BIBLE FUN 2 IN 1

SCRAMBLES •• AND •• WORD SEARCHES

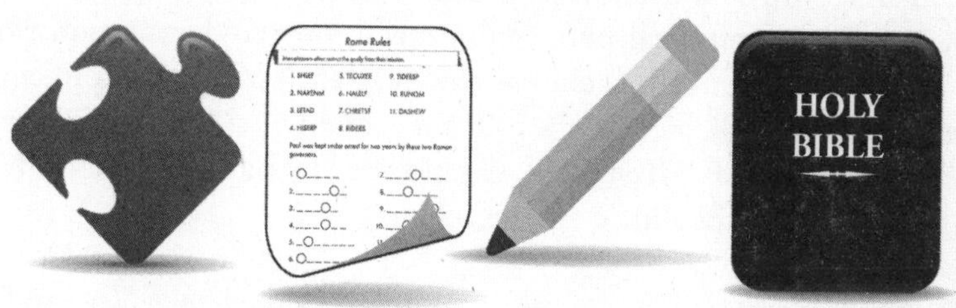

OVER 300 FUN PUZZLES

© 2009 by Barbour Publishing, Inc.

Bible Scrambles © 2009 by Barbour Publishing, Inc.
Secret Message Bible Word Searches © 2009 by Barbour Publishing, Inc.

ISBN 978-1-60260-658-6

All rights reserved. No part of this publication may be reproduced or transmitted for commercial purposes, except for brief quotations in printed reviews, without written permission of the publisher.

Churches and other noncommercial interests may reproduce portions of this book without the express written permission of Barbour Publishing, within the following limitations: No more than one puzzle per month in a physical publication made for free distribution (for example, church bulletins, club newsletters, etc.). When reproducing text from this book, include the following credit line: "From *Bible Fun 2-in-1: Scrambles and Word Searches* published by Barbour Publishing, Inc. Used by permission."

All scripture quotations are taken from the King James Version of the Bible.

Published by Barbour Publishing, Inc., P.O. Box 719, Uhrichsville, Ohio 44683, www.barbourbooks.com

Our mission is to publish and distribute inspirational products offering exceptional value and biblical encouragement to the masses.

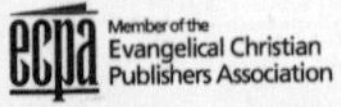

Printed in the United States of America.

Welcome to *Bible Fun 2-in-1: Scrambles and Word Searches*!

If you like Bible word games, you'll love this book. Here are 303 great puzzles to expand your Bible knowledge and test your solving skills.

Bible Scrambles: Each puzzle features a numbered list of jumbled words, each one (or a form of it) found within the stated reference in the King James Version of the Bible. Unscramble those words, placing them into the numbered blanks below. Then use the circled letters to answer the Bible-based question that follows. Answers appear at the back of the book.

Secret Message Bible Word Searches: Each puzzle features a scripture passage with the search word printed in **bold type**. When a phrase is **<u>bold and underlined</u>**, those words will be found together in the puzzle grid. Once you've found all the search words, begin at the top left-hand corner of the puzzle and read the leftover letters in order—they'll spell out the trivia question that adds to the fun. If you run into the letter "X" repeated, the question is complete. Answers appear at the back of the book.

BIBLE SCRAMBLES

1–The Better Things

In Ecclesiastes, Solomon made many distinctions between the wise and foolish things of this world. Solve this puzzle to discover one of the better things we would be wise to choose. (Ecclesiastes 7)

1. WNMOA
2. OIMGRNNU
3. YFLOL
4. MIDSOW
5. EAMSDNS
6. ENFCDEE
7. TTGRISHA
8. OMYEN
9. ODCKERO

1. ___ ___ ___ ◯ ___
2. ___ ___ ___ ___ ___ ___ ___ ◯
3. ___ ◯ ___ ___ ___
4. ___ ___ ___ ___ ◯ ___
5. ___ ___ ◯ ___ ___ ___ ___
6. ___ ___ ___ ___ ◯ ___ ___
7. ___ ___ ___ ◯ ___ ___ ___ ___
8. ◯ ___ ___ ___ ___
9. ___ ___ ___ ___ ___ ◯ ___

Better than precious ointment.

Answer: ___ ___ ___ ___ ___ ___ ___ ___ ___ ___ ___

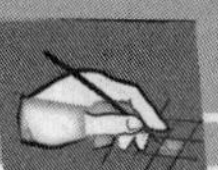

2–Praise!

A concurrent cacophony of sound? Only the Lord could make sense of it—and receive it as an expression of gratitude! Solve to discover what we should raise in praise! (Psalm 98)

1. TLVNSAOAI
2. DUJGE
3. THOEEGTR
4. CYOVRIT
5. OFSODL
6. DLUO
7. AMPLS
8. SANHD
9. IJROCEE
10. CIVOE
11. DNSUO
12. YMECR

1. _◯_________

2. ◯____

3. _◯______

4. ______◯

5. ◯_____

6. __◯_

7. ___◯_

8. __◯__

9. ___◯___

10. __◯__

11. ◯____

12. _◯___

All the earth. . .make this unto the Lord.

Answer: __ __ __ __ __ __ __ __ __ __ __ __ __

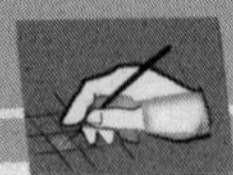

3–The Joy of Parenting

Bringing up children is a challenging endeavor. Solve to discover what end result a parent can look forward to. (Proverbs 15)

1. OESNSA
2. AWHTR
3. SEDERSIP
4. RESUETAR
5. TDPEAR
6. CNSRO
7. SEOAFKR
8. EUNEVER

1. ___ ___ ◯ ___ ___ ___

2. ◯ ___ ___ ___ ___

3. ___ ◯ ___ ___ ___ ___ ___ ___

4. ___ ___ ___ ___ ◯ ___ ___ ___

5. ___ ◯ ___ ___ ___ ___

6. ◯ ___ ___ ___ ___

7. ___ ◯ ___ ___ ___ ___ ___

8. ___ ___ ___ ___ ◯ ___ ___

This really makes a man glad.

Answer: ___ ___ ___ ___ ___ ___ ___ ___

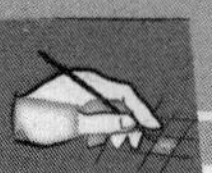

4–Ultimate Authority

God's power is the greatest on earth, as Moses and his brother proved to Pharoah. Unscramble the words to discover one of the tools God used to prove His ultimate authority. (EXODUS 7)

1. CANGIAIM
2. EICRLMA
3. TEPNSRE
4. ADOCMMN
5. WDNO
6. RSSATME
7. VREES
8. LPOSO
9. EADNHR

1. ___ ◯ ___ ___ ___ ___ ___ ___
2. ___ ___ ___ ◯ ___ ___ ___
3. ___ ___ ◯ ___ ___ ___ ___
4. ___ ◯ ___ ___ ___ ___ ___
5. ___ ___ ___ ◯
6. ___ ___ ___ ___ ___ ___ ◯
7. ___ ___ ◯ ___ ___
8. ___ ___ ◯ ___ ___
9. ___ ___ ___ ◯ ___ ___

Became a serpent.

Answer: ___ ___ ___ ___ ___ ' ___ ___ ___ ___

5–Poof! They're Gone!

Obadiah was a chief in the household of King Ahab and the author of the shortest book in the Old Testament. Solve to discover what he envisioned to be the demise of these people, who would become as though they'd never been. (OBADIAH 1)

1. LXATE
2. HELDRCNI
3. ITMYGH
4. GSAEULTRH
5. GHIH
6. AFMLE
7. IPNAL
8. MCITLAYA
9. HSLNSEIO
10. OSEKNP

1. __ __ ○ ○ __
2. __ __ __ ○ __ __ __ __
3. __ __ __ __ ○ __
4. __ __ __ __ __ ○ __ ○ __
5. ○ __ __ __
6. __ __ __ __ ○
7. __ __ ○ __ __
8. __ __ __ __ __ __ ○ __
9. ○ __ __ __ __ ○ __ __
10. __ __ __ __ __ ○

The day of the Lord is near upon them.

Answer: __ __ __ __ __ __ __ __ __ __ __ __ __

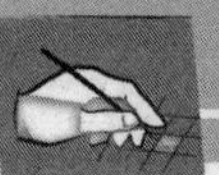

6–Cut Apart

God broke two shepherd staffs, one to represent breaking His covenant with all the people and the other the brotherhood between Judah and Israel. Solve to discover the names of these two symbolic staffs. (ZECHARIAH 11)

1. ABELNNO
2. TTRPEO
3. EULSGHRTA
4. ISTVI
5. NOYUG
6. ARUNDSE
7. HAROB
8. KANRDE
9. RACED
10. SHELF

1. __ __ ○ __ __ __ __
2. __ __ __ __ ○ __
3. __ __ ○ ○ __ __ __ __ __
4. __ __ __ __ ○
5. ○ __ __ __ __
6. ○ __ __ ○ ○ __ __
7. __ ○ __ __ __
8. __ ○ __ __ __ ○
9. __ __ ○ __ __
10. __ __ __ ○ __

The broken staves of the Lord.

Answer: __ __ __ __ __ __ __ __ __ __ __ __ __ __ __

7–Right Hand Clan

Out this clan, made famous for its archers and slingers, would come the first king of the Jews. Solve for the name that means "son of my right hand." (1 Samuel 10)

1. REBIT
2. RRDBEO
3. KNEAT
4. JDECREET
5. MYFIAL
6. MUSELA
7. SINGROAR
8. NSPERET

1. ___ ___ ___ ◯ ___
2. ___ ___ ___ ___ ◯ ___
3. ___ ___ ___ ___ ◯
4. ___ ___ ◯ ___ ___ ___ ___ ___
5. ___ ◯ ___ ___ ___ ___
6. ___ ___ ◯ ___ ___ ___
7. ___ ___ ___ ___ ◯ ___ ___ ___
8. ___ ___ ___ ___ ___ ◯ ___

An issue of Israel.

Answer: ___ ___ ___ ___ ___ ___ ___ ___

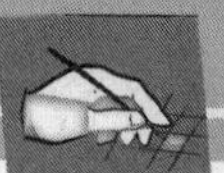

8–*Prayer and Praise*

Poetry has changed a lot over the years but the Hebrew versions live on right here. Unscramble these words for clues to this tome of chapters and verses. (OLD TESTAMENT TOME)

1. SBENO
2. EETRRSO
3. OYLH
4. RKNDI
5. ERVPEOR
6. RFEFO
7. HRPESI
8. ALART
9. SARMON
10. THOUS

1. ◯__ __ __ __
2. __ __ __ __ ◯__ __
3. __ ◯__ __
4. __ __ __ __ ◯
5. __ __ __ __ ◯__ __
6. __ __ ◯__ __
7. ◯__ __ __ ◯__
8. ◯◯__ __ __
9. __ __ __ __ __ ◯
10. ◯ __ __ __ __

Words of happiness and delight.

Answer: __ __ __ __ __   __ __   __ __ __ __ __ __ __

9–Good Reading

When Shaphan the scribe read a tome to King Josiah, the ruler tore his clothes and repented of his evil. Solve to discover the name of this reforming record. (2 Kings 22)

1. RHCABE
2. UHSEO
3. SAMNOS
4. IIKAHLH
5. SDOWR
6. SOEKNAFR
7. ITHGM
8. UHJAD
9. IELV
10. LIKEND
11. PRARIE
12. RWBEAROD

1. ◯ ___ ___ ___ ___ ___
2. ___ ◯ ___ ___ ___
3. ___ ___ ___ ◯ ___ ___
4. ___ ___ ___ ◯ ___ ___ ___
5. ___ ◯ ___ ___ ___
6. ◯ ___ ___ ___ ___ ___ ___ ___
7. ___ ___ ___ ___ ◯
8. ___ ___ ___ ___ ◯
9. ◯ ___ ___ ___
10. ___ ___ ___ ___ ◯ ___
11. ___ ___ ___ ◯ ___ ___
12. ◯ ___ ___ ___ ___ ___ ___ ___

Hilkiah the priest found this, first given by Moses.

Answer: ___ ___ ___ ___   ___ ___   ___ ___ ___   ___ ___ ___

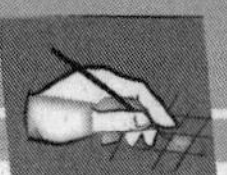

10–Stone by Stone

Nehemiah was a cupbearer on a mission. Do you know what he felt called to do in defense of God's people? Unscramble each clue to "construct" the right answer. (NEHEMIAH 13)

1. EBHCRAM
2. NEEDCUAI
3. DGOEL
4. EBDAR
5. EOTRPRS
6. AHSVEES
7. DWASR
8. SNECLAE
9. ARSELI
10. RLELSES

1. __ __ __ __ ◯ __ __

2. __ ◯ __ ◯ __ __ __ __

3. ◯ __ __ __ __

4. __ __ __ __ ◯

5. __ __ __ ◯ __ __ __

6. __ ◯ __ __ __ ◯ __

7. ◯ __ __ __ __

8. __ __ __ ◯ __ __ __

9. __ __ __ __ __ ◯

10. __ __ ◯ __ __ __ __

Nehemiah's first decree.

Answer: __ __ __ __ __   __ __ __   __ __ __ __

11–Aiming to Please

God gave instructions regarding the kinds of sacrifices He required. Work these clues to find the one that pleased the Lord's olfactories. (EXODUS 29)

1. ASMBL
2. ROULF
3. TONNIA
4. THAWE
5. SOCAT
6. ECFOIF
7. EFARSW
8. INS
9. NOYGU

1. ___ ___ ___ ◯ ___

2. ___ ___ ___ ◯ ◯

3. ___ ___ ___ ___ ◯ ___

4. ___ ___ ___ ___ ◯

5. ___ ◯ ___ ___ ___

6. ___ ◯ ◯ ___ ___ ___

7. ___ ___ ___ ◯ ◯ ___

8. ___ ◯ ◯

9. ___ ___ ___ ___ ◯

The Lord finds this sweet.

Answer: ___ ___ ___ ___ ___   ___ ___ ___ ___ ___ ___ ___ ___

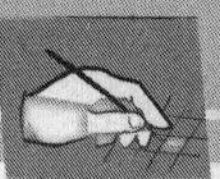

12–Praise before the Ark

Some of Israel's descendents were appointed to perform special duties. Solve to uncover those who worked in the Tabernacle. (Hint: Ministering was in their "jeans.") (1 Chronicles 16)

1. NVOCAETN
2. ETPDRA
3. HHTA
4. SNVATRE
5. CJEIEOR
6. TONAIN
7. EBSDSEL
8. IDVAD
9. UNSNMRITET
10. DOSNU

1. ◯ ___ ___ ___ ___ ___ ___ ___
2. ___ ◯ ___ ___ ◯ ___
3. ___ ___ ◯ ___
4. ___ ___ ___ ___ ◯ ___ ___
5. ___ ___ ___ ___ ◯ ___ ___
6. ◯ ___ ___ ___ ___ ___
7. ___ ◯ ___ ___ ___ ◯ ___
8. ___ ___ ◯ ___ ___
9. ◯ ___ ___ ◯ ___ ___ ___ ◯ ___ ___
10. ◯ ___ ___ ___ ___

Ministers of the ark.

Answer: __ __ __ __ __ __ __ __ __ __ __ __ __ __ __ __ __

13–Terrors

For a certain period of time, Job's aching bones gave him no rest, but that wasn't the worst of his troubles. Work this puzzle to discover the term Job used to describe his season of terrors. (JOB 30)

1. ULCDO
2. LORIATSY
3. RUEPUS
4. UHYTO
5. FCOER
6. RAFET
7. REBDIL
8. MICAYTAL
9. SCTA
10. SOIRIDEN
11. WISSEN

1. __ __ __ __ ○
2. __ __ __ __ __ ○ __ ○
3. __ __ __ ○ __ __
4. __ ○ __ __ __
5. ○ __ __ __ __
6. ○ ○ __ __ __
7. __ __ __ __ ○ __
8. __ __ __ __ __ ○ __ __
9. ○ __ __ ○
10. __ __ __ ○ __ __ ○ __
11. __ __ ○ __ __ __

Job declared this having taken hold of him.

Answer: __ __ __ __ __ __ __ __ __ __ __ __ __ __ __ __

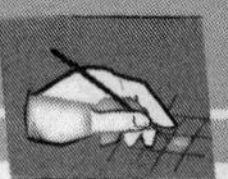

14–Faithfulness

Some day the unfaithful will hunger and thirst, but those who put their trust under His wings will not go wanting. Unscramble the words below to get clued in on this time of "no satisfaction" for the wicked. (Psalm 37)

1. THEGILD
2. LYSA
3. KOSME
4. CMRUEILF
5. RFKAEOS
6. NODMECN
7. THNIREI
8. ABCNAUEND

1. ◯ ___ ___ ___ ___ ___ ___
2. ___ ___ ◯ ◯
3. ◯ ___ ◯ ___ ___
4. ___ ___ ___ ___ ___ ◯ ___ ___
5. ◯ ___ ___ ___ ◯ ___ ___
6. ___ ___ ___ ___ ___ ◯ ___
7. ◯ ◯ ___ ___ ___ ___ ___
8. ___ ___ ___ ___ ___ ___ ___ ___ ◯

The Lord promises that in this time, the upright will be satisfied.

Answer: ___ ___ ___ ___   ___ ___   ___ ___ ___ ___ ___ ___

15–"Ungolden" Years

There is a time to really enjoy the things in life, but our true satisfaction must come from God. Solve to uncover the term describing our fleeting "ungolden" years. (Ecclesiastes 11)

1. EBDAR
2. TINYVA
3. HOSUT
4. SLEHF
5. LOWHITDH
6. MYTEP
7. RYULT
8. USCOLD
9. RPSTII
10. RATHE

1. __ __ __ __ ◯
2. __ ◯ __ __ __ ◯
3. ◯ ◯ __ __ __
4. ◯ __ __ __ __
5. __ __ ◯ __ ◯ __ __ __
6. __ __ __ __ ◯
7. __ __ __ __ ◯
8. __ __ ◯ ◯ __ __
9. __ __ __ __ __ ◯
10. ◯ __ __ __ __

You should rejoice in this.

Answer: __ __ __ __ __   __ __ __   __ __ __ __   __ __ __ __ __ __

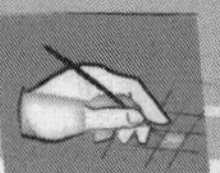

16–Deceptive Love

One biblical bad girl proved she was definitely not a cut above the rest. Solve to discover the name of this deceptive female. (Judges 16)

1. CEMKDO
2. EAGNDVE
3. AELN
4. TFALIFC
5. CLSKO
6. ZAROR
7. IESTHSLNIIP

1. ___ ___ ___ ___ ___ ◯
2. ___ ___ ◯ ___ ___ ___ ___
3. ◯ ___ ___ ___
4. ___ ___ ___ ___ ◯ ___ ___
5. ◯ ___ ___ ___ ___
6. ___ ◯ ___ ___ ___
7. ___ ◯ ___ ___ ___ ___ ___ ___ ___ ___ ___

A woman of the Sorek Valley.

Answer: ___ ___ ___ ___ ___ ___ ___

17–Massacre at Nob

This man was doggedly faithful in following his master Saul's orders. Unscramble the clues below to discover his appropriate appellation. (1 Samuel 22)

1. PRATED
2. RISONPCE
3. UGELAE
4. NASTAGI
5. HENIT
6. TRIESP
7. EDLWT
8. NOTEFOM
9. DELFI
10. NAPTAIC
11. UHSEO

1. ◯ __ __ __ __ __
2. __ ◯ __ __ __ __ __ __
3. __ __ __ __ __ ◯
4. __ ◯ __ __ __ __ ◯
5. __ ◯ __ __ ◯
6. __ __ __ ◯ __ __
7. ◯ __ __ __ __
8. __ ◯ __ __ ◯ __ __
9. __ ◯ __ __ __
10. __ __ __ ◯ __ __ __
11. __ __ __ __ ◯

Obeyed Saul's order to kill.

Answer: __ __ __ __ __ __ __ __ __ __ __ __ __ __ __ __

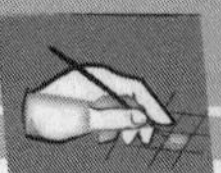

18–Watch What You Say!

The Bible tells us to be careful about the words we use. Solve to discover what kind of "opening" we need to diligently guard. (Psalm 141)

1. ODWO
2. OECVI
3. LOUS
4. STRUT
5. REVPORE
6. TFRHO
7. IMALACSITE
8. RERYAP
9. NFLIGIT
10. AESPCL

1. ___ ___ ___ ◯
2. ___ ◯ ___ ___ ___
3. ___ ◯ ___ ___
4. ___ ◯ ___ ___ ___
5. ___ ___ ___ ___ ◯ ___ ___
6. ◯ ___ ___ ___ ___
7. ___ ___ ___ ___ ◯ ___ ___ ___ ___ ___
8. ___ ___ ___ ◯ ___ ___
9. ◯ ___ ___ ___ ◯ ___ ___
10. ◯ ___ ___ ___ ◯

Don't leave this ajar.

Answer: ___ ___ ___ ___ ___ ___ ___ ___ ___ ___ ___ ___

19–Hungry for Prophecy

Ezekiel was instructed to "take in" God's instruction in an unusual way. Work this puzzle to discover the command the prophet followed to sate his spiritual appetite. (EZEKIEL 3)

1. EDPEON
2. GLUGNAEA
3. SGARTNE
4. OSGRTN
5. NRUSHGI
6. IDKCEW
7. RQREUIE
8. ENIOS
9. HEDCLINR
10. THASL

1. __ __ __ __ ◯ __

2. __ __ __ __ __ ◯ __ __

3. __ ◯ __ __ __ __ __

4. __ ◯ __ __ __ __

5. __ __ __ ◯ __ __ __

6. __ __ __ __ ◯ __

7. __ __ __ __ __ ◯ __

8. __ ◯ __ __ __

9. __ __ __ ◯ __ __ __ __

10. __ __ __ ◯ __

Before Ezekiel spoke to Israel, God gave him this instruction.

Answer: __ __ __ __ __ __ __ __ __ __

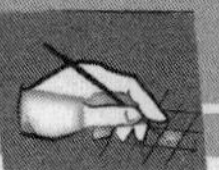

20–Second Visit

At Christ's first appearance, John the Baptist was a type of Old Testament prophet.Solve to discover the same "type" of prophet that will be seen before Christ returns. (MALACHI 3–4)

1. DRATE
2. VEIL
3. EEWLJ
4. SCLAEV
5. AHTRE
6. GLEANIH
7. SPORPSE
8. SELSO
9. URPO
10. HLASL
11. SLETNAPA

1. __ __ ◯ __ __
2. ◯ __ __ ◯
3. ◯ __ __ __ __
4. __ ◯ __ __ __ __
5. ◯ __ __ __ ◯
6. ◯ ◯ __ __ __ __ __
7. __ ◯ __ ◯ __ __ __
8. __ ◯ __ __ __
9. ◯ __ __ __
10. __ ◯ __ __ __
11. __ __ ◯ __ __ __ __ ◯

He will come before the dreadful day of the Lord.

Answer: __ __ __ __ __ __ __ __ __ __

__ __ __ __ __ __ __

21–*Two of a Kind*

These two boys had a hairy sibling rivalry. Unscamble the clues to uncover their respective names. (Genesis 25–26)

1. ABGET
2. IRTSES
3. MAGNERT
4. RDGUTLSEG
5. ONTNAI
6. EEHRNRTB
7. TDAHE
8. JRUOSON
9. PTAERD
10. APCLE
11. NFUDO
12. HRBETOR

1. __ ◯ __ __ __
2. __ __ ◯ __ __ __
3. __ ◯ __ __ __ __ __
4. __ __ __ ◯ __ __ __ __ __
5. __ ◯ __ __ __ __
6. __ __ __ __ __ __ __ ◯
7. ◯ __ __ __ __
8. __ __ ◯ __ __ __ __
9. __ __ __ ◯ __ __
10. __ __ __ ◯ __
11. __ ◯ __ __ __
12. ◯ __ __ __ __ __ __

One right after the other.

Answer: __ __ __ __ __ __ __ __ __ __ __ __

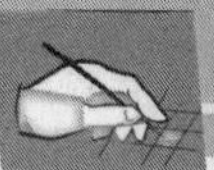

22–Amazing Wonders

The things this Old Testament prophet beheld were wondrous. May the "fours" be with you as you solve to discover what so amazed him. (CHAPTER 1 OF THE 26TH OLD TESTAMENT BOOK)

1. MEARNTIMF
2. ZIUB
3. ELSNSEIK
4. NKIG
5. EWESHL
6. GALEE
7. SCRATLY
8. NLIVGI
9. EOSNI
10. GWNSI
11. WDAROT
12. OILN

1. __ __ __ __ __ __ ◯ __ __
2. __ __ ◯ __
3. __ __ __ __ __ ◯ __ __
4. ◯ ◯ __ __
5. __ __ ◯ __ __ __
6. __ __ __ ◯ __
7. __ __ __ ◯ __ __ __
8. __ __ ◯ __ __ __
9. __ __ ◯ ◯ __
10. __ ◯ __ __ __
11. __ ◯ __ __ __ __
12. __ __ __ ◯

A whirlwind from the north.

Answer: __ __ __ __ __ __ __ ' __ __ __ __ __ __ __

23–Woe to Them!

Jeremiah is one who would look ahead and see truth, but woe to these ones who would lead the people astray. Solve to discover the term describing these navigationally challenged shepherds. (Jeremiah 23)

1. ASLYEF
2. OSPRTAS
3. CLOKF
4. HESAM
5. APEHROCR
6. NERGA
7. OOMSD
8. PPYHROSE
9. DAERH
10. RMDASE
11. OEGTRF
12. DOLFS

1. __ __ ○ __ __ __
2. __ ○ __ __ __ __ __
3. __ ○ __ __ __
4. ○ __ __ __ ○
5. __ __ ○ __ __ __ __ __
6. __ __ __ __ ○
7. __ ○ __ __ __
8. __ __ __ ○ __ __ __ __
9. ○ __ __ __ __
10. __ __ ○ __ __ __
11. __ __ __ __ __ ○
12. __ __ __ __ ○

Ones worthy of rebuke.

Answer: __ __ __ __ __ __   __ __ __ __ __ __ __ __

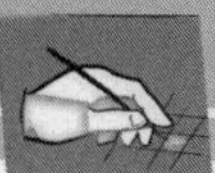

24–The Leftovers

Ruth needed to find a way to feed herself and mother-in-law. Work this puzzle to find her place of employment. (BOOK OF RUTH)

1. CFFEALTDI
2. CUDFSEIF
3. EENLDAG
4. MLADSE
5. KDRNIED
6. ODRUGN
7. NFDI
8. NUSDBHA
9. MWNAO
10. HEPZAR

1. __ __ ◯ __ __ __ __ __ __
2. __ __ __ __ ◯ __ __ __
3. __ __ __ __ __ ◯ __
4. __ __ __ __ __ ◯
5. __ __ __ ◯ __ __ __
6. __ __ ◯ __ __ __
7. ◯ __ __ __
8. __ __ __ ◯ __ __ __
9. __ ◯ __ ◯ __
10. __ __ __ __ __ ◯

It was here that Ruth met someone special.

Answer: __ __ __ __ __ __ __ __ __ __ __ __

25–A Barrier

On the second day, God separated the waters. Unscramble the clues below to discover what He called this expansive barrier. (GENESIS 1)

1. TFSIR
2. IEKLSNSE
3. RGOMNNI
4. DOIMNINO
5. OEASNSS
6. EGIAM
7. VNEIGNE
8. VANEEH
9. PLUMYILT

1. ◯ ___ ___ ___ ___
2. ___ ◯ ___ ___ ___ ___ ___ ___
3. ___ ___ ◯ ___ ___ ___ ___
4. ___ ___ ◯ ___ ___ ___ ___ ___
5. ___ ___ ◯ ___ ___ ___ ___
6. ___ ◯ ___ ___ ___
7. ___ ___ ◯ ___ ___ ___ ___
8. ___ ___ ___ ___ ___ ◯
9. ___ ___ ___ ◯ ___ ___ ___ ___

Created to divide water from water.

Answer: ___ ___ ___ ___ ___ ___ ___ ___ ___

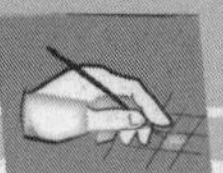

26–It Was a Long Week!

We were made in God's image to not only work and create but to rest, at least once a week. After all, He started it. Got a clue as to what we're referring to? (Genesis 2–3)

1. UTFRI
2. EISW
3. SPRNOA
4. PRNTESE
5. NECDOS
6. ANEDRG
7. UBSIER
8. HRABET
9. HESTTISL
10. OHRTME

1. ◯ ___ ___ ___ ___
2. ___ ◯ ___ ___
3. ___ ___ ◯ ___ ___ ___
4. ◯ ___ ___ ___ ___ ___ ◯
5. ◯ ___ ___ ___ ___ ___
6. ___ ◯ ___ ___ ___ ___
7. ◯ ___ ___ ___ ___ ___
8. ◯ ___ ___ ◯ ___ ___
9. ___ ___ ___ ___ ◯ ___ ___ ___
10. ___ ___ ___ ◯ ___ ___

Made for man.

Answer: ___ ___ ___ ___ ___ ___   ___ ___ ___ ___ ___ ___ ___ ___ ___

27–A Dark Night. . .

The Egyptians were plagued with trouble. Solve to reveal what happened one dark night. (Exodus 12)

1. MASLFEII
2. EVERSOB
3. ANOSB
4. STOPS
5. TABES
6. ATRSO
7. RAINME
8. FALSEESM
9. POSHSY
10. NITELL
11. TNEEA

1. ○ __ __ ○ __ __ __ __
2. __ __ __ ○ __ __
3. __ __ ○ __ __
4. __ __ __ ○ __
5. ○ __ __ __ __
6. __ ○ __ __ __
7. ○ __ __ __ __ ○
8. ○ __ __ __ __ __ ○ __
9. __ __ __ __ ○ __
10. __ __ __ ○ __ __
11. ○ __ __ __ __

Last judgment against Pharaoh.

Answer: __ __ __ __ __ __ __ __ __ __ __ __ __ __ __ __

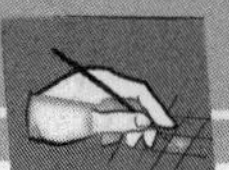

28–Hot Ones!

God sends celestial beings, intense and ablaze with truth, to guide His people. Solve to discover what God makes some of these heavenly ministers. (Psalm 104)

1. UDNDEFO
2. SLGENA
3. LYVEAL
4. NAMGO
5. EFLID
6. UHNCEQ
7. IGSN
8. WOLFS
9. RCNAITU
10. CREBAMH
11. ALCTET

1. ◯_ _ _ _ _ _

2. _ _ _ _ ◯ _

3. _ ◯ _ _ _ _

4. _ ◯ _ _ _

5. _ ◯ _ _ _

6. _ _ _ ◯ _ _

7. _ _ _ ◯

8. ◯ _ _ _ _

9. _ _ _ _ _ ◯ _

10. _ _ _ _ _ _ ◯

11. _ _ _ _ _ ◯

His ministers are made a. . .

Answer: _ _ _ _ _ _ _ _ _ _ _ _ _ _ _ _

29–Smart Man!

Jesse's grandson asked God for one thing. Do you have the smarts to discover his request? (1 Kings 3)

1. FYNAIIFT
2. EHRONT
3. HRUGTIP
4. TENBWEE
5. SCENENI
6. SCRINDE
7. EWDLL
8. ROOHUN
9. MARED

1. __ __ ◯ __ __ __ __ __
2. __ __ __ ◯ __ __
3. __ __ ◯ __ __ __ __
4. __ __ __ ◯ __ __ __
5. ◯ __ __ __ __ __ __
6. __ __ ◯ __ __ __ __
7. ◯ __ __ __ __
8. __ __ __ ◯ __ __
9. __ __ __ __ ◯

What Solomon asked.

Answer: __ __ __ __ __ __ __ __ __

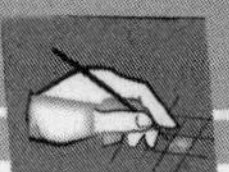

30–Spirits of Heaven

Zechariah envisioned these rollers, symbolic of heavenly spirits executing judgment for the Lord. Unscamble the clues below and the answer will be conveyed to you. (ZECHARIAH 6)

1. DETILF
2. TURNYOC
3. WCONRS
4. ABKCL
5. EDAH
6. LAMERIOM
7. RHSEO
8. LETMEP
9. UESCLNO

1. __ __ ○ __ __ __
2. __ ○ ○ __ __ __ __
3. __ ○ __ __ __ __
4. __ __ __ ○ __
5. ○ __ ○ __
6. __ __ __ __ ○ ○ __ __
7. __ ○ __ __ __
8. ○ __ __ __ __ __
9. __ __ __ __ ○ __ __

They came out from brass mountains.

Answer: __ __ __ __ __ __ __ __ __ __ __ __

31–Mighty Warrior

This well-known warrior appeared to Daniel. Hopefully, you'll wing right through this one. (Daniel 9)

1. LAREM
2. ERNPCI
3. EGRTA
4. ELBER
5. GUEJSD
6. SWLA
7. YEOBDE
8. AARYSTUCN
9. OIINSV
10. UREDDLAF
11. SLAIER

1. __ __ ◯ __ __
2. __ __ __ ◯ __ __
3. ◯ __ ◯ __ __
4. __ __ __ __ ◯
5. __ __ __ ◯ __ __
6. __ ◯ __ __
7. __ ◯ __ __ __ __
8. __ __ __ __ __ __ __ ◯ __
9. __ ◯ __ __ __ __
10. __ __ ◯ __ __ __ __ __
11. __ __ __ __ __ ◯

Came to comfort Daniel.

Answer: __ __ __ __ __ __   __ __ __ __ __ __ __ __

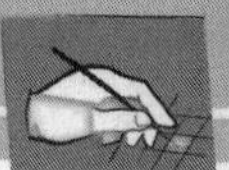

32–An Eyeful

These men made Moses' spies seem so small in their own eyes. Have "tons" of fun solving this puzzle! (NUMBERS 13)

1. SPRAGE	4. SCIIET	7. EHOYN	10. OADNRJ
2. NBRIG	5. NESTT	8. TSHUO	11. GEAROCU
3. GASNIY	6. GRNETORS	9. HFTRAE	12. IKLM

1. ◯ ___ ___ ___ ___ ___
2. ___ ___ ◯ ___ ___
3. ___ ◯ ___ ___ ◯ ___
4. ___ ___ ◯ ___ ___ ◯
5. ___ ___ ___ ___ ◯
6. ___ ___ ___ ◯ ___ ___ ___ ___
7. ___ ___ ◯ ___ ___
8. ◯ ◯ ___ ___ ___
9. ◯ ___ ___ ___ ___ ___
10. ___ ___ ___ ___ ◯ ◯
11. ___ ___ ___ ___ ◯ ___ ___
12. ___ ___ ___ ◯

The spies returned from Canaan, feeling as grasshoppers because of these men.

Answer: ___ ___ ___ ___ ___ ___ ___, ___ ___ ___ ___ ___ ___ ___ ___ ___ ___ ___

33–Moral Virtues

Peter desired the saints to attain this virtue along with life. Hope you get this one "right"! (2 Peter 1)

1. ECRAG
2. CREPOSIU
3. CIGENIDLE
4. RYOGL
5. HIFTA
6. DONBAU
7. DRUEPG
8. RIST
9. APLESDE

1. ◯ __ __ __ __

2. __ __ __ __ __ ◯ __ __

3. ◯ __ __ __ __ __ __ __ __

4. __ ◯ __ __ __

5. __ __ ◯ __ __

6. __ __ __ __ ◯ __

7. __ __ __ __ ◯ __

8. ◯ __ __ __

9. __ __ __ __ ◯ __ __

The promise of knowledge of Christ.

Answer: __ __ __ __ __ __ __ __ __

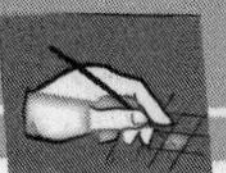

34–Something to Count On

David experienced this again and again, and so do we. What a relief! (PSALM 52)

1. GDSNOSEO
2. EVOLI
3. OSTEDYR
4. HSRAP
5. SLIMHFE
6. SCHIRE
7. RUDENE
8. FISHMCEI
9. EHYTLSF

1. ○ ___ ___ ___ ___ ___ ___ ___
2. ○ ___ ___ ___ ___
3. ○ ___ ___ ___ ___ ___ ___
4. ○ ___ ___ ___ ___
5. ___ ___ ○ ___ ___ ___ ___
6. ___ ___ ___ ___ ○ ___
7. ___ ___ ___ ___ ○ ___
8. ___ ___ ___ ○ ___ ___ ___ ___
9. ___ ___ ○ ___ ___ ___ ___

We give thanks because we are confident of. . .

Answer: ___ ___ ___'___ ___ ___ ___ ___ ___

35–A Light to See

A heavenly being helped Zechariah see this "lamp" in a dark room. May the clues below enlighten you. (ZECHARIAH 4)

1. ERTAG
2. LOBEDH
3. KODELO
4. YESE
5. LAGNE
6. GRINCY
7. NAPIL
8. SHDNA
9. KLEDTA
10. EDASHNOTE
11. SHINIF
12. EAMC
13. DAKNEWE

1. ◯ _ _ _ _
2. _ _ _ ◯ _ _
3. ◯ _ _ _ _ ◯
4. _ _ ◯ _
5. _ ◯ _ _ _
6. ◯ _ _ _ _ _
7. _ _ ◯ _ ◯
8. _ _ _ ◯ _
9. _ _ ◯ _ ◯ _
10. _ _ _ _ _ ◯ ◯ _ _ _
11. _ ◯ _ _ _ _
12. ◯ _ _ _
13. _ _ ◯ _ _ _ _ _

A vision of Zechariah.

Answer: _ _ _ _ _ _

_ _ _ _ _ _ _ _ _ _ _ _ _ _

36–Water-Proofing

History would have ended had there not been an abundance of this, which allowed a major figure in the Bible to "go forward" with God's plan. Hope you have smooth sailing as you solve this puzzle. (GENESIS 6)

1. HUDRGAEST
2. OTRPCRU
3. TCHPI
4. ALETCT
5. LERDNHIC
6. DWNIOW
7. WNNEOR
8. HAFNSIO
9. YSEOTDR

1. __ __ __ ○ __ __ __ __ __
2. __ ○ __ __ __ ○ __
3. __ __ __ __ ○
4. __ __ __ __ __ ○
5. __ __ __ __ __ ○ __ __
6. ○ __ __ __ __ __
7. __ __ __ ○ __ __
8. __ __ __ __ __ ○ __
9. ○ __ __ __ __ __ __

Useful for boat building.

Answer: __ __ __ __ __ __ __ __ __ __

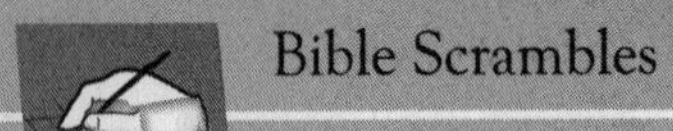

37–Watch Out!

Out of their corruption, the Israelites would build these when they took their eyes off the Lord. This puzzle reminds us that there's nothing like the real thing—God. (DEUTERONOMY 4)

1. LNGAO
2. PRECE
3. SELBTA
4. CIVEO
5. ATNHEHE
6. GFERIU
7. CMYRE
8. KDSARESN
9. GEPYT
10. IDGWEN
11. ETSAB

1. ◯ ___ ___ ___ ___
2. ___ ◯ ___ ___ ___
3. ___ ◯ ___ ___ ___ ___
4. ◯ ___ ___ ◯
5. ___ ___ ___ ___ ___ ___ ◯
6. ___ ◯ ___ ___ ___ ___
7. ◯ ___ ___ ___ ___
8. ___ ◯ ___ ___ ___ ___ ___ ___
9. ___ ◯ ___ ___ ___
10. ___ ___ ___ ___ ◯ ___
11. ___ ___ ___ ◯ ___

Looking for something solid.

Answer: ___ ___ ___ ___ ___ ___ ___ ___ ___ ___ ___ ___ ___ ___ ___

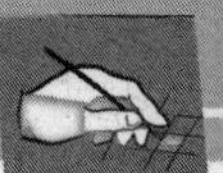

38–Belly Tremble

In Hebrew, his name means *embrace*—and indeed he did embrace this vision from God, so that it caused all his body to shake and quiver. This one's a clincher. (CHAPTER 3 OF THE 35TH OLD TESTAMENT BOOK)

1. PHECES
2. ARCTEST
3. OSBEN
4. TATNHIOBIA
5. AEKDN
6. RKOW
7. EROVUD
8. WNKNO

1. ___ ___ ___ ___ ___ ○
2. ___ ___ ○ ___ ___ ___ ___
3. ○ ___ ___ ___ ___
4. ___ ___ ___ ___ ___ ○ ___ ___ ___ ___
5. ___ ___ ○ ___ ___
6. ___ ___ ___ ○
7. ___ ___ ___ ___ ○ ___
8. ○ ___ ___ ___ ___

He trembled at God's majesty.

Answer: ___ ___ ___ ___ ___ ___ ___ ___

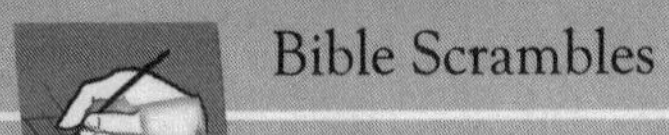

39–*A Perfect Yet Troubled Man!*

His submissive heart and attitude caused God to hold this man in high esteem and uphold him even against arrogant and evil accusations. Don't anguish over this one. (Chapter 3 of the 18th Old Testament Book)

1. TMOHU
2. ERSNPCI
3. TLEPS
4. SUCEDR
5. IBHTR
6. VEINECOC
7. GAINWND
8. WILIHTTG
9. YOULFJ
10. MWOB

1. ___ ___ ___ ___ ◯
2. ___ ___ ◯ ___ ___ ___ ◯
3. ◯ ___ ___ ___ ___
4. ___ ___ ___ ___ ◯ ___
5. ___ ___ ◯ ___ ___
6. ___ ___ ___ ___ ___ ___ ◯ ___
7. ___ ◯ ___ ◯ ___ ___ ___
8. ___ ___ ___ ___ ___ ___ ___ ◯
9. ◯ ___ ___ ___ ___ ___
10. ___ ◯ ___ ◯

One whose greatest fear came upon him.

Answer: ___ ___ ___   ___ ___ ___ ___ ___ ___ ___   ___ ___ ___

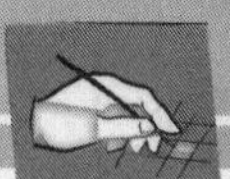

40–A Glorious Outfit

Only a true king can be arrayed in this. Can you work out the kind of attire fit for the Lord of all? (PSALM 104)

1. SAEHT
2. OAIUMNTN
3. SFOLW
4. DHRETUN
5. EVHNASE
6. DETLPAN
7. FINLOMDA
8. JRCEEIO
9. RISISTP
10. RLGYO

1. ◯__ __ __ __

2. __ ◯ __ __ __ __ __ ◯

3. __ ◯ __ __ __

4. __ __ ◯ __ __ __ ◯

5. __ __ ◯ __ __ ◯ __

6. __ __ __ __ __ __ ◯

7. ◯ ◯ __ __ __ __ __ __

8. __ __ ◯ __ __ __ ◯

9. ◯ __ __ __ __ ◯ __

10. __ __ __ __ ◯

God is so great, and clothed with. . .

Answer: __ __ __ __ __ __ __ __ __ __

__ __ __ __ __ __ __

41–The Lord Gives a Sign

Isaiah saw a sign of the little Lord's arrival. May God be with you as you work on this puzzle. (ISAIAH 7)

1. HLCID
2. AUSMSCAD
3. TTPME
4. YAARSIS
5. RFEANKSO
6. UNDOTIC
7. VARPELI
8. LEFLUR

1. ___ ___ ◯ ___ ___
2. ___ ___ ◯ ___ ___ ___ ___ ___
3. ___ ___ ◯ ___ ___
4. ◯ ___ ___ ___ ___ ___ ___
5. ___ ___ ___ ___ ___ ___ ___ ◯
6. ___ ___ ___ ___ ◯ ___ ___
7. ___ ___ ◯ ___ ___ ___ ___
8. ___ ___ ___ ◯ ___ ___

"He will refuse the evil, and choose the good."

Answer: ___ ___ ___ ___ ___ ___ ___ ___

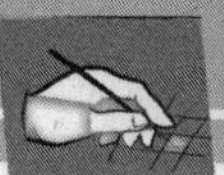

42–Back to School

From cover to cover, the Bible is full of this. And if you've had any schooling, you'll easily solve this one. (PROVERBS 12)

1. LIDGEITN
2. ARSEDN
3. UTLEROB
4. NDEERR
5. LUCRE
6. WKDCEI
7. HTTUR
8. TURSGHEIO
9. DCMNNEO

1. _ _ _ ◯ _ _ ◯ _
2. ◯ _ _ _ _ _
3. ◯ _ _ _ _ _ _
4. _ _ _ _ _ ◯
5. _ _ ◯ _ _
6. _ _ ◯ _ _ _
7. ◯ _ _ _ _
8. _ ◯ _ _ _ _ ◯ _ _
9. _ _ _ _ _ _ ◯

Whoever loves this, loves knowledge.

Answer: _ _ _ _ _ _ _ _ _ _ _

43–Looking for Love in All the Wrong Places

Many times the faithfulness of God's people waned. Solve this scramble to discover what activity His people pursued. (JEREMIAH 3)

1. SEDIRNSEWL
2. THOARL
3. REGAN
4. OULPLET
5. MAHES
6. CWKEDI
7. CREATESHOUR
8. SCABLKDEI
9. TNNASOI
10. DRAYTLEU
11. EUSLYR

1. ___ ◯ ___ ___ ___ ___ ___ ___ ___ ◯
2. ___ ___ ◯ ___ ___ ___
3. ◯ ___ ___ ◯ ___
4. ___ ___ ◯ ___ ___ ___ ___
5. ◯ ___ ___ ___ ___
6. ___ ◯ ___ ___ ___ ◯
7. ___ ___ ___ ___ ___ ___ ___ ___ ◯ ___ ___
8. ___ ___ ___ ___ ___ ◯ ___ ___ ___
9. ___ ◯ ◯ ___ ___ ___ ___
10. ___ ___ ___ ___ ___ ___ ◯ ___
11. ___ ___ ___ ___ ___ ◯

In this, they were as guilty as Hosea's wife.

Answer: ___ ___ ___ ___ ___ ___ ' ___ ___ ___ ___ ___ ___ ___ ___ ___

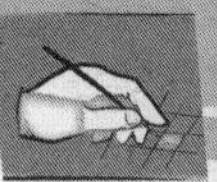

44–An Old Phrase. . .

This king was known long ago as an ally to the ruler of Israel. You'll be "jumping" to solve this puzzle. (1 Kings 22)

1. SEMLJRUEA
2. CARTNENE
3. DHRDUEN
4. MOISTDOSE
5. BAAH
6. KRPVOEO
7. SHRON
8. TRGHEA

1. ○ ___ ___ ___ ___ ___ ___ ___ ___
2. ___ ___ ___ ___ ___ ___ ___ ○
3. ○ ___ ___ ___ ___ ___ ___
4. ___ ○ ___ ___ ___ ___ ___ ___ ___ ○
5. ___ ○ ○ ___
6. ○ ___ ___ ___ ___ ___ ___
7. ○ ___ ___ ___ ___
8. ___ ○ ○ ___ ___ ___

A king of Judah.

Answer: ___ ___ ___ ___ ___ ___ ___ ___ ___ ___ ___

45–A New Name

God is the ultimate provider. Solve to uncover Abraham's term to describe this aspect of our Lord. (Genesis 22–23)

1. UESONRRJO
2. ILHDTHWE
3. HSERO
4. LIVRES
5. ECVA
6. KSLHESE
7. PHILJAD
8. BEAID
9. DTHERESTC
10. ADHN

1. __ __ ◯ __ __ __ __ ◯ __

2. __ __ __ ◯ __ __ __ __

3. __ __ ◯ __ __

4. __ __ __ ◯ __ __

5. __ ◯ __ __

6. __ ◯ __ __ __ __ __

7. ◯ __ __ __ __ __ __

8. __ __ ◯ __ __

9. __ __ ◯ __ __ __ __ __ ◯ __

10. ◯ __ __ __

Abraham's name for a giving God.

Answer: __ __ __ __ __ __ __ – __ __ __ __ __

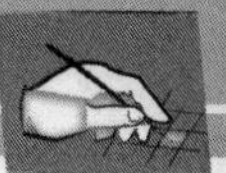

46–Because He Was Sad

This nation, built and torn apart again and again, brought such sorrow to Nehemiah's heart. Can you determine this cupbearer's destination? (NEHEMIAH 2)

1. DJHAU
2. SCENERPE
3. ARHTFE
4. HEPLURCES
5. TOFERS
6. SWEAT
7. BNLLEOIRE
8. SLOBNE
9. ROOMERVE

1. ○ __ __ __ __
2. __ __ __ __ __ __ __ ○
3. __ __ __ __ __ ○
4. __ __ __ ○ __ __ __ __ __
5. __ __ __ __ ○ __
6. __ ○ __ __ __
7. __ __ __ __ ○ __ __ __ __
8. __ __ __ __ ○ __
9. ○ __ __ __ __ __ __ __

Nehemiah leads the way here.

Answer: __ __ __ __ __ __ __ __ __

47–*Warrior Gives Thanks*

This was built to give thanks to the Lord for a rock-solid victory. (You'll love the "iron-y" of this one.) (CHAPTER 8 OF THE 6TH OLD TESTAMENT BOOK)

1. GDUSJE
2. OSETNS
3. LHFA
4. NBRTU
5. SGATAIN
6. ZEEIS
7. ADRCOC
8. NSLSEGISB
9. OHRTF
10. SHABUM
11. NRRGTEAS

1. ◯ _ _ _ _ _
2. _ _ ◯ _ _ ◯
3. ◯ _ _ _
4. _ ◯ _ _ _
5. _ _ ◯ _ _ _ _
6. ◯ _ _ _ _
7. ◯ _ _ _ _ _
8. _ ◯ _ _ _ _ _ _ _
9. _ _ _ ◯ _
10. ◯ _ _ _ _ _
11. _ _ _ _ _ _ _ ◯

Built for the Lord in Mount Ebal.

Answer: _ _ _ _ _ _ ' _   _ _ _ _ _

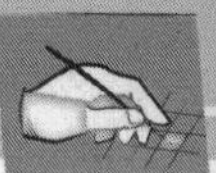

48–Glory to Shame

Without this, only destruction lies ahead. Are you clever enough to solve this one? (HOSEA 4)

1. GLUHNASI
2. CEETRJDE
3. LINKGLI
4. AWDHSO
5. OGFETR
6. KRBAE
7. RRSNTOOEYCV
8. RAWES
9. FELT
10. CRADLEE
11. GNIODS
12. FEERIH

1. ◯ ◯ ___ ___ ___ ___ ___ ___

2. ___ ___ ___ ___ ◯ ___ ___ ___

3. ◯ ___ ___ ___ ___ ___ ___

4. ___ ___ ___ ___ ◯ ___

5. ◯ ___ ___ ___ ___ ___

6. ___ ___ ___ ___ ◯

7. ___ ___ ◯ ___ ___ ◯ ___ ___ ___ ___ ___

8. ___ ◯ ___ ___ ___

9. ◯ ◯ ___ ___

10. ◯ ___ ___ ___ ___ ___ ___

11. ___ ___ ___ ___ ◯ ___

12. ___ ___ ___ ___ ◯ ___

His people would perish because of this.

Answer: ___ ___ ___ ___ ___ ___ ___ ___ ___ ___ ___ ___ ___ ___ ___ ___

49–Heavy Heart

Jeremiah wrote pages and pages expressing this. The answer will make you howl! (JEREMIAH 6)

1. SAILRE
2. BLESSMAY
3. HSSEA
4. NURDET
5. SAKEBT
6. MENCHTAW
7. FIRGE
8. CCOAKTLHS
9. GHNAUIS

1. __ __ __ __ __ ◯
2. ◯ __ __ __ ◯ __ __ __
3. __ __ __ ◯ __
4. __ __ __ ◯ __ __
5. __ __ __ __ __ ◯
6. __ ◯ ◯ __ __ __ __ __
7. __ __ ◯ __ __
8. __ __ __ __ __ __ ◯ __ __
9. __ ◯ __ __ __ __ __

A prophet's words of sorrow.

Answer: __ __ __ __ __ __ __ __ __ __ __

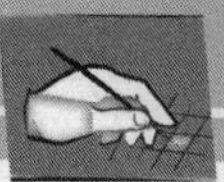

50–*Jaws*

If this creature were still around today, we'd never go in the water! Have fun getting your hooks into this puzzle. (Job 41)

1. EOCALNC
2. IHENS
3. NAVI
4. LRIEDB
5. RLADNOC
6. BTERLREI
7. TIHGL
8. EBBDRA
9. RSNLTOSI

1. ___ ___ ___ ___ ___ ___ ◯
2. ___ ___ ___ ___ ◯
3. ◯ ___ ___ ___
4. ___ ___ ◯ ___ ___ ___
5. ___ ◯ ___ ___ ___ ___ ___
6. ◯ ___ ___ ___ ___ ___ ___ ___
7. ___ ___ ___ ◯ ___
8. ___ ◯ ___ ___ ___ ___
9. ◯ ___ ___ ___ ___ ___ ___ ___

"Canst thou. . .bore his jaw through with a thorn?"

Answer: ___ ___ ___ ___ ___ ___ ___ ___ ___

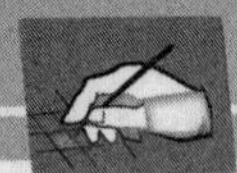

51–He Knew God Well

David was confident of this aspect of God's character. If you know Him well, it shouldn't be too hard to solve this scramble. (Psalm 51)

1. TBOL
2. VAINTOLAS
3. IENRSN
4. GONEUT
5. GNAKIM
6. BTRNU
7. DHNEID
8. DTRENE
9. NSNDEI
10. SLANGSED

1. ___ ◯ ◯ ___
2. ___ ___ ___ ◯ ___ ___ ◯ ___ ___
3. ___ ___ ___ ◯ ___ ___
4. ___ ___ ___ ◯ ___ ___
5. ___ ___ ◯ ◯ ___ ___
6. ___ ___ ___ ◯ ___
7. ___ ___ ◯ ___ ___ ___
8. ___ ___ ◯ ___ ◯ ___
9. ◯ ___ ___ ___ ___ ___
10. ___ ___ ___ ___ ___ ___ ◯ ___

David prayed for mercy according to God's. . .

Answer: ___ ___ ___ ___ ___ ___ ___ ___ ___ ___ ___ ___ ___ ___ ___ ___

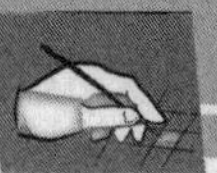

52–Refiner's Fire

Dwell on a royal line to help you figure out the description of this One who was, and is, and is to come. (MALACHI 3)

1. ORMREF
2. REAPS
3. CBAOJ
4. EEVSR
5. FISTW
6. YRFUIP
7. IROTPF
8. TCSA
9. EFHSTAR
10. SWESTIN
11. NLATPSAE

1. ___ ___ ___ ○ ___ ___
2. ___ ___ ○ ___ ___
3. ○ ___ ___ ___ ___
4. ___ ___ ___ ___ ○
5. ○ ___ ___ ___ ○
6. ___ ___ ___ ___ ___ ○
7. ___ ___ ○ ○ ___ ___
8. ○ ___ ___ ___
9. ___ ___ ___ ○ ___ ○ ___
10. ___ ○ ___ ___ ___ ___ ___
11. ___ ___ ___ ___ ○ ___ ___ ○

A prophecy of Malachi.

Answer: ___ ___ ___ ___ ___ ___ ___ ___ ___ ___ ___ ___ ___ ___ ___ ___ ___

53–We're Covered

The sanctuary contained several pieces of furniture. Sit down for a moment and think on this as a symbol of God's wonderful grace to come! (Exodus 25)

1. RHMBECIU
2. EHGNTL
3. EBRNO
4. RVCEO
5. RVYLAEO
6. ASTVSE
7. LONDEG
8. EPSCLA
9. ITUCB

1. __ __ __ __ __ __ __ ◯
2. __ ◯ __ __ __ __
3. __ __ ◯ __ __
4. ◯ __ __ __ __
5. __ __ __ __ __ __ ◯
6. ◯ __ __ __ __ __
7. __ __ __ __ ◯ __
8. __ __ ◯ __ __ __
9. __ __ __ __ ◯

Covered by angels' wings.

Answer: __ __ __ __ __   __ __ __ __

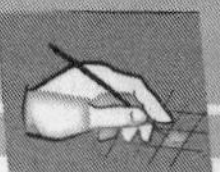

54–Little Known

This small-town prophet saw the King coming. Solve to discover "Who is like the Lord?" (33RD OLD TESTAMENT BOOK)

1. IDMRNO
2. NZOI
3. CRABUILNE
4. OHPETPR
5. ENBRETRH
6. YAMILF
7. FSRETO
8. SREIA
9. EEHVSSA
10. NSRGTO
11. OHNR
12. TWHNII
13. VEDINI

1. ___ ___ ◯ ___ ___ ___
2. ___ ◯ ___ ___
3. ___ ___ ◯ ___ ___ ◯ ___ ___ ___
4. ___ ___ ___ ___ ◯ ___ ◯
5. ___ ___ ___ ___ ◯ ___ ◯ ___
6. ___ ___ ◯ ___ ___ ___
7. ___ ◯ ◯ ___ ___ ___
8. ___ ◯ ___ ___ ___
9. ___ ___ ___ ___ ___ ___ ◯
10. ___ ◯ ___ ___ ___ ___
11. ◯ ___ ___ ___
12. ___ ◯ ◯ ___ ___ ___
13. ___ ___ ___ ___ ___ ◯

He proclaimed the promised ruler.

Answer: ___ ___ ___ ___ ___ ___ ___ ___ ___

___ ___ ___ ___ ___ ___ ___ ___ ___ ___

55–A Threshing Floor

Solomon built the temple of the Lord here. Good luck threshing this one out. (2 CHRONICLES 3)

1. ESABM
2. MTOUAN
3. RHUEDDN
4. LESTANT
5. GIAEM
6. REOCS
7. MORICNS
8. LIARSPL
9. BRUCHE

1. __ __ __ ◯ __
2. __ __ ◯ ◯ __ __
3. __ __ ◯ __ __ __ __
4. __ __ __ __ __ ◯ __
5. __ ◯ __ __ __
6. __ __ ◯ __ __
7. __ ◯ __ __ __ __ __
8. __ ◯ __ __ ◯ __ __
9. __ ◯ __ __ __ __

The Lord appeared here once to David.

Answer: __ __ __ __ __   __ __ __ __ __ __

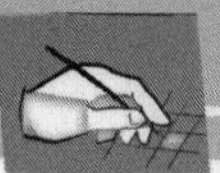

56–Kingdom Come

This place will be rendered one day and, no doubt, nothing upon it will survive. Solving this puzzle will not be a fruitless endeavor. (Zechariah 14)

1. EULM
2. MOUSENC
3. WNRIET
4. OHRFT
5. CRONER
6. SFEHL
7. THOFUG
8. ULGAEP
9. PVYIACITT
10. LVLEAY
11. ORESH
12. ASNTSI

1. ◯ __ __ __
2. __ ◯ __ __ ◯ __ __
3. __ __ ◯ __ __ __
4. __ __ __ ◯ __
5. __ ◯ __ __ __ __
6. ◯ __ __ __ __
7. __ ◯ __ __ __ __
8. __ ◯ __ __ __ __
9. __ __ __ __ __ __ ◯ __ __
10. ◯ __ __ __ __ __
11. __ __ __ __ ◯
12. __ __ __ __ __ ◯

On that day, where He will stand.

Answer: __ __ __ __ __   __ __   __ __ __ __ __ __ __

57–A Furnace!

One more time, the Lord came down here to command his people in the ways of righteousness and obedience. This puzzle will take you to old heights! (Exodus 19)

1. NADMOCM
2. ULDOC
3. CUTOH
4. NERTDURE
5. MUPTTER
6. CASTINYF
7. GWNIS
8. EXDAW
9. TINGGHILN

1. __ __ ◯ __ __ __ __
2. __ __ ◯ __ __
3. __ __ ◯ __ __
4. __ __ __ __ __ ◯ __ __
5. __ __ __ __ __ __ ◯
6. ◯ __ __ __ __ ◯ __ __
7. __ __ ◯ __ __
8. __ ◯ __ __ __
9. __ ◯ __ __ __ __ __ __ __

Here was the fire of God.

Answer: __ __ __ __ __ __ __ __ __ __

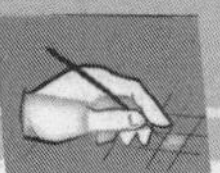

58–Hot Rocks!

Sometimes the Lord gets inflamed, as He did here. As you solve, be sure not to let let the difficulty of this puzzle quench *your* fire. (DEUTERONOMY 4)

1. SEMSO
2. LEHODB
3. DISTILEMIU
4. NARLE
5. WRATSDAE
6. DISTM
7. EHTRNIE
8. SSESOPS
9. SIFH
10. GREUIF
11. PEREC
12. AVEELC

1. ○ __ __ __ __

2. __ __ __ ○ __ __

3. __ __ __ __ __ __ __ ○ __ __

4. __ __ __ __ ○

5. __ __ __ ○ __ ○ __ __

6. __ ○ __ __ __

7. ○ __ __ __ __ __ __

8. __ ○ __ __ __ __ __

9. ○ __ __ __

10. ○ ○ __ __ __ __

11. __ ○ __ __ __

12. __ __ __ __ __ ○

The covenant delivered here.

Answer: __ __ __ __ __ __ __ __ __ __ __ __ __ __ __ __

59–Vile Verbage

Hearing oration from this orifice would not be sweet or righteous. Remember that silence really can be golden as you solve this. (PROVERBS 15)

1. MOABIOTAINN
2. ESREFU
3. TMEHRO
4. FROROPE
5. HRAWT
6. SEEPAPA
7. SIEW
8. TORECRC
9. OESKARF
10. RMYER
11. RINEDN

1. ___ ___ ___ ○ ___ ___ ___ ___ ___ ○ ___
2. ___ ___ ___ ○ ___ ___
3. ___ ___ ○ ○ ___ ___
4. ___ ___ ___ ___ ○ ___ ○
5. ___ ___ ___ ○ ○
6. ___ ___ ___ ___ ___ ___ ○
7. ○ ○ ___ ___
8. ○ ___ ___ ___ ___ ___ ___
9. ___ ___ ___ ___ ___ ○ ___
10. ___ ○ ___ ___ ___
11. ○ ___ ___ ___ ___ ___

Only evil pours out.

Answer: ___ ___ ___ ___ ___ ___ ___ ___ ___ ___
___ ___ ___ ___ ___ ___

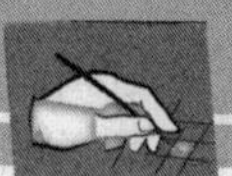

60–They Wouldn't Stop

Endless whiners can become more than irritating. Solve to discover what Miriam's brother got tired of hearing. (Exodus 16)

1. OESSM
2. ODUNR
3. MROWS
4. LURRES
5. IMRNGON
6. ASKTN
7. TGHNNIO
8. ESKAP

1. ○__ __ __ __
2. __ __ ○ __ __
3. __ __ ○ ○ __
4. __ ○ __ __ __ __
5. __ __ ○ __ ○ __ __
6. __ __ __ ○ __
7. __ __ __ __ __ __ ○
8. ○ __ __ __ __

During the Exodus, the children of Israel were guilty of this.

Answer: __ __ __ __ __ __ __ __ __ __ __

61–Only for the Lord

When they vowed their lives to God, long hair was an outward sign, and for Samson, a source of his strength. Don't "tress" out on this one! (JUDGES 13)

1. RABERN
2. CANULEN
3. OARZR
4. SHUNDAB
5. KNDIR
6. AINTDE
7. ANTENOUNCCE
8. SEERBOV

1. __ __ __ __ __ ◯
2. __ __ __ __ __ ◯ __
3. __ __ ◯ __ __
4. __ __ __ __ ◯ __ __
5. __ ◯ __ __ __
6. __ __ __ __ ◯ __
7. __ __ __ __ ◯ __ __ __ __ __ ◯
8. __ __ ◯ __ __ __ __

No haircuts.

Answer: __ __ __ __ __ __ __ __ __ __ __

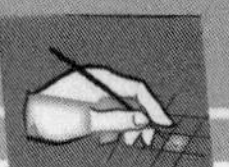

62–Short but Powerful

There's a very short book in the Old Testament, written by a prophet whose name means "servant of the Lord." Solve to uncover his book's main gist. (30TH BOOK OF THE OLD TESTAMENT)

1. LSOALWW
2. SBEUTBL
3. TCPIAIYTV
4. ADLI
5. ENMARI
6. DWRRAE
7. OENHLISS
8. CDIEVEE
9. DSISPEDE
10. EPSSOSS
11. KLIEDN
12. UWODN

1. _ _ _ _ _ ◯ _
2. _ _ _ ◯ _ _ _
3. _ ◯ _ _ _ _ _ _ _
4. _ _ _ ◯
5. _ _ _ _ ◯ _
6. _ _ _ ◯ _ _
7. ◯ _ _ _ _ _ _ ◯
8. _ _ _ _ _ ◯ _
9. _ _ _ _ ◯ _ _ _
10. _ _ _ _ _ _ ◯
11. _ ◯ _ _ _ _
12. _ ◯ _ ◯ _

All of God's nation's a fire, according to this.

Answer: _ _ _ _ _ _ _ _ ' _ _ _ _ _ _ _ _ _

63–A Heart Transplant

To help His people obey Him, God said He would replace their heart of stone with a heart of flesh. Work this puzzle to find a different term for these Holy Orders that required heart surgery. (EZEKIEL 11)

1. INISOV
2. DRROBE
3. EDDRINK
4. EIPNRC
5. BASTEDELET
6. ANFLEL
7. CRATEST
8. KPESA
9. STESTUAT

1. ___ ___ ___ ___ ○ ___
2. ___ ___ ○ ○ ___ ___
3. ___ ○ ___ ___ ___ ___ ___
4. ___ ___ ___ ○ ___ ___
5. ___ ___ ___ ___ ___ ___ ○ ___ ___ ___
6. ___ ___ ___ ___ ___ ○
7. ___ ○ ___ ___ ___ ___ ___
8. ___ ___ ○ ___ ___
9. ○ ___ ___ ___ ___ ___ ___ ___

If they kept these, He would be their God.

Answer: ___ ___ ___ ___ ___ ___ ___ ___ ___ ___

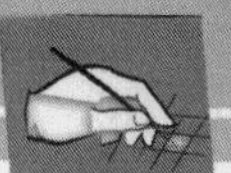

64–Vision Impaired

This officer's household was blessed when Joseph was its overseer. Unscramble these clues to uncover the name of this "short-sighted" man of rank. (Genesis 39)

1. OPRRESP
2. CMKO
3. RHWTA
4. EIKCDW
5. RINSESPOR
6. WHSBERE
7. NMRNEA
8. TRAGERE

1. __ __ __ __ ◯ __ __
2. __ ◯ __ __
3. __ __ __ ◯ __
4. __ ◯ __ __ __ __
5. ◯ __ __ __ __ __ __ __ __
6. ◯ __ __ __ __ __ __
7. __ ◯ __ __ __ __
8. __ __ __ __ __ __ ◯

An officer of the Pharaoh.

Answer: __ __ __ __ __ __ __ __

65–Gave Up One of Seven

A stranger in a strange land offered his help and was rewarded with the hand of this noble man's daughter. (Exodus 2)

1. AHOAPRH
2. RDECI
3. NECODS
4. HHDERSPES
5. OTSDO
6. OKLCF
7. TMESI
8. TUDRAGHE
9. VEIRR
10. AETNRGRS
11. ABOGEDN

1. ◯ ___ ___ ◯ ___ ___ ___
2. ___ ___ ◯ ___ ___
3. ___ ◯ ___ ___ ___ ___
4. ___ ___ ___ ___ ___ ___ ___ ___ ◯
5. ___ ◯ ___ ◯ ___
6. ◯ ___ ___ ___ ___
7. ___ ◯ ◯ ___ ___
8. ◯ ___ ___ ___ ___ ___ ___ ___
9. ___ ◯ ___ ___ ___
10. ___ ___ ___ ◯ ___ ___ ___ ___
11. ___ ___ ◯ ___ ___ ___ ___

Father-in-law of a "once-prince."

Answer: ___ ___ ___ ___ ___ ___ ___   ___ ___   ___ ___ ___ ___ ___ ___

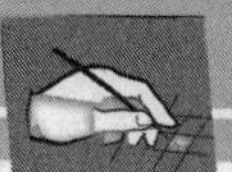

66–Road Work

Malachi predicted that a man would do this prior to the coming of the Lord. Solve to find the work once performed by John the Baptist. (Malachi 3)

1. UPGRE
2. TNRUER
3. OVPER
4. FDEREA
5. ONAVCENT
6. GHLINIRE
7. NEFERRI
8. FWTIS
9. EIADB
10. PYPAH

1. ◯ __ ◯ __ __
2. __ ◯ __ __ __ __
3. ◯ __ __ __ __
4. __ __ ◯ ◯ __ __
5. __ __ __ ◯ __ __ __ ◯
6. ◯ __ __ __ __ __ __ __
7. __ __ __ __ __ ◯ __
8. __ ◯ __ __ __
9. ◯ __ __ __ __
10. __ __ __ __ ◯

Role of a messenger.

Answer: __ __ __ __ __ __ __ __ __   __ __ __   __ __ __

67–A Great Light

Isaiah foretells of One who will give to us what the world cannot give. The clues below should illuminate His royal appellation. (Isaiah 9)

1. SOPERSPOR
2. CIJREEO
3. SCARENIE
4. ETHTCRS
5. TUNESOSST
6. FASTF
7. OPILS
8. STEALVINERG
9. SCUONLE
10. CUTJSEI

1. _ O _ O _ _ _ _ _

2. _ _ _ _ O _ _

3. _ O O _ _ _ _ _

4. _ _ _ O _ _ _

5. _ _ O _ _ _ _ _ _

6. _ _ _ O _

7. _ O _ _ _

8. O _ _ _ _ O _ _ _ _ _

9. O _ _ _ _ _ _

10. _ _ _ _ _ _ O

Isaiah speaks of this one. . .

Answer: _ _ _ _ _ _ _ _ _ _ _ _ _ _

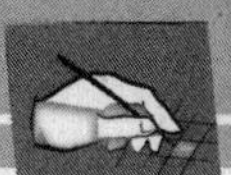

68–Lighten Up

This ruler was advised to lighten the loads of his people. No yoke!
(1 Kings 12)

1. POORICNS
2. ROUSEFORC
3. VHAEY
4. IRUSVOGE
5. TNRUB
6. ATCOHIR
7. SEATHCSI
8. EFPRRMO

1. ___ ___ ___ ◯ ___ ___ ___ ___
2. ___ ___ ___ ___ ___ ___ ___ ___ ◯
3. ◯ ___ ___ ___ ___
4. ___ ___ ___ ___ ___ ◯ ___ ___
5. ◯ ___ ___ ___ ___
6. ___ ___ ___ ___ ___ ◯ ___
7. ___ ___ ◯ ___ ___ ___ ___ ___
8. ___ ___ ___ ___ ___ ___ ◯

Solomon's son who spurned the advice of his counselors.

Answer: ___ ___ ___ ___ ___ ___ ___ ___

69–Judgment

In the Day of the Lord, this idolatrous group will never see the "sun" again. (ZEPHANIAH 1)

1. REAPLAP
2. THARMECN
3. SCHRAGNI
4. TESTEL
5. THUPOSSOE
6. SHSEIF
7. CLOBSK
8. RADINECD
9. LEDNACS

1. _ _ _ _ ◯ ◯ _
2. ◯ _ _ _ _ _ ◯ _
3. _ _ ◯ _ _ _ ◯ _
4. _ _ ◯ _ _ _
5. _ ◯ _ _ _ _ _ _ _
6. ◯ _ _ _ _ _
7. ◯ _ _ _ _ _
8. _ _ _ _ ◯ _ _ _
9. _ ◯ _ _ ◯ _ _

Zephaniah declares who will be cut off.

Answer: _ _ _ _ _ _ _ _ _ _ _ _ _ _

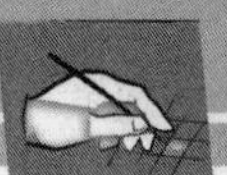

70–*Refreshing Grace*

As we follow His leading, God renews us! Solve to discover what He did for David. (Psalm 23)

1. SETAPUSR
2. NIEMSEE
3. TOAINN
4. MCROTFO
5. EKMA
6. THADE
7. MANE
8. RUYSLE
9. PSDHHERE
10. SONGDOSE
11. SHUOE
12. LISTL

1. ___ ___ ___ ___ ___ ◯ ___ ___
2. ◯ ___ ___ ___ ___ ___ ◯
3. ___ ___ ___ ___ ___ ◯
4. ___ ◯ ___ ___ ___ ◯ ___
5. ___ ___ ___ ◯
6. ___ ___ ___ ◯ ◯
7. ___ ___ ◯ ___
8. ___ ___ ___ ___ ___ ◯
9. ◯ ___ ___ ___ ___ ___ ___ ___
10. ___ ◯ ___ ___ ___ ___ ___ ___
11. ___ ___ ◯ ___ ___
12. ___ ___ ___ ___ ◯

A promise from God.

Answer: ___ ___ ___ ___ ___ ___ ___ ___ ___ ___ ___ ___ ___ ___ ___ ___ ___ ___ ___

71–True Value

God's wisdom is more precious than gold or silver. "Ken" you discover its true value? (PROVERBS 8)

1. PROMACE
2. EEVECIR
3. SLCUDO
4. GOTSEHIUR
5. ELDABRU
6. SNIFONUAT
7. UNCEPERD
8. REAPERP
9. ACPEL

1. __ __ __ __ __ ◯ __
2. __ __ __ __ ◯ __ __
3. ◯ __ __ __ __ __
4. __ __ __ ◯ ◯ __ __ __ __
5. __ __ ◯ __ __ __ ◯
6. __ __ __ __ __ ◯ __ __ ◯
7. __ __ ◯ __ __ __ __ __
8. __ ◯ __ __ __ __ __
9. __ __ __ __ ◯

Wisdom is a. . .

Answer: __ __ __ __ __ __ __ __ __ __ __ __

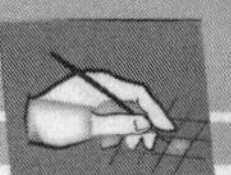

72–Built Strong

David found that with each act of deliverance, God was building his faith so that he would know his Lord as a mighty refuge on which he could stand. Work this puzzle to uncover terms David used to describe our Lord. (2 Samuel 22)

1. SAREI
2. TNSLORSI
3. UOMSCEN
4. EUCLRBK
5. ANCLE
6. LFELNA
7. IGDEDR
8. AORWFRD
9. PREDAT
10. HEUBCR
11. GBETSRHINS
12. NWISG

1. __ ◯ __ __ __
2. __ ◯ __ __ __ __ __ __
3. ◯ __ __ __ __ __ __
4. __ __ __ ◯ __ __ __
5. __ __ __ ◯ __
6. __ __ __ __ __ ◯
7. __ __ __ ◯ __ __
8. ◯ __ ◯ __ __ __ __
9. __ __ __ __ ◯ ◯
10. __ __ __ ◯ __ __
11. __ __ __ __ __ __ __ ◯ __ ◯
12. __ __ __ __ ◯

David was delivered and knew that God was his. . .

Answer: __ __ __ __ __ __ __ __ __ __ __ __ __ __ __ __ __ __

73–Strike One

The outcome would have been horrible if God had not helped Moses out at this place. (EXODUS 17)

1. DELRSE
2. UTGFHO
3. EHSCOO
4. OBKO
5. DIHEC
6. PGYSAIENT
7. IRHTTS
8. USJHAO
9. VPELRAI
10. ULBIT

1. ___ ___ ___ ___ ◯ ___

2. ___ ◯ ___ ___ ___ ___

3. ◯ ___ ___ ___ ___ ___

4. ___ ___ ___ ◯

5. ___ ___ ◯ ___ ___

6. ___ ___ ___ ___ ___ ___ ___ ◯ ___

7. ___ ◯ ___ ___ ___ ___

8. ___ ◯ ___ ___ ___ ___

9. ___ ◯ ◯ ___ ___ ___ ___

10. ◯ ___ ___ ___ ___

Smitten for water.

Answer: ___ ___ ___ ___ ___ ___ ___ ___ ___ ___ ___

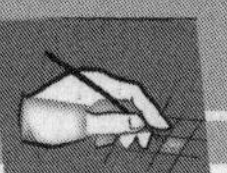

74–King Me!

When the Israelites demanded a king, this man envisioned the consequences. Solve to discover the name of this farseeing individual. (Chapter 8 of the 9th Old Testament Book)

1. ORNIBFRST	4. EJDGU	7. SHCNOE	10. EEPLOP
2. RKEAB	5. EDHLBO	8. PACNITA	11. RASHEERE
3. DMSAI	6. NPTIAPO	9. NROUDG	12. VSETRAH

1. ___ ___ ___ ◯ ___ ___ ___ ___ ___

2. ___ ◯ ___ ___ ___

3. ◯ ___ ___ ___ ___

4. ___ ◯ ___ ___ ___

5. ___ ◯ ___ ___ ◯ ___

6. ___ ___ ___ ___ ___ ___ ◯

7. ___ ◯ ___ ___ ◯ ___

8. ___ ___ ◯ ___ ___ ___ ___

9. ___ ◯ ___ ___ ___ ___

10. ___ ___ ◯ ◯ ___ ___

11. ___ ___ ◯ ___ ___ ___ ___ ___

12. ___ ___ ___ ___ ◯ ___ ◯

He tried to tell the Israelites they didn't need an earthly ruler.

Answer: ___ ___ ___ ___ ___ ___ ___   ___ ___ ___ ___   ___ ___ ___ ___ ___ ___ ___ ___ ___ ___

75–David's Desire

David's desire for his son was that he walk in the ways of the Lord, that he might be strong and "reveal" this quality to all who would see. Work these words to reveal David's fatherly advice. (1 KINGS 2)

1. NSVARET
2. HNTOER
3. WLEKTAS
4. HIBELATSS
5. SAYER
6. VEENS
7. FEIL
8. CABEALYPE
9. MDSIWO
10. DRAINCCOG

1. ◯ _ _ _ _ _ _
2. _ ◯ _ _ _ ◯
3. ◯ _ _ _ _ _ _
4. _ _ ◯ _ _ _ _ _ ◯
5. ◯ _ _ _ _
6. ◯ _ _ ◯ _
7. ◯ _ ◯ _
8. _ _ ◯ _ _ _ _ _ _
9. _ _ _ _ _ ◯
10. ◯ _ _ _ _ _ _ ◯ _

A charge to Solomon.

Answer: "_ _ _ _ _ _ _ _ _ _ _ _ _ _ _ _ _"

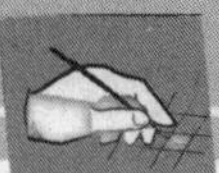

76–Job's Trial

Satan implied that Job would rather see the very "flesh of his flesh," his children, be killed rather than lose his own flesh. Hope that hint helps you uncover his exact remark—word for word! (JOB 2)

1. ESLO
2. LIWNGKA
3. OSFHOLI
4. NRESCEPE
5. TFHOR
6. EOTRYSD
7. TOESRPHD
8. ESLKRNIP
9. ILSBO
10. TEAMNL

1. ◯__ __ __
2. __ __ __ ◯ __ __ __
3. __ __ __ __ ◯ __ __
4. __ __ __ __ __ ◯ __ __
5. ◯ __ __ __ __
6. __ __ __ __ __ ◯ __
7. __ __ __ __ __ __ ◯ __
8. ◯ __ __ __ __ ◯ __ __
9. __ __ ◯ __ __
10. __ __ ◯ __ __ __

Satan's answer to God.

Answer: "__ __ __ __ __ __ __ __ __ __ __ __"

77–Pass It On

To solve this scramble, know that he shared this title with One who was to come. (1 Kings 5)

1. SHREEW
2. ANOSDUHT
3. NYCVEO
4. EOIFCFR
5. RDCEA
6. VENSTAR
7. ULBDI
8. IDSEER

1. ___ ___ ___ ___ ___ ○
2. ___ ___ ○ ___ ___ ___ ○ ___
3. ___ ○ ___ ___ ___ ___
4. ___ ___ ○ ___ ___ ___ ___
5. ___ ___ ○ ○ ___
6. ___ ___ ___ ○ ___ ___ ___
7. ___ ___ ○ ___ ___
8. ○ ___ ___ ___ ___ ___

He would build the house of the Lord.

Answer: ___ ___ ___   ___ ___   ___ ___ ___ ___ ___ ___ ___

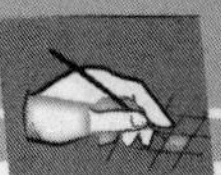

78–*Calling Out*

Not the longest book in the Bible, but one that clearly "plays out" a vision of the greatest love story ever told. (22nd Old Testament Book)

1. WLFSEOR
2. ONHSR
3. OENRDWC
4. ERAPG
5. MYCEOL
6. XFOSE
7. ETWRO
8. EEDOVBL
9. FEMREUP
10. BNAENOL
11. IONUNTAF

1. ___ ___ ___ ___ ___ ___ ○
2. ___ ___ ○ ___ ___
3. ___ ___ ___ ___ ○ ___ ___
4. ○ ___ ___ ___ ___
5. ___ ○ ___ ___ ___ ___
6. ○ ___ ___ ___ ○
7. ___ ○ ___ ___ ___
8. ___ ___ ○ ○ ___ ___ ___
9. ___ ___ ___ ___ ___ ○ ___
10. ___ ___ ___ ___ ___ ○ ___
11. ___ ___ ___ ○ ___ ___ ___ ___

Courtship is only the beginning.

Answer: ___ ___ ___ ___ ___ ___ ___ ___ ___ ___ ___ ___ ___

79–A *Promise*

God stores this up for true believers. Unscramble these clues and you'll "know" the answer! (PROVERBS 2)

1. GRANTRES
2. OMTUH
3. SNUTREDDNA
4. AWNMO
5. TUYQIE
6. RASHEC
7. REDCIINSTO
8. GUMDENJT

1. ◯ ___ ___ ___ ___ ___ ___ ___
2. ___ ◯ ◯ ___ ___
3. ___ ◯ ___ ___ ___ ___ ___ ___ ___ ◯
4. ◯ ___ ___ ___ ___
5. ___ ___ ___ ◯ ___ ___
6. ◯ ___ ___ ___ ___ ___
7. ◯ ___ ___ ___ ___ ___ ___ ___ ◯ ___
8. ___ ___ ___ ___ ◯ ___ ___ ___

For the righteous, God gives. . .

Answer: ___ ___ ___ ___ ___   ___ ___ ___ ___ ___ ___

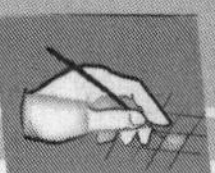

80–Thanksgiving

After the yearly harvest and for seven days, every male was commanded to attend this glad festival. (Leviticus 23)

1. GRHTEA
2. AFSET
3. NBECSHAR
4. RIVELSE
5. OHMTN
6. EFHAS
7. RCMPIAOL
8. MSBEHIL
9. ONMESL

1. __ __ ◯ __ __ __
2. __ __ ◯ __ __
3. ◯ __ __ __ __ __ ◯ __
4. __ __ ◯ __ __ __ __
5. __ __ ◯ __ __
6. __ __ __ ◯ __
7. __ __ __ ◯ __ __ __ __
8. __ ◯ ◯ __ __ __ __
9. ◯ __ __ __ __ __

An ingathering of fruits.

Answer: __ __ __ __ __ __ __ __ __ __ __

81–Bedtime Story

This history book, read before a sleepless king, prevented the hanging of Mordecai. Stay awake and solve! (Esther 6)

1. ITHGN
2. ESRETH
3. DORCESR
4. RVDECOE
5. OSHER
6. LWASOGL
7. UNATQEB
8. GUMNORIN
9. ALMICEBHARN
10. LEFBLEAN
11. ISNTRIME

1. _ _ _ _ ◯
2. _ _ _ ◯ _ _
3. _ ◯ _ _ _ _ _
4. ◯ _ _ _ _ _ _
5. ◯ _ ◯ _ _
6. _ _ _ _ ◯ _ _
7. _ _ ◯ _ _ _ _
8. _ _ _ _ _ ◯ _ _
9. ◯ _ _ _ _ _ _ ◯ _ _ _
10. _ _ _ _ _ _ ◯ _
11. _ _ _ _ ◯ _ _ _

The words of the foregoing days.

Answer: _ _ _   _ _ _ _ _ _ _ _ _ _

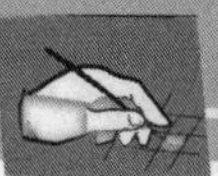

82–Lies and Deceit

Because of their lies and deceit, these men had blurred vision. Solve to discover those who were rebuked. (2 PETER 2)

1. RCTHEEA
2. SHEYER
3. EFGIN
4. EAGNL
5. UHPISN
6. TERBU
7. REPSCOINIU
8. VRPOREB
9. NUOP
10. YLHO
11. ETTEPSM
12. UVEOCSTO

1. ◯ ___ ___ ___ ◯ ___ ___
2. ___ ___ ___ ◯ ___ ___
3. ◯ ___ ___ ___ ___
4. ◯ ___ ___ ___ ◯
5. ___ ___ ___ ___ ◯ ___
6. ___ ___ ___ ___ ◯
7. ◯ ___ ___ ___ ___ ___ ___ ___ ___ ___
8. ___ ◯ ◯ ___ ___ ___ ___
9. ___ ◯ ___ ___
10. ◯ ___ ___ ___
11. ___ ◯ ___ ___ ___ ___ ___
12. ___ ___ ___ ___ ◯ ___ ___ ◯

Seer-ious liars.

Answer: ___ ___ ___ ___   ___ ___ ___ ___ ___ ___ ___   ___ ___ ___ ___ ___ ___ ___ ___ ___ ___ ___ ___ ___

83–Night Sight

Because of one man's gift of interpreting dreams, many were saved from this. (GENESIS 41)

1. ATROHCI
2. TIFHF
3. TCDRESEI
4. UAFVRO
5. AHROPHA
6. EMTI
7. NINLE
8. EUDNGNO
9. RDVOEU

1. ___ ___ ___ ___ ___ ___ ◯
2. ___ ___ ___ ___ ◯
3. ___ ___ ___ ___ ___ ◯ ___ ___
4. ◯ ___ ___ ___ ___ ___
5. ___ ___ ___ ___ ◯ ___ ___
6. ___ ___ ◯ ___
7. ___ ◯ ___ ___ ___
8. ___ ___ ◯ ___ ___ ___ ___
9. ___ ◯ ___ ___ ___ ___

Meaning of a dream.

Answer: ___ ___ ___ ___ ___ ___ ___ ___ ___

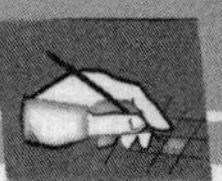

84–Sate Your Appetite

Want to avoid famine and death? Eat the Word of God and head in this direction. (Proverbs 6)

1. NNTTCOE
2. THANGUY
3. OORFPRE
4. IEKCWD
5. PLMA
6. EYUBTA
7. HLCSTEO
8. SFLEA
9. DELEISY
10. ONNNCEIT
11. DREFNI

1. ___ ___ ___ ◯ ___ ___ ___
2. ___ ___ ___ ___ ◯ ___ ___
3. ___ ◯ ___ ___ ___ ___ ___
4. ◯ ___ ___ ___ ___ ___
5. ___ ◯ ___ ___
6. ___ ___ ___ ___ ___ ◯
7. ___ ___ ◯ ___ ___ ___ ___
8. ◯ ___ ___ ___ ___
9. ___ ___ ___ ◯ ___ ___ ___
10. ◯ ___ ___ ___ ___ ___ ___ ___ ___
11. ◯ ___ ___ ◯ ___ ___

Reproofs of instruction are. . .

Answer: ___ ___ ___ ___   ___ ___ ___ ___   ___ ___   ___ ___ ___ ___

85–Changing Times

Everything moves in cycles, as this puzzle reveals. To solve, try not to "turn, turn, turn" to the answers in the back of the book. (Ecclesiastes 3)

1. NOHGNIT
2. SOUPREP
3. MAERCBE
4. FEARRIN
5. LICEESN
6. RALUBO
7. TUDS
8. REVICEPE
9. FMETNISA
10. IRNOPOT
11. QYINTIUI

1. __ __ ◯ ◯ __ __ __

2. __ __ __ __ __ __ ◯

3. __ __ __ ◯ __ __ ◯

4. __ __ __ __ __ ◯ __

5. ◯ __ __ __ __ __ __

6. __ ◯ __ __ __ __

7. __ __ ◯ __

8. __ __ __ __ ◯ __ __ __

9. __ ◯ __ __ __ __ ◯ __

10. __ __ __ __ __ ◯ __

11. __ ◯ __ __ __ __ __ __

A timeless phrase.

Answer: __ __ __ __ __ __ __ __ __ __ __ __ __ __ __ __ __

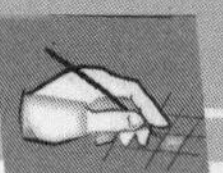

86–Never Forget

Throughout your days remember that you are God's property and He is this. (ECCLESIASTES 12)

1. CRSTEE
2. ERHERACP
3. EEYVR
4. SCCONONLUI
5. ONRMU
6. RLPSEAUE
7. DLMONA
8. ETBERML
9. NOSDIWW
10. EPBVRSOR

1. _ _ _ _ _ ◯
2. _ _ _ _ _ ◯ _ _
3. _ _ _ _ ◯
4. _ _ _ ◯ _ _ _ _ _ _
5. _ _ _ ◯ _
6. _ _ ◯ _ _ _ _ _
7. ◯ _ _ _ _ _
8. ◯ _ _ _ _ _ _
9. _ _ _ _ ◯ _ _
10. _ ◯ _ _ _ _ _ _

Remember throughout your days. . .

Answer: _ _ _ _ _ _ _ _ _ _

87–A Dog's Life

Sick dogs and senseless people aren't the smartest creatures in the world. Solve to discover the tail end of a disgusting proverb that's quoted by Peter in 2 Peter 2:22. (PROVERBS 26)

1. NICEOTC
2. RAWRO
3. SHGNEI
4. BRIEFDRNA
5. LFLUSHOT
6. DORMEF
7. TVMIO
8. LEDEMD
9. BRATLEAREE
10. LEYBL

1. ___ ___ ___ ___ ___ ___ ◯
2. ___ ___ ___ ◯ ___
3. ◯ ___ ___ ___ ___ ___
4. ___ ◯ ___ ___ ___ ___ ___ ___ ___
5. ◯ ___ ___ ___ ___ ___ ___ ___
6. ◯ ___ ___ ___ ___ ___
7. ___ ◯ ___ ___ ___
8. ___ ___ ___ ___ ◯ ___
9. ___ ___ ◯ ___ ___ ___ ___ ___ ___ ___
10. ___ ___ ___ ___ ◯

A fool always returns. . .

Answer: ___ ___   ___ ___ ___   ___ ___ ___ ___ ___

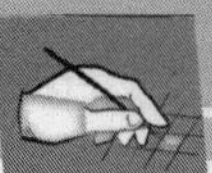

88–Not Just for Tasting

Reckless words can hurt deeply, but a certain organ used with a specific attribute will bring only goodness. (Proverbs 12)

1. VSRNTEA
2. ULCSONE
3. HISTERGOU
4. NRRDEE
5. OSDRW
6. HEMISFIC
7. TMUHO
8. RRNETOVOWH
9. NETRED
10. NWSTSEI
11. VAINSEHSE
12. ESDITASIF

1. _ _ _ _ _ _ ◯
2. _ ◯ _ ◯ _ _ _
3. _ _ ◯ _ _ _ _ ◯ _
4. _ _ _ _ ◯ _
5. _ _ ◯ _ _
6. _ _ _ _ _ _ _ ◯
7. _ _ _ ◯ _
8. _ _ _ _ _ ◯ _ _ _ _
9. _ _ _ _ ◯ _
10. ◯ _ _ _ _ _ _
11. _ _ _ _ ◯ _ _ _ _
12. ◯ _ _ _ _ _ _ ◯ _

This brings health!

Answer: _ _ _ _ _ _ _ _   _ _ _   _ _ _ _   _ _ _ _ _

89–Then There Were Many

Scrambles may seem confusing at times, but with effort you can "rise" to the occasion and solve the puzzle. (GENESIS 11)

1. AHETR
2. DLOFO
3. HEOWL
4. DRABOA
5. NUNCFOOD
6. LIBDU
7. DREETACST
8. KRBCI
9. PECEHS
10. UNGLAGEA

1. __ __ __ ◯ __
2. __ __ __ ◯ __
3. ◯ __ __ __ ◯
4. __ __ ◯ ◯ __ __
5. __ __ __ ◯ __ __ __ __
6. ◯ __ __ __ __
7. __ __ ◯ __ __ __ __ __ __
8. ◯ __ __ __ __
9. __ __ ◯ __ __ __
10. ◯ __ __ __ __ __ __ __

Symbol of man's arrogance.

Answer: __ __ __ __ __ __ __ __ __ __ __ __ __ __

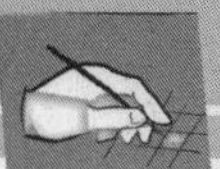

90–Ram Tough

The goat had these placed on it, foreshadowing the One who would one day be pierced by them. Ready to take a stab at finding the answer? (LEVITICUS 16)

1. ANSMGETR
2. BTCNEEARLA
3. ESNCNEI
4. RSENGSRAT
5. SCERNE
6. ASTE
7. UOSSL
8. IRGFNE
9. BDOLO
10. IKSN
11. IKSNRELP

1. ___ ___ ___ ___ ___ ___ ◯ ___
2. ___ ___ ___ ___ ◯ ___ ◯ ___ ___ ___
3. ___ ◯ ___ ___ ___ ◯ ___
4. ___ ___ ___ ___ ___ ◯ ___ ◯ ___
5. ___ ◯ ___ ___ ___ ___
6. ◯ ___ ___ ___
7. ___ ___ ___ ___ ◯
8. ___ ◯ ___ ___ ___ ___
9. ___ ___ ___ ◯ ___
10. ___ ___ ___ ◯
11. ◯ ___ ___ ___ ___ ___ ___ ___

Placed on the head of a goat.

Answer: ___ ___ ___ ___ ___ ___ ___ ___ ___ ___ ___ ___ ___ ___

91–Special Diet

Even today, a lot of us would have a hard time putting most of these items on the barbecue! Solving this one will be no picnic. (Leviticus 11)

1. EVTRULU
2. FNSICATY
3. VNOELC
4. CLESSA
5. LEAPNIC
6. MGONA
7. NEOMAEHCL
8. SOOTIERT
9. POSYAR
10. SOULCT

1. ___ ◯ ___ ___ ___ ___ ___
2. ___ ___ ◯ ◯ ___ ___ ___ ___
3. ___ ◯ ___ ___ ___ ___
4. ___ ___ ___ ___ ◯ ___
5. ___ ___ ___ ___ ___ ◯ ___
6. ___ ___ ___ ◯ ___
7. ___ ___ ___ ◯ ___ ___ ___ ___ ___
8. ___ ___ ___ ___ ___ ___ ___ ◯
9. ___ ___ ___ ___ ◯ ___
10. ___ ___ ___ ___ ___ ◯

Lizard would be on this list.

Answer: ___ ___ ___ ___ ___ ___ ___ ___ ___ ___ ___ ___ ___

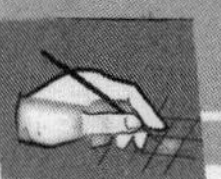

92–A Little Flat!

When the Israelites had to leave in a hurry, there was no time to loaf around. Can you rise to the occasion in solving this puzzle? (Exodus 12)

1. OESUH
2. ITMNGHDI
3. ODLIEPS
4. YGAINS
5. RVESOSAP
6. GRUTEN
7. ICECFSIRA
8. ETERDYOSR
9. HRUTBOG
10. EASMIR
11. TFASE
12. ESHDR

1. __ __ ◯ __ __
2. __ __ __ ◯ __ __ __ __
3. __ __ __ __ ◯ ◯ __
4. __ ◯ __ __ __ __
5. __ __ __ __ __ ◯ ◯ __
6. __ __ __ __ ◯ __
7. __ __ __ __ __ __ __ __ ◯
8. ◯ __ __ __ __ __ __ __ __
9. ◯ __ __ __ __ __ __
10. __ ◯ __ __ __ __
11. __ ◯ ◯ __ __
12. __ __ __ ◯ __

Part of the Hebrew diet.

Answer: __ __ __ __ __ __ __ __ __ __ __   __ __ __ __ __

93–*Lamentable Demise*

This was a place where a good ruler was fatally wounded by his *arch*er enemies. Ready to take a shot at this one? (2 Chronicles 35)

1. SIOVSDINI
2. LIAIMSFE
3. OEEPLP
4. SUDGEIDSI
5. YLLGLIINW
6. RSFFEOIGN
7. RDEONUM
8. ENISGSR
9. NSKIG
10. SEDDE
11. SAABARMOSD

1. __ __ ◯ __ __ __ __ __ __

2. __ ◯ __ __ ◯ __ __ __

3. __ __ __ __ ◯ __

4. __ __ __ __ __ __ __ ◯ __

5. __ __ __ __ __ __ __ __ ◯

6. ◯ __ ◯ __ __ __ __ __ __

7. ◯ __ __ __ __ ◯ __

8. __ __ __ ◯ __ __ __

9. __ ◯ __ __ __

10. ◯ __ __ ◯ __

11. __ __ __ __ __ __ __ __ ◯ __

Josiah was sorely wounded at this place.

Answer: __

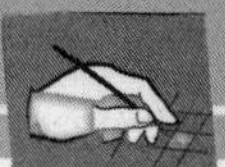

94–Graven Images

Adoring anything or anyone other than God is a worthless endeavor. Unscramble words below to find a phrase describing this futile enterprise. (Isaiah 44)

1. IRVESIND
2. VHNEAE
3. RPHIOWS
4. KNEOST
5. UYSRC
6. STRAO
7. FGRIPOSNF
8. CYAED
9. SMCSPOA
10. RECDAEL
11. AESIRD

1. __ __ ◯ __ __ __ __ __
2. __ __ ◯ __ __ ◯
3. __ __ __ __ __ ◯ __
4. ◯ __ __ __ __ __
5. __ ◯ __ __ __
6. __ ◯ __ __ __
7. __ __ ◯ __ __ __ ◯ __ __
8. ◯ __ __ __ __
9. __ ◯ __ __ __ __ __
10. __ __ __ ◯ __ __ __
11. __ __ __ ◯ __ __

Profitable for nothing.

Answer: __ __ __ __ __ __ __ __   __ __   __ __ __ __ __ __ __

95–Good Grief

Nothing on earth is as satisfying as knowing God. Work this puzzle to find a term describing what worldly things bring us. (ECCLESIASTES 1)

1. REVOEFR
2. XSDRCEIEE
3. SEATET
4. AYVTNI
5. NNCOECR
6. FRPOTI
7. ERISA
8. EPEVRECI
9. SCARENIE
10. UIICCTR

1. _ _ _ _ ○ ○ _
2. _ ○ _ _ _ _ _ _ _
3. _ _ _ ○ ○ _
4. _ _ _ ○ _ _
5. _ ○ _ _ _ _ ○
6. _ _ ○ ○ _ _
7. _ _ _ ○ _
8. ○ _ _ _ _ ○ _ _
9. _ _ _ ○ _ _ _ _
10. _ ○ _ _ _ _ ○

All is vanity and. . .

Answer: _

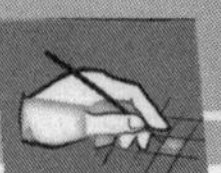

96–Don't Be Lame

Don't worry about money. Instead, stay upright and do this on the road of life. (PROVERBS 19)

1. AGTIWNN
2. LAEFS
3. SKEINSND
4. EHATLW
5. MSAEH
6. EELRIVD
7. QITYNIUI
8. ENGRA
9. NAITTER
10. GRNPODIP
11. VEOERRP
12. GRRNOIA
13. MCILATAY

1. ◯ __ __ __ __ __ __
2. __ ◯ ◯ __ __
3. ◯ __ __ __ __ __ __ __
4. __ ◯ __ __ ◯ __
5. __ ◯ __ __ __
6. __ __ __ ◯ __ __ __
7. __ ◯ __ __ __ ◯ __ __
8. __ ◯ __ __ __
9. __ __ ◯ __ ◯ __ __
10. __ __ __ __ __ __ __ ◯
11. ◯ __ __ __ __ __ __
12. __ __ __ __ ◯ __ __
13. __ __ __ __ __ __ ◯ ◯

A fool is perverse in his lips, but better are the poor that. . .

Answer: __

97–*Definition of Bitter*

It took a tree to sweeten this enough that the Israelites' anger was finally "quenched." Don't grumble—you'll be able to brook any challenges this puzzle presents. (EXODUS 15)

1. WOLWALS
2. AETSUSTT
3. ENCDEAPM
4. SERTCOEERH
5. NNRCODEAI
6. FISTEDASI
7. EMTRLBI
8. CDNSAE
9. AESPSIR
10. PURTIMH

1. __ __ __ __ __ __ ○
2. __ __ ○ __ __ ○ __ __
3. ○ __ __ __ __ __ __ __
4. __ __ ○ __ __ ○ __ __ __
5. ○ __ __ __ __ __ __ __ __
6. __ __ __ __ __ ○ __ __ __
7. __ __ ○ __ __ __ __
8. __ ○ __ __ __ __
9. __ ○ ○ __ __ __ __
10. __ __ __ __ __ __ ○

Too bitter at first.

Answer: __ __ __ __ __ __ __ __ __ __ __ __ __ __

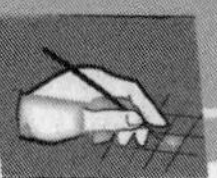

98–Marvelous Work

To unscramble this scramble, just take a long look in the mirror. . .and see what God sees! (PSALM 139)

1. KAWEA
2. UOGNTE
3. ASRDNKSE
4. TCEESR
5. ETHRA
6. AFRA
7. CPUSEIRO
8. ILCYORUSU
9. RYLUES

1. _ ◯ _ _ _
2. _ ◯ ◯ _ _ _
3. ◯ _ _ _ _ _ _ _
4. _ _ _ _ ◯ _
5. _ _ _ ◯ _
6. _ ◯ _ _
7. _ _ _ _ _ _ ◯ _
8. _ _ _ _ _ _ _ ◯ _
9. _ _ _ _ ◯ ◯

David knew he was made fearfully and. . . !

Answer: _ _ _ _ _ _ _ _ _ _ _ _ _ _ _

99–Seven Times Seven

Slaves loved the trumpet blast that would announce the coming of this celebration! You'll feel a sense of freedom as you solve this puzzle. (LEVITICUS 25)

1. TCYI
2. OSPRESP
3. EASTYF
4. WGHOTR
5. EFNLAL
6. DEUGJ
7. UUSRBSB
8. HOTUBG
9. LVEGSALI
10. AEYRLY
11. RLSAEI

1. __ __ __ ○
2. __ __ __ __ ○ __ __
3. __ ○ __ __ __ __
4. __ ○ ○ __ __ __
5. ○ __ __ __ __ __
6. ○ __ __ __ __
7. __ __ __ ○ __ __ __
8. ○ __ __ __ __ __
9. __ ○ __ __ __ __ __ __
10. __ __ __ __ ○ __
11. __ __ __ __ ○ __

Rest and redemption for the good earth.

Answer: __ __ __ __ __ __ __ __ __ __ __ __

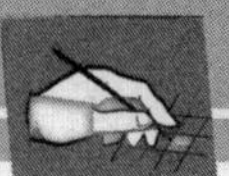

100–Easy Load

With His coming, Christ fulfills His promise of what will be easy and what will be light. Take a load off as you work these scrambles. (Isaiah 9)

1. AYAW
2. EOPLEP
3. KIHTTSCE
4. NMTUO
5. FGITNIL
6. HBNIDE
7. UDNETR
8. DLAREES
9. CNTIENA

1. ___ ___ ___ ◯
2. ___ ___ ◯ ___ ___ ___
3. ___ ___ ___ ___ ◯ ◯ ___ ___
4. ___ ◯ ___ ___ ___
5. ___ ___ ◯ ___ ___ ___ ___
6. ◯ ___ ___ ___ ___ ___
7. ___ ◯ ◯ ___ ___ ◯
8. ___ ◯ ___ ___ ___ ___ ___
9. ___ ___ ___ ___ ___ ◯ ___

The Prince of Peace has broken this.

Answer: ___ ___ ___ ___ ___ ___ ___ ___ ___ ___ ___ ___ ___

101–Freedom

Redeemed from the law, the Spirit of God comes into our hearts, and we gain a very special standing in the eyes of our Father. After all, it's a family affair. (GALATIANS 4)

1. ARETUN
2. OGDNBEA
3. RFHTO
4. TONPAIP
5. RIJNEU
6. ROUSTT
7. RREVSOGON
8. AFDRIA
9. RBOVESE
10. RONB
11. TESEEMLN

1. __ ◯ __ __ __ __

2. __ __ __ ◯ __ __ __

3. __ ◯ __ __ __

4. __ ◯ __ __ __ __ ◯

5. ◯ __ __ __ __ __

6. __ __ __ ◯ __ __

7. __ __ __ __ __ ◯ ◯ __ __

8. __ ◯ __ __ __ __

9. __ __ ◯ __ __ __ __

10. __ ◯ __ __

11. __ __ __ __ __ ◯ __ ◯

We receive this.

Answer: __ __ __ __ __ __ __ __ __   __ __   __ __ __ __

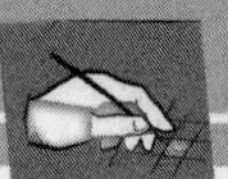

102–A Bad Read

There may be many of these, but that which is true is found only in the grace of Christ—the only really good news! Carefully read the text below to uncover this answer. (GALATIANS 1)

1. ENVTSRA
2. EAGNL
3. LDOBO
4. SOAPLET
5. UCRCHH
6. RLVAEM
7. CPRAHE
8. NELIORGI
9. ARPEDEUS
10. TVRERPE
11. CFTIRYE
12. DRVLEEI

1. ___ ___ ___ ___ ◯ ___ ___
2. ___ ◯ ___ ___ ___
3. ___ ___ ___ ◯ ___
4. ___ ___ ___ ___ ◯ ___ ___
5. ___ ___ ___ ___ ___ ◯
6. ___ ___ ___ ___ ◯ ___
7. ___ ◯ ___ ___ ___ ___
8. ___ ___ ___ ___ ◯ ___ ◯ ___
9. ___ ___ ___ ◯ ___ ___ ___ ___
10. ◯ ___ ___ ___ ___ ___ ___
11. ___ ◯ ___ ___ ___ ___ ___
12. ___ ___ ◯ ___ ___ ___ ___

It is a curse!

Answer: ___ ___ ___ ___ ___ ___ ___ ___ ___ ___ ___ ___ ___ ___ ___

103–Looking Good!

When the enemy comes, prowling around, we need to be prepared. Are you ready to battle this one out? (EPHESIANS 6)

1. SMARTE
2. AWHTR
3. DOOMNIAITN
4. RUNETATEC
5. ROMPIES
6. SAFIRFA
7. IAGNKM
8. DEBEIECNO
9. YLDOBL

1. __ ○ __ __ __ __

2. __ ○ __ __ __

3. __ __ ○ __ __ __ __ __ __ ○ __

4. ○ __ __ __ __ __ __ __ __

5. __ ○ ○ __ __ __ __

6. __ __ ○ __ __ __ __

7. __ __ __ __ __ ○

8. ○ __ __ __ __ __ __ __ __

9. __ __ __ ○ __ __

The only defense.

Answer: __ __ __ __ __ __ __ __ __ __ __ __

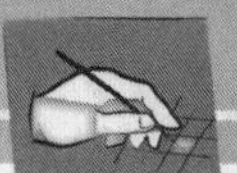

104–Labor On!

Like productive farmers, we can't be sleeping on the job when there's a chance to bring in a goodly harvest. So get your pencil ready, work these words, and reap a wonderful answer. (GALATIANS 6)

1. NERDUB
2. ORETSER
3. ESSNOA
4. NRCSNOIAT
5. PURCTOR
6. TRITEWN
7. RGECA
8. LAFUT
9. KARTEVNOE
10. CLASPEEIYL

1. ◯ ___ ___ ___ ___ ___
2. ___ ___ ___ ___ ___ ___ ◯
3. ___ ___ ___ ___ ___ ◯
4. ___ ◯ ___ ___ ___ ___ ___ ___ ___
5. ___ ___ ___ ___ ___ ___ ◯
6. ◯ ___ ___ ___ ___ ___ ___
7. ___ ___ ___ ___ ◯
8. ___ ◯ ___ ___ ___
9. ___ ___ ___ ◯ ___ ___ ___ ___ ___
10. ___ ___ ___ ___ ___ ___ ___ ___ ___ ◯

In well doing. . .

Answer: ___ ___ ___ ___ ___ ___ ___ ___ ___ ___

105–Fearless

These were so evident with the imprisoned Paul and, seen by all, gave others the courage they needed to proclaim the gospel. Take courage as you solve this puzzle. (PHILIPPIANS 1)

1. PHOSIB
2. UOABDN
3. EEDRIS
4. CEJEROI
5. RECESNI
6. RFHTERU
7. FREIST
8. EXWITBT
9. FISTEMNA

1. ◯ ___ ___ ___ ___ ___
2. ___ ___ ◯ ___ ◯ ___
3. ◯ ___ ◯ ___ ___ ___
4. ___ ___ ___ ___ ◯ ___ ___
5. ___ ___ ◯ ◯ ___ ___ ___
6. ___ ___ ___ ___ ◯ ___ ___
7. ___ ___ ◯ ___ ___ ___
8. ___ ___ ___ ___ ◯ ___ ___
9. ___ ___ ___ ___ ___ ___ ◯ ◯

A prisoner of love.

Answer: ___ ___ ___ ___ ___   ___ ___   ___ ___ ___ ___ ___ ___ ___

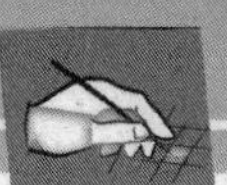

106–One Big Family

God desires that all His children would find this genuine affection in their hearts for each other. Be careful "*philly*-ing" all the blanks. (Romans 12)

1. BROYLES
2. WTRDOA
3. HLUFTSOL
4. REEPRF
5. EVTERNF
6. ELSIBSPO
7. CIYMTPLSII
8. RYDALE
9. TROXEH
10. EEVGAN

1. ___ ___ ◯ ___ ◯ ___ ___
2. ___ ◯ ___ ___ ___ ___
3. ___ ___ ___ ◯ ◯ ___ ___ ___
4. ___ ___ ___ ___ ◯ ___
5. ___ ___ ◯ ___ ___ ___ ___
6. ___ ___ ___ ___ ___ ___ ◯ ___
7. ___ ___ ___ ___ ___ ___ ___ ___ ___ ◯
8. ___ ___ ___ ___ ◯ ___
9. ___ ___ ___ ◯ ___ ___
10. ___ ◯ ___ ___ ___ ◯

Very touching.

Answer: ___ ___ ___ ___ ___ ___ ___ ___ ___   ___ ___ ___ ___

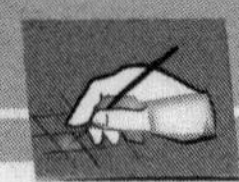

107–Phrase of Praise

Here's a phrase of praise that He deserves to hear from everyone. (PHILIPPIANS 2)

1. BEENSAC
2. LBUMEH
3. SENTSRVA
4. GRAVYNIOL
5. WBESOL
6. PRUTINTEAO
7. CBSUEAE
8. SHRASMLE
9. OSWROR
10. BROYEBR
11. DRILSEO

1. __ __ __ __ __ ◯ __
2. ◯ __ __ __ __ __
3. __ __ ◯ __ __ __ __ __
4. __ __ ◯ __ __ __ __ __ __
5. __ __ __ __ __ ◯
6. __ __ __ __ ◯ __ __ ◯ __ __
7. __ __ __ __ __ ◯ __
8. __ __ __ __ ◯ __ __ __
9. __ __ __ __ ◯ __
10. __ __ __ __ __ ◯ __
11. __ __ __ ◯ __ __ __

Will one day be said by all!

Answer: __ __ __ __ __ __ __ __ __ __ __ __ __ __ __

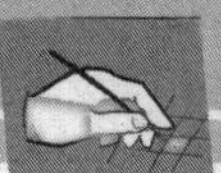

108–The Removal

There are both physical and spiritual versions of this procedure. You'll finish this puzzle in a snap—or should we say a snip. (Romans 15)

1. SHRTIC
2. DYEIF
3. PHRRACOE
4. AGECR
5. OHTUM
6. NMDEID
7. NARCLA
8. RHIDDNEE
9. SKAPTRARE
10. VISTERD
11. TREBOSD
12. GNIER

1. ◯__ __ __ __ __
2. __ __ ◯ __ __
3. ◯__ __ __ __ __ __ __
4. __ __ __ ◯ __
5. __ __ ◯ __ __
6. ◯ __ __ __ __ __
7. ◯__ __ __ __ __
8. __ ◯ __ __ __ __ __ __
9. __ __ __ __ __ __ __ __ ◯
10. __ __ __ ◯ __ __ __
11. __ __ __ __ ◯ __ __
12. __ __ __ __ ◯

"Cut it out!"

Answer: __ __ __ __ __ __ __ __ __ __ __ __

109–Stay Awake!

Those who are of the day and not the night will not be asleep when the Day of the Lord does this. Ready? Set? Solve! (1 THESSALONIANS 5)

1. ESHCBEE
2. OGMNA
3. LETMEH
4. ABNTIO
5. EREHRTBN
6. LAMBSELSE
7. SANCEGI
8. IAHLFTFU
9. EPTNATI
10. ELBEFE
11. MTORCFO

1. __ __ __ __ __ ◯ __
2. __ __ ◯ __ __
3. __ __ __ ◯ ◯ __
4. __ __ ◯ __ __ __
5. __ __ __ __ ◯ __ __ __
6. __ __ ◯ __ __ __ __ ◯ __
7. __ __ ◯ __ __ __ __
8. __ __ __ ◯ ◯ __ __ __
9. __ __ __ ◯ __ __ __
10. __ ◯ __ __ __ __
11. __ __ __ ◯ __ __ __

Sneaking in.

Answer: __ __ __ __ __ __ __ __ __ __ __ __ __ __ __ __ __

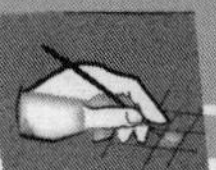

110–Contentment

To solve this one, just think on another promise of God that nothing is impossible for Christ, and we are heirs to that as well. In other words, you *will* be able to solve this puzzle! (PHILIPPIANS 4)

1. TNDAS
2. LOFEWL
3. UABNDO
4. OLVYEL
5. RUFSOLIH
6. LSETAU
7. KHNTSA
8. ISOGUORL
9. MWENO
10. YHGNRU
11. ASCARE

1. __ __ __ __ ◯
2. __ __ __ __ ◯ __
3. ◯ __ __ __ __ __
4. __ __ __ __ ◯ __
5. __ ◯ __ __ __ __ __ __
6. __ __ __ __ ◯ __
7. __ ◯ __ __ __ __
8. __ __ __ __ ◯ __ __ __
9. __ __ __ __ ◯
10. __ __ __ ◯ __ __
11. __ __ __ ◯ __ __

In Christ's strength, we can. . .

Answer: __ __ __ __ __ __ __ __ __ __ __

111–*Beware*

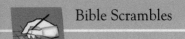

Paul uses these strong words for ones who do not worship by the Spirit but put all their confidence in their own flesh. Solve until you find the "boneified" answer. (Philippians 3)

1. VIESOURG
2. SCIONCNOI
3. SELHF
4. ATRWDO
5. UNCTO
6. FROONMC
7. CTSKO
8. PLENASEM
9. FRSUEF
10. BESTULOSD

1. __ __ __ ◯ ◯ __ __ __
2. __ __ __ __ ◯ __ __ __ __
3. __ ◯ __ __ __
4. __ __ ◯ __ __ __
5. __ ◯ __ __ __
6. __ __ __ __ __ ◯ __
7. __ __ __ __ ◯
8. ◯ __ __ __ __ __ __ __
9. __ __ __ __ __ ◯
10. __ __ __ __ __ __ __ ◯ __

Beware of these dogs!

Answer: __ __ __ __   __ __ __ __ __ __ __ __

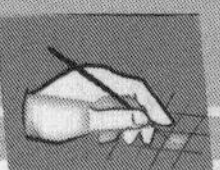

112–In the Light

Christ shows us the way to God. If you are walking behind Him, you are considered one of these. The scrambled words below will lead you to the ultimate answer. (Ephesians 5)

1. RHFREETOE
2. GWRINOK
3. VEALE
4. KNEWLIR
5. EROREPV
6. RHWTA
7. RHHISCE
8. VEREREECN
9. ISTRIP

1. ___ ___ ___ ___ ___ ○ ___ ___ ___

2. ___ ○ ___ ___ ___ ___ ___

3. ○ ___ ___ ___ ___

4. ___ ___ ___ ___ ___ ○ ___

5. ___ ___ ___ ___ ○ ___ ___

6. ○ ___ ___ ___ ___

7. ___ ___ ○ ___ ___ ___ ___

8. ___ ___ ___ ___ ○ ___ ___ ___ ___

9. ○ ___ ___ ___ ___ ___

Seen as dear children.

Answer: ___ ___ ___ ___ ___ ___ ___ ___ ___

113–Confused Christians

Who were these that took their eyes off Christ, and so fell under what seemed like a spell? The answer here is less than charming. (CHAPTER 3 OF A NEW TESTAMENT LETTER)

1. ESEFEOR
2. COLOSH
3. TWECIBH
4. STEMRA
5. TTHRU
6. GRIAEHN
7. NAUDSNIL
8. SLHEF
9. DATERMIO
10. UFIETIDSJ
11. DRAINO
12. LSNBIGES

1. ○ ○ _ _ _ _ _
2. _ _ _ ○ _ ○
3. _ _ _ ○ _ _ _
4. _ _ ○ _ _ _
5. _ _ _ _ ○
6. _ _ _ _ _ _ ○
7. _ _ _ ○ _ _ _ _
8. _ ○ _ _ _
9. _ _ _ _ ○ _ _ _
10. _ _ _ ○ _ _ ○ _ _
11. _ _ _ ○ _ ○
12. _ _ _ ○ _ _ _ _

They were deluded.

Answer: _

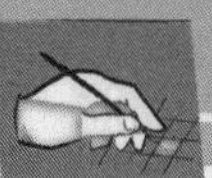

114–Holy Matrimony

This is not a building but one half of a loving union that will be forged on a very special day. Vow to solve this one. (Ephesians 5)

1. RGATE
2. FIMSEHL
3. AUOIRVS
4. DRAETLIO
5. WEUNSI
6. RNESTEP
7. HERHCSI
8. UNIHORS
9. VOTCE
10. SNWGHIA

1. ◯_ _ _ _
2. _ _ _ _ _ ◯ _
3. _ _ _ _ ◯ _ ◯
4. ◯ _ ◯ _ _ _ _ _
5. ◯ _ _ _ _ _
6. _ _ _ ◯ _ _ _
7. ◯ _ _ _ _ _ ◯
8. _ _ ◯ ◯ _ _ _
9. ◯ _ _ _ _
10. _ _ _ ◯ _ _ _

Presented as something very special.

Answer: _

115–An Earthly Picture

Like Christ and His church, the bond of husband and wife is very much like this. The answer to this one is an enigma within an enigma. (Ephesians 3 and 5)

1. EHGTNL
2. TIERSMIN
3. ALEVRE
4. CSESCA
5. CUTEAFLFE
6. ALOFDMIN
7. YFMILA
8. SHICER
9. NTEALRE
10. GHITHE
11. NAKSDSRE
12. BHWREEY

1. ___ ___ ___ ◯ ___ ___
2. ___ ___ ___ ___ ___ ___ ___ ◯
3. ___ ___ ___ ◯ ___ ___
4. ◯ ___ ___ ___ ___ ___
5. ___ ___ ___ ___ ___ ◯ ___ ___ ___
6. ◯ ___ ___ ___ ___ ___ ___ ___
7. ___ ___ ___ ___ ___ ◯
8. ___ ___ ___ ___ ___ ◯
9. ___ ◯ ___ ___ ___ ___ ___
10. ___ ◯ ___ ___ ___ ___
11. ___ ___ ◯ ___ ___ ___ ___ ___
12. ___ ___ ___ ___ ___ ___ ◯

Joined and one.

Answer: ___ ___ ___ ___ ___   ___ ___ ___ ___ ___ ___ ___

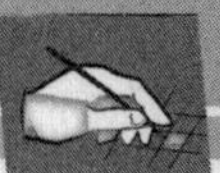

116–Above All

No principality, no power, no might, and no dominion of earth reaches here, where we see the true glory of Christ. If you get stuck, don't hesitate to "look up" the answer. (EPHESIANS 1)

1. RHATGE
2. NENTMOI
3. PATOD
4. LVEIBEE
5. RANETSE
6. NNLTGHIEE
7. SERARYP
8. WPEOR
9. PEOSGL
10. LEADES
11. SHEOCN
12. DSIOWM

1. __ __ __ ◯ __ __
2. __ ◯ __ __ __ __ __
3. ◯ __ __ __ __
4. __ __ __ __ __ ◯ __
5. ◯ __ __ ◯ __ __ __
6. __ __ ◯ __ __ __ __ __ __
7. __ __ __ ◯ __ __ __
8. ◯ __ __ __ __
9. __ __ __ __ __ ◯
10. __ __ ◯ __ __ __
11. ◯ __ __ __ ◯ __
12. __ __ ◯ __ __ __

Our destination.

Answer: __ __ __ __ __ __ __ __ __ __ __ __ __ __ __ __ __

117–A Promise

The New Testament itself is a clue to solving this scramble, as it speaks of something far different from what was before. (GALATIANS 3)

1. TUCNEION
2. EMNNRA
3. OOHSFIL
4. ALNER
5. ICREAML
6. EWNTRTI
7. DEDAD
8. ONSNTIA
9. UYCRFIC
10. DIVETNE

1. ___ ___ ___ ___ ◯ ___ ___ ___
2. ___ ___ ◯ ___ ___ ___
3. ___ ___ ___ ___ ___ ___ ◯
4. ___ ◯ ___ ___ ___
5. ___ ___ ◯ ___ ___ ___ ___
6. ___ ___ ◯ ___ ◯ ___ ___
7. ◯ ___ ___ ___ ___
8. ___ ___ ___ ___ ___ ◯ ___
9. ◯ ___ ___ ___ ___ ___ ___
10. ___ ___ ___ ___ ◯ ___ ___

Like given to Abraham.

Answer: ___ ___ ___ ___ ___ ___ ___ ___ ___ ___ ___

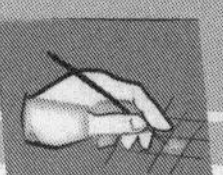

118–The Only Way

Heavenly justice requires only one thing of us and only in this do we have redemption and become true sons of God. We trust you'll have no problems finding the right answer. (GALATIANS 2)

1. SJSUE
2. EHNTAEH
3. HMITYG
4. AESLF
5. AVPYERILT
6. RWORFDA
7. TYRILBE
8. AURTSERFT
9. MICMTO
10. THWSEOMA

1. ◯ __ __ ◯ ◯

2. __ __ __ ◯ __ __ __

3. __ ◯ __ __ __ __

4. ◯ __ __ __ __

5. __ __ ◯ __ __ __ ◯ __ __

6. __ __ __ __ __ __ ◯

7. __ __ ◯ __ __ __ ◯

8. ◯ __ __ __ __ __ ◯ __ __

9. __ __ __ __ ◯ ◯

10. __ __ __ __ __ ◯ __ __

Not for the flesh.

Answer: __ __ __ __ __ __ __ __ __ __ __ __   __ __   __ __ __ __ __ __

119–Working Hard

Unlike false teachers, Paul experienced this as he provided for himself while preaching the true Word. Have fun working out the answer. (1 Thessalonians 2)

1. HELASFMU
2. LOSPSATE
3. HEVBEA
4. USOLS
5. ERTNETA
6. LISPAGEN
7. ERISED
8. RTHTU
9. EOVRDNEA
10. GRANFTELIT
11. ULEIG

1. __ __ __ __ __ __ __ ○
2. ○ __ __ __ __ __ __ __
3. ○ __ __ __ __ __
4. __ ○ ○ __ __
5. __ __ __ ○ __ ○ __
6. __ __ __ __ __ __ ○ __
7. ○ __ __ __ __ __
8. ○ ○ __ __ __
9. __ __ __ __ ○ ○ __ __
10. __ __ ○ __ __ __ __ __ ○ __ __
11. __ __ __ ○ __

For the sake of the Gospel.

Answer: __ __ __ __ __ __ __   __ __ __ __   __ __ __ __ __ __ __ __ __

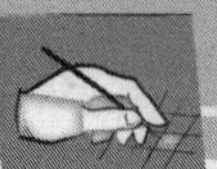

120–Hanging On

There is much delicious fruit on the spiritual "tree." Do you have the forbearance to pick the right one here? (GALATIANS 5)

1. GYLOR
2. EROVUD
3. CUAELNN
4. GYNVENI
5. FHESL
6. UIFYTJS
7. NFCEEFO
8. VRESE
9. FORTPI
10. GNENEALT
11. NGIATSA

1. __ ◯ __ __ __
2. __ __ __ ◯ __ __
3. __ ◯ __ __ __ __ __
4. __ __ __ __ __ __ ◯
5. __ __ __ ◯ __
6. __ ◯ __ __ __ ◯ __
7. __ ◯ __ __ __ __ __
8. __ __ __ __ ◯
9. __ ◯ __ __ ◯ __
10. __ __ __ __ ◯ __ __ __
11. __ ◯ __ __ __ __ __

Only in the Spirit.

Answer: __ __ __ __ __ __ __ __ __ __ __ __ __ __ __ __

121–The Highest

Walking worthy of the Lord, fruitful in every good work, and increasing in the knowledge of God, comes only from this attribute. (Colossians 1)

1. EWLFOL
2. ROIGEVF
3. EAGS
4. VGNEI
5. TRHWYO
6. HEPO
7. OWMSDI
8. PDMEIOTERN
9. HIYLCR
10. EIVBSIL
11. GTILH

1. __ __ ○ __ __ __
2. __ ○ __ __ __ ○ __
3. __ __ ○ __
4. __ ○ __ __ ○
5. __ __ __ ○ __ __
6. ○ __ __ ○
7. __ __ ○ __ __ __
8. __ __ __ __ __ ○ __ ○ __ __
9. ○ __ __ __ __ __
10. __ ○ __ __ __ __ __
11. __ __ __ __ ○

Ministers of Christ declare.

Answer: __ __ __ __ __ __ __ __ __ __ __ __ __ __ __ __ __ __ __

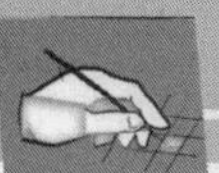

122–Not a Pretty Sight

There is a war on, and only in the Spirit can we bear His fruit rather than this that so easily tempts us. (GALATIANS 5)

1. LFILULF
2. DMRRSUE
3. ISFRET
4. ROCYNTAR
5. UTFIR
6. TOREWIHSE
7. ETYFTIS
8. ETNGEL
9. SKENEMSE
10. DRTHAE

1. __ __ __ __ __ __ ◯
2. __ ◯ __ __ __ __ ◯
3. __ ◯ __ __ __ __
4. __ ◯ __ __ __ __ __ __
5. ◯ __ __ __ ◯
6. __ __ ◯ __ __ __ __ __ ◯
7. __ __ __ __ __ ◯ __
8. __ __ __ __ ◯ __
9. __ ◯ __ __ __ __ ◯ __
10. ◯ __ __ __ __ __

Do not fulfill this.

Answer: __ __ __ __   __ __   __ __ __   __ __ __ __ __ __

123–Deception

Many will be deceived by this and other powerful delusions, but not those who have within the love of the truth. Solving this puzzle might be a bit tricky. (2 Thessalonians 2)

1. OYGRL
2. TREDYOS
3. DRITNEPOI
4. GUTTHA
5. LWYAAS
6. PSEPOO
7. KHAESN
8. EADRLYA
9. THARES
10. OEPSGL

1. __ ○ __ __ __
2. __ __ __ __ __ __ ○
3. __ __ __ __ ○ __ __ __ ○
4. __ __ __ ○ __ __
5. __ __ ○ __ __ __
6. __ __ __ ○ __ __
7. __ __ __ __ __ ○
8. __ __ __ __ __ ○ __
9. __ ○ __ ○ __ __
10. __ __ ○ __ __ __

From Christ's enemy.

Answer: __ __ __ __ __ __ __ __ __ __ __ __

124–Another Lie

Unbelivers will fall for another deception—a calm before the big storm. And what a price they'll pay! But believers know this answer is something only Christ can truly bring! (1 Thessalonians 5)

1. FCERPTE
2. DREENR
3. TIPETNA
4. EPACES
5. SIBATNA
6. EPSDSIE
7. SETPIEL
8. CAFTSIYN
9. ETMSEE
10. RLUYNU

1. ◯_ _ _ _ _ _
2. _ _ _ _ ◯ _
3. _ ◯ _ _ _ _ _
4. _ _ ◯ _ _ ◯
5. ◯ _ _ _ _ _ ◯
6. ◯ _ _ _ _ _ _
7. _ _ _ ◯ _ _ _
8. _ ◯ _ _ _ _ ◯ _
9. ◯ _ ◯ _ _ _
10. _ _ _ _ _ ◯

Won't last long.

Answer: _ _ _ _ _ _ _ _ _ _ _ _ _ _ _

125–A Good Work Here

Paul wrote a letter to these people who lived in a Macedonian mecca. Although these scambled words may seem like Greek to you, they are solvable. (Chapter 4 of a New Testament Letter)

1. ECTPESR
2. CESEBEH
3. CREFISICA
4. ATULES
5. GIANA
6. YPRERA
7. PREOTR
8. GHSTNI
9. DARNEEL
10. UHYNGR
11. SQRSTEEU

1. ___ ___ ___ ◯ ___ ___ ___

2. ___ ___ ___ ___ ___ ___ ◯

3. ___ ___ ___ ___ ___ ___ ◯ ___ ___

4. ___ ___ ◯ ___ ___ ___

5. ___ ___ ___ ◯ ___

6. ◯ ___ ___ ___ ___ ___

7. ___ ___ ◯ ___ ___ ___

8. ___ ___ ◯ ___ ___ ___

9. ___ ___ ◯ ___ ___ ___ ___

10. ___ ___ ◯ ___ ___ ___

11. ___ ___ ___ ___ ___ ◯ ___ ___

Dearly beloved brethren.

Answer: ___ ___ ___ ___ ___ ___ ___ ___ ___ ___ ___

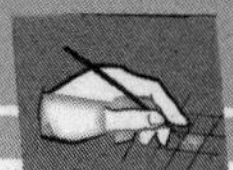

126–Stand Strong

Without the armor of God to stand against this, you may find at some point, your morals, principles, and values easily compromised. Stand strong as you wrestle with this puzzle. (Ephesians 6)

1. OOPVEKR
2. BTRLMEE
3. GILNES
4. YCEIRNIST
5. EOIMSRP
6. FRIAFAS
7. TEALP
8. HMGTI
9. EWLIS
10. SNPEOSR

1. ◯ __ __ __ __ __ __

2. __ ◯ __ __ __ __ __

3. __ ◯ __ __ __ __

4. __ __ ◯ ◯ __ __ ◯ __ __

5. ◯ __ __ __ __ __ __

6. ◯ __ __ __ __ __ __

7. __ ◯ __ __ __

8. __ ◯ __ __ ◯

9. __ ◯ __ ◯ __

10. __ __ __ __ __ __ __ ◯

Wrestling against.

Answer: __ __ __ __ __ __ __ __ __ __ __ __ __ __

127–A Gift

This is found only in Christ and is given to each of His believers by faith and not by works. With these clues, you'll be sure to find the correct answer. (ROMANS 3)

1. SMIRINOES
2. NTUGOE
3. ASBSHLTIE
4. FWIST
5. RIMSYE
6. CASOREL
7. BUELNFEI
8. RNISEN
9. DUDRANTESN
10. IONSPO
11. DRNALSE

1. ◯ __ __ ◯ __ __ __ __ __
2. __ __ __ ◯ __ __
3. __ __ __ __ __ __ __ __ ◯
4. __ __ __ __ ◯
5. __ __ __ ◯ __ __
6. ◯ __ __ __ __ __ __
7. ◯ __ __ __ __ __ __ __
8. ◯ __ __ __ __ __
9. __ ◯ __ ◯ __ __ __ __ __ __
10. __ __ __ ◯ __ __
11. ◯ __ __ __ __ __ __

Not of the law.

Answer: __ __ __ __ __ __ __ __ __ __ __ __ __

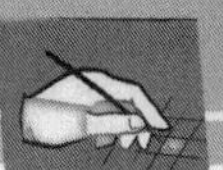

128–To the Finish

Paul would desire to rejoice that his work was not for nothing as he proclaimed the gospel. See how fast you can figure out this one. (PHILIPPIANS 2)

1. FROTOCM
2. BRAOLU
3. KNSLEIES
4. SINFHAO
5. NIBEEDOT
6. NAIVHSESE
7. SCABEEN
8. ISIRTP
9. TLAARUN

1. __ __ __ __ __ ◯ __
2. __ __ __ __ ◯ __
3. __ __ __ __ ◯ __ __ __
4. __ __ __ __ ◯ __ __
5. __ __ __ __ __ __ ◯ __
6. __ __ __ ◯ __ __ __ __ __
7. ◯ __ __ __ __ __ __
8. __ __ __ __ ◯ __
9. ◯ __ __ __ __ __ __

A very quick pace, but not. . .

Answer: __ __ __   __ __   __ __ __ __

129–Held High

This piece of equipment will make all the difference when the evil one aims at you. Use all your mettle to figure this one out. (EPHESIANS 6)

1. VENATRSS
2. TAWHR
3. NIOGD
4. LDVEBOE
5. STERELW
6. VLEID
7. MRROUA
8. LYFLNAI
9. EFRA
10. SPRSLEAE
11. STISNA
12. VHANEE

1. ◯ ___ ___ ___ ___ ___ ___ ___
2. ___ ___ ___ ___ ◯
3. ___ ___ ◯ ___ ___
4. ___ ___ ___ ___ ___ ◯ ___
5. ___ ___ ___ ___ ___ ◯ ___
6. ◯ ___ ___ ___ ___
7. ___ ___ ___ ◯ ___ ___
8. ◯ ___ ___ ___ ___ ___ ___
9. ◯ ___ ___ ___
10. ___ ___ ___ ◯ ___ ___ ___ ___
11. ___ ___ ◯ ___ ◯ ___
12. ◯ ___ ___ ___ ___ ___

Fire extinguisher.

Answer: ___ ___ ___ ___ ___ ___ ___ ___ ___ ___ ___ ___ ___ ___ ___

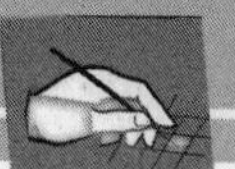

130–Be Gentle

Fellowship and relationship. . .not always easy, but God would desire His children to treat one another with this in mind. Easy does it in solving this puzzle. (EPHESIANS 4)

1. ASETL
2. TFHRAE
3. USNFSEL
4. DVEICEE
5. NDRDKEAE
6. ARHTER
7. ODNJEI
8. SASTLPEO
9. GRCNINOAE
10. TEEACRD
11. SDLEAE

1. __ O __ __ __
2. __ __ __ __ O __
3. __ __ __ O __ __ __
4. O __ __ __ __ __ O
5. __ __ O __ __ __ __ __
6. __ __ __ O __ __
7. __ __ __ __ O __
8. O __ __ __ __ __ __ __
9. __ __ __ __ O __ __ __ __
10. __ __ __ __ O O __
11. __ __ __ __ __ O

Attitude of love.

Answer: __ __ __ __ __ __ __ __ __ __ __ __ __ __ __ __ __

131–A Good Pace

If you head down this road, you won't fulfill the desires of the flesh. (GALATIANS 5)

1. CCFTTAIRWH
2. BTUEORL
3. KNRDU
4. RLYBETI
5. CRAVEINA
6. RHETNAO
7. TEEENNSSLG
8. PRNCEEEAMT
9. TRUFI
10. DEARTH
11. RESIDE
12. HATFI

1. ◯ __ __ __ __ __ __ ◯ __ __
2. __ __ __ __ __ ◯ __
3. __ __ __ __ ◯
4. __ ◯ __ __ __ __ __
5. __ __ __ __ __ ◯ __ __
6. __ __ __ ◯ ◯ __ __
7. __ __ __ __ __ ◯ __ __ __ ◯
8. __ __ __ ◯ __ __ __ __ __ __
9. __ __ __ ◯ __
10. __ __ __ ◯ __ __
11. __ __ __ ◯ __ __
12. __ __ __ ◯ __

A holy stroll.

Answer: __ __ __ __ __ __ __ __ __ __ __ __ __ __ __ __ __

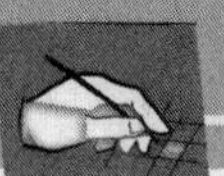

132–Singing with Grace

It is rich wisdom and the source of all we need. (Colossians 3)

1. MSIWOD
2. AOGREVF
3. PREAAP
4. SHADUBSN
5. WOELBS
6. EFLHS
7. EEPRCTS
8. UMLBHE
9. NERIS
10. BUTISM
11. CRIEESM
12. MHUOT

1. ◯_ _ _ _ _
2. _ ◯_ _ _ _ _
3. _ _ _ _ _ ◯
4. _ _ _ _ _ _ ◯_
5. _ ◯_ _ _ _
6. ◯_ _ _ _
7. _ _ _ _ _ ◯_
8. ◯_ _ _ _ _
9. ◯_ _ _ _
10. _ _ _ _ ◯_
11. _ _ _ _ _ _ ◯
12. _ _ _ ◯_

Dwelling within.

Answer: _ _ _ _ _ _ _ _ _ _ _ _ _ _ _

133–Radiant Appearance

This face shone like the sun. The answer may appear easy, but be careful here. (REVELATION 1)

1. RIEDEPC
2. NETGEBOT
3. CANFERU
4. THWEI
5. HTRTSNEG
6. DERAH
7. NEARGTM
8. DENCLA

1. _ _ _ _ ◯ _ _
2. _ _ _ ◯ _ _ _ _
3. _ ◯ _ ◯ _ _ _
4. _ _ _ ◯ _
5. _ _ _ ◯ ◯ _ _ _
6. _ _ ◯ _ _
7. _ _ _ _ _ ◯ _
8. ◯ _ _ _ _ ◯

After seeing this, John fell at His feet.

Answer: _ _ _ _ _ _ _ _ _ _ _

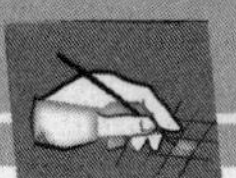

134–God's Right-Hand Man

He was a real superhero from way back. Hopefully, you'll wing right through these scrambles. (JUDE 1)

1. GDUJTNEM
2. DEHSPEIR
3. TUCEXEE
4. PSESEHCE
5. LANRETE
6. TAFES
7. ATLPESOS

1. ___ ___ ___ ___ ◯ ___ ___ ___
2. ___ ___ ___ ◯ ___ ___ ___ ___
3. ___ ___ ___ ◯ ___ ___ ___
4. ___ ___ ___ ___ ___ ◯ ___ ___
5. ___ ___ ___ ___ ___ ◯ ___
6. ___ ◯ ___ ___ ___
7. ___ ___ ___ ___ ___ ◯ ___ ___

He and his band fought for God.

Answer: ___ ___ ___ ___ ___ ___ ___

135–An Assiduous Plan

Although Jude planned strongly to write of salvation, he chose a different topic. Can you carefully figure out what it was? (JUDE 1)

1. TONECDN
2. NAISTS
3. NDLOGYU
4. LEIDEF
5. HANCARGLE
6. PETRC
7. TRESGAN
8. CARGE
9. TSIEINIDG

1. __ __ __ __ __ __ ◯
2. __ __ ◯ __ __ __
3. __ __ __ __ __ ◯ __
4. __ __ __ ◯ __ __
5. __ __ __ __ __ __ ◯ __ __
6. __ __ ◯ __ __
7. __ __ __ __ ◯ __ __
8. __ __ __ ◯ __
9. __ __ __ __ __ __ __ ◯ __

He gave all this to his writing.

Answer: __ __ __ __ __ __ __ __ __

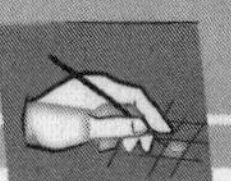

136–No Favoritism

God's command is to love your neighbor as yourself. This rule reigns! (JAMES 2)

1. POSERSP
2. SOTOFOLOT
3. THYWRO
4. RSGSSERTNA
5. PAERLAP
6. TARPILA
7. MINAERT
8. EWMADR

1. ___ ___ ___ ◯ ___ ___ ___
2. ___ ___ ___ ___ ___ ___ ◯ ___ ___
3. ___ ___ ___ ___ ___ ◯
4. ___ ___ ◯ ___ ___ ___ ___ ___ ___ ___
5. ___ ___ ___ ___ ___ ___ ◯
6. ___ ___ ___ ___ ___ ___ ◯
7. ___ ◯ ___ ___ ___ ___ ___
8. ◯ ___ ___ ___ ___ ___

All are to fulfill this.

Answer: ___ ___ ___ ___ ___   ___ ___ ___

137–*Highly Regarded*

He was known for his truthfulness. Honest! (3 John 1)

1. ESIRFND
2. CREDRO
3. MELHIFS
4. PORERSP
5. TEUR
6. OTHRF
7. GNIRB
8. HCRHUC
9. TORS

1. ___ ___ ___ ___ ___ ◯ ___
2. ___ ◯ ___ ___ ___ ___
3. ___ ___ ◯ ___ ___ ___ ___
4. ___ ___ ___ ___ ___ ◯ ___
5. ◯ ___ ___ ___
6. ___ ___ ◯ ___ ___
7. ___ ___ ◯ ___ ___
8. ___ ___ ◯ ___ ___ ___
9. ◯ ___ ___ ___

Everyone had good things to say about this man.

Answer: ___ ___ ___ ___ ___ ___ ___ ___ ___

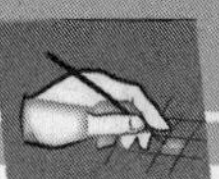

138–A Trusted Helper

This man, with a woodsy name, traveled with Paul and was trusted with important documents. (1 PETER 5)

1. POCALSMHIC
2. STISWNE
3. PAXLEME
4. REVSHIGOT
5. TRIHYCA
6. ANOGRRI
7. FREDFUSE
8. PSSOEUP

1. ___ ___ ___ ___ ___ ___ ___ ___ ◯ ___
2. ___ ◯ ___ ___ ___ ___ ___
3. ___ ___ ___ ___ ___ ◯ ___
4. ___ ◯ ___ ___ ___ ___ ___ ___ ___
5. ___ ___ ◯ ___ ___ ___ ___
6. ___ ___ ___ ___ ___ ◯ ___
7. ___ ◯ ___ ___ ___ ___ ___ ___
8. ◯ ___ ___ ___ ___ ___ ___

He was a faithful brother.

Answer: ___ ___ ___ ___ ___ ___ ___ ___ ___ ___

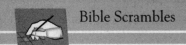

139–A Chosen Woman

This title may refer to one woman or to a church. Choose to unscramble carefully. (2 John 1)

1. TEEERND
2. KANIGWL
3. WEARDR
4. MANDTEMONMC
5. TIREW
6. DLERE
7. ESAK
8. CRIDENOT
9. TRAYGEL

1. __ __ __ __ __ ○ __
2. __ __ ○ __ __ __ __
3. __ ○ __ __ __ __
4. ○ __ __ __ __ __ __ __ __ __ __
5. __ __ __ ○ __
6. __ ○ __ __ __
7. __ ○ __ __
8. ○ __ __ __ __ __ __ __
9. __ __ __ __ __ __ ○

An epistle was written to this name.

Answer: __ __ __ __ __ __ __ __ __

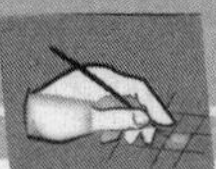

140–All Christians

The fellowship of believers is the most important group to belong to. (1 Peter 2)

1. DOBY
2. PRSEIA
3. SONICEECNC
4. TOMUH
5. EHESP
6. PUMSEER
7. FARE
8. LOIOFSH
9. NOHSET
10. RODNACINE

1. ◯ __ __ __
2. __ ◯ __ __ __ __
3. __ ◯ __ __ __ __ __ __ __ __
4. __ __ __ ◯ __
5. __ ◯ __ __ __
6. __ __ __ __ ◯ __ __
7. __ __ __ ◯
8. __ __ __ __ __ __ ◯
9. __ ◯ __ __ __ __
10. ◯ __ ◯ __ __ __ __ __ __

Instructions were given to love this collection of Christians.

Answer: __ __ __ __ __ __ __ __ __ __ __

141–*Treat Others Kindly*

Christ was the ultimate expression of this attribute. Take care in solving this puzzle. (1 PETER 3)

1. EFAC
2. LDOG
3. MEZANTAME
4. TIFILUP
5. MANREN
6. STEACH
7. TOCURSUOE
8. DENDIH
9. LOHY
10. TUGONE

1. __ __ ◯ __
2. __ ◯ __ __
3. __ __ __ __ __ ◯ __ __ __
4. ◯ __ __ __ __ __ __
5. __ ◯ __ __ __ __
6. __ __ __ ◯ __ __
7. __ __ __ __ __ __ __ __ ◯
8. __ ◯ __ __ __ __
9. __ ◯ __ __
10. __ __ ◯ __ __ __

We are to show this for others.

Answer: __ __ __ __ __ __ __ __ __ __

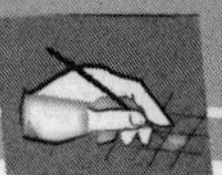

142–No Fire Damage

Through faith, Old Testament figures stopped the effects of fire in a furnace. Don't let the difficulty of unscrambling these clues dampen your spirit. (HEBREWS 11–12)

1. AEKUQ
2. THUGWOR
3. FEIR
4. NOBDS
5. CEIOLVEN
6. TLFGIH
7. CEVAS
8. RWSOD

1. ◯ ___ ___ ___ ___
2. ___ ___ ___ ◯ ___ ___ ___
3. ___ ___ ___ ◯
4. ___ ___ ◯ ___ ___
5. ___ ___ ___ ___ ___ ___ ◯ ___
6. ___ ___ ___ ___ ◯ ___
7. ___ ___ ___ ◯ ___
8. ___ ___ ___ ___ ◯

What was done to a fire before it could cause harm.

Answer: ___ ___ ___ ___ ___ ___ ___ ___

143–More Than Just a King

This king had a second, more important job. Peace be with you as your solve. (HEBREWS 7)

1. MATTENTES
2. TREPSI
3. LEAMS
4. ECREVIE
5. NETHT
6. NKIG
7. TYRSUE
8. REDOR
9. THETIS
10. CTDESEN

1. __ __ __ __ __ ◯ __ __ __
2. __ __ __ ◯ __ __
3. __ __ ◯ __ __
4. __ __ ◯ __ __ __ __
5. __ __ __ __ ◯
6. __ ◯ __ __
7. ◯ __ __ ◯ __ __
8. __ __ ◯ __ __
9. __ __ __ __ ◯ __
10. __ __ __ ◯ __ __ __

His name means "king of righteousness."

Answer: __ __ __ __ __ __ __ __ __ __ __ __

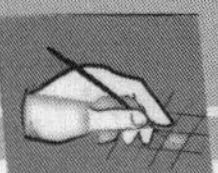

144–Take Heed!

Be on guard for these charlatans who would steal your faith. Hopefully, it won't take a "sentry" to solve this one. (TITUS 1)

1. DELER
2. FEEDLDI
3. ACEPE
4. KRASTLE
5. DCLIRHEN
6. VEOLR
7. VNCOIENC
8. ATPREMETE
9. BESFAL

1. __ __ ◯ __ __
2. __ ◯ __ __ __ __ __
3. __ __ __ ◯ __
4. __ __ __ __ ◯ __ __
5. __ __ ◯ __ __ __ __ __
6. __ __ ◯ __ __
7. __ __ __ __ __ __ __ ◯
8. __ __ __ __ __ ◯ __ __ __
9. __ __ __ __ __ ◯

Paul warns us of these.

Answer: __ __ __ __ __ __ __ __ __ __

145–Our High Priest

Christ is this, for He has gone ahead and can plead for us continually to God. (HEBREWS 6)

1. TAMONFCRINOI
2. OHTA
3. ONRCAH
4. IRSHE
5. NOGSRT
6. SLOU
7. IDGILECEN
8. NEAM
9. OCNEUSL
10. HEINITR

1. ___ ___ ___ ◯ ___ ___ ___ ___ ___ ___ ___ ___
2. ◯ ___ ___ ___
3. ___ ___ ___ ___ ___ ◯
4. ___ ◯ ___ ___ ___
5. ___ ___ ◯ ___ ___ ___
6. ___ ___ ◯ ___
7. ___ ___ ___ ___ ___ ___ ◯ ___ ___
8. ◯ ___ ___ ___
9. ___ ___ ___ ___ ___ ◯ ___
10. ___ ___ ___ ___ ◯ ___ ___

Christ is this for us as a high priest.

Answer: ___ ___ ___ ___ ___ ___ ___ ___ ___ ___

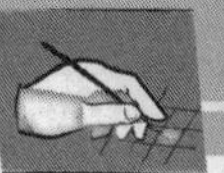

146–*Heaven's Gift*

True believers have been endowed with this gift. (Hebrews 6)

1. FTIHA
2. TRONDICE
3. RETEALN
4. CYIRCUF
5. LITEDENGEHN
6. ROWLD
7. TADSTE
8. STROHN

1. ___ ___ ___ ___ ◯
2. ___ ◯ ___ ___ ___ ___ ___ ___
3. ___ ___ ___ ___ ___ ___ ◯
4. ___ ___ ___ ___ ___ ___ ◯
5. ___ ___ ___ ___ ◯ ◯ ___ ___ ___ ___ ___
6. ___ ◯ ___ ___ ___
7. ___ ___ ◯ ___ ___ ___
8. ◯ ___ ___ ___ ___ ___

Some were made partakers of this.

Answer: ___ ___ ___ ___   ___ ___ ___ ___ ___

147–God Sees Everything

Don't try to hide anything from God! Hope the answer isn't too obvious. (Hebrews 4)

1. RWORAM
2. THRAW
3. CRANETI
4. OITSJN
5. SSORNFIPEO
6. NARDEH
7. STHIG
8. EHRTA

1. ◯__ __ __ __ __
2. __ __ ◯ __ __
3. __ __ __ __ __ __ ◯
4. __ __ ◯ __ __ __
5. __ __ __ ◯ __ __ __ __ __ __
6. __ __ __ __ ◯ __
7. ◯ __ __ __ __
8. __ __ __ __ ◯

All things are this to God.

Answer: __ __ __ __ __ __ __ __

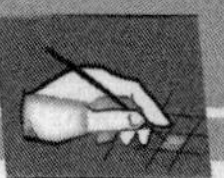

148–Bless His House

One good turn deserves another. Be refreshed as you solve for this man's name. (2 Timothy 1)

1. ERWPO
2. DSAHN
3. LEPSOG
4. EVADS
5. ITGF
6. EPKE
7. SUHOE
8. YMECR
9. SORUEPP
10. UDNOS

1. __ ◯ __ __ __
2. __ __ ◯ __ __
3. __ __ __ __ ◯ __
4. ◯ __ __ __ __
5. __ ◯ __ __
6. __ __ __ ◯
7. ◯ ◯ __ __ __
8. __ __ ◯ __ __
9. __ ◯ __ __ __ __ __
10. ◯ __ __ __ __

Paul asked the Lord for blessings on this person and his family.

Answer: __ __ __ __ __ __ __ __ __ __ __

149–Among Paul's Travels

The people here received a personal visit from Paul. Hope these scrambled words don't trip you up! (1 TIMOTHY 1)

1. IRTIMSEN
2. GGNNIAJL
3. HCEGRA
4. EPRU
5. DAEBI
6. ROMALMTI
7. FOREPAN
8. RASIL

1. ◯ __ __ __ __ __ __ __
2. __ ◯ __ __ __ __ __ __
3. ◯ __ __ __ __ __
4. __ __ __ ◯
5. __ __ __ ◯ __
6. __ __ __ ◯ __ __ __ __
7. __ __ __ __ __ ◯ __
8. __ ◯ ◯ __ __

Paul left Timothy in charge at Ephesus while he went here.

Answer: __ __ __ __ __ __ __ __ __ __

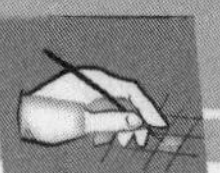

150–A Fortunate Church

The name of an American city was first a church in Asia. Don't use a pen to work this one. (REVELATION 1)

1. HAPAL
2. CEPNIR
3. RULNOITIBAT
4. MODGNIK
5. LEIS
6. SDLUCO
7. NOPAINOMC
8. RETBOHR
9. CEIOV
10. GOMEA

1. __ __ ◯ ◯ __
2. __ __ ◯ __ __ __
3. __ __ __ __ __ ◯ ◯ __ __ __ __
4. __ __ __ __ ◯ __ __
5. __ __ __ ◯
6. __ ◯ __ __ __ __
7. __ __ __ ◯ __ __ __ __ __
8. __ __ __ __ ◯ __ __
9. __ __ ◯ __ __
10. __ __ __ __ ◯

John was to send a book of his visions here.

Answer: __ __ __ __ __ __ __ __ __ __ __ __

151–Very Happy

How John responded to good news about Gaius. Happy solving! (3 John 1)

1. AGTYRLE
2. EMCO
3. NYOREUJ
4. DYLOG
5. SNIETWS
6. OISLIMUCA
7. TOCNNET
8. REDLE

1. __ ◯ __ __ __ __ __
2. __ __ __ ◯
3. ◯ __ __ __ __ __ __
4. __ ◯ __ __ __
5. __ ◯ __ __ __ __ __
6. __ __ __ __ ◯ __ __ __ __
7. __ __ __ __ ◯ __ __
8. __ __ ◯ __ __

John did this with enthusiasm.

Answer: __ __ __ __ __ __ __ __

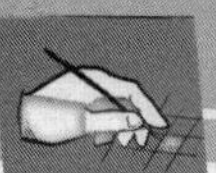

152–A High Office

Levi and his descendants had no choice in their career. Can you guess what it was? (HEBREWS 7)

1. RAHPTICAR
2. LVIREY
3. BEIRT
4. TNHET
5. NCDSETE
6. SNCODERTECA
7. EHPO
8. ATOH
9. DROER

1. ◯ __ __ __ __ __ __ __ __

2. __ __ ◯ __ __ __

3. __ __ ◯ __ __

4. __ ◯ __ __ __

5. __ __ ◯ __ __ __ __

6. __ __ __ __ __ __ __ __ ◯ __ __

7. ◯ ◯ __ __

8. ◯ __ __ __

9. __ __ ◯ __ __

Levi was given this office.

Answer: __ __ __ __ __ __ __ __ __ __

153–From Root to Fruit

The Gospel of Matthew begins with a genealogical tree of our Lord Jesus Christ. See if your understanding of this tree—from "root to fruit"—will help you solve this puzzle. (MATTHEW 1)

1. LFDIULFLE
2. VADDI
3. THEPPOR
4. HEJOPS
5. OTMERH
6. DUNBASH
7. EVIONCDEC
8. RIVING
9. NELMEUMA

1. ◯ __ __ __ __ __ __ __ __
2. __ __ __ ◯ __
3. __ ◯ __ __ __ __ __
4. __ __ ◯ __ __ __
5. __ __ ◯ __ __ __
6. __ __ __ ◯ __ __ __
7. __ ◯ __ __ __ __ __ __ __
8. __ __ ◯ __ __ __
9. __ __ __ __ ◯ __ __ __

Jesus was this to Mary.

Answer: __ __ __ __ __ __ __ __ __ __

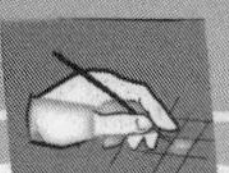

154–John the Baptist

John pointed out the Way to us. Once unscrambled, these clues will point out the way to the puzzle's answer. (MARK 1)

1. TATIGYSRWHA
2. ZATDIBEP
3. SOLONUE
4. DRJANO
5. CEDDESGINN
6. CATPREENEN
7. NSEGMEERS
8. SHAVENE
9. SCLOTSU
10. ISERMONSI

1. __ __ __ __ __ __ __ __ ◯ __ __
2. __ __ __ __ ◯ __ __ __
3. __ __ ◯ __ __ __ __
4. __ __ __ ◯ __ __
5. __ __ __ __ ◯ __ __ __ __ __
6. ◯ __ __ __ __ __ __ __ __ __
7. __ __ __ __ __ ◯ __ __ __
8. __ __ __ __ ◯ __ __
9. __ __ __ __ __ __ ◯
10. __ __ __ __ ◯ __ __ __ __

Where John the Baptist cried.

Answer: In the __ __ __ __ __ __ __ __ __ __

155–Blessed among Women

All of God's promises about the birth of the Messiah have come true. Luke can help you solve this puzzle with his clues about Jesus' birth. (Luke 1)

1. USMCFOHAR
2. IRCHASZAA
3. REIGNTEANO
4. SLEBESD
5. MINKDOG
6. ABELIGR
7. FNGYIAM
8. SEPSUEDO
9. BLISTEEHA
10. NATIOLSTUA

1. ___ ___ ___ ◯ ___ ___ ___ ___ ◯
2. ___ ___ ___ ___ ___ ___ ___ ◯ ___
3. ___ ___ ◯ ___ ___ ___ ___ ___ ___ ___
4. ___ ___ ___ ___ ___ ___ ◯
5. ___ ___ ___ ___ ___ ___ ◯
6. ___ ◯ ___ ___ ___ ___ ___
7. ___ ___ ___ ___ ◯ ___ ___
8. ___ ___ ___ ___ ___ ___ ___ ◯
9. ___ ___ ___ ___ ___ ___ ◯ ___ ___
10. ___ ___ ___ ___ ___ ___ ___ ___ ___ ◯

Before she was called mother, Mary was called this.

Answer: ___ ___ ___ ___ ___ ___ ___ ___ ___ ___ ___ ___

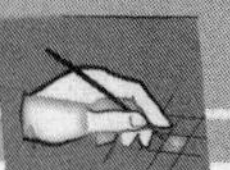

156–CNN in the Wilderness

BREAKING NEWS from field reporter, John the Baptist: "This was he of whom I spake." (JOHN 1)

1. SINWETS
2. VEENHA
3. SAISAE
4. TLHTCAE
5. GINPTIBZA
6. SOMES
7. GBNNIGENI
8. ETTNBOGE
9. DRFERPERE
10. AGRNIINME
11. PHMEODCRNE

1. __ __ ◯ __ __ __ __
2. ◯ __ __ __ __ __
3. ◯ __ __ __ __ __
4. ◯ __ __ __ __ __ __
5. __ ◯ __ __ __ __ __ __ __
6. ◯ __ __ __ __
7. ◯ __ __ __ __ __ __ __ __
8. __ __ __ ◯ __ __ __ __
9. __ __ __ ◯ __ __ __ __ __
10. __ __ __ __ __ __ __ __ ◯
11. __ ◯ __ __ __ __ __ __ __ __ ◯

John's "breaking news story" might have been entitled this.

Answer: __ __ __ __ __ __ __ __ __ __ __ __ __

157–Forty Days

For forty days from the Passion of Christ to His ascension, Jesus' followers were solving the puzzle of the Messiah's life, death, and rebirth. Can you solve this puzzle in less than forty *minutes*? (Acts 1)

1. MELSERJAU
2. PREUP MORO
3. ADDIONER
4. TINYRIMS
5. THIMSATA
6. INOPLCUITSPA
7. SCPIEDILS
8. DEBLESSMA

1. __ __ __ __ __ ○ __ __ __
2. __ __ ○ __ __ __ __ __ __
3. ○ __ __ __ __ __ __ __
4. __ __ __ __ ○ __ __ __
5. __ __ __ ○ __ __ __ __
6. __ __ __ __ ○ __ __ __ __ __ __ __
7. __ __ __ __ __ __ __ ○ __
8. __ ○ __ __ __ __ __ __ __

What the eleven plus one were numbered to be.

Answer: __ __ __ __ __ __ __ __ __

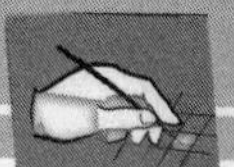

158–When in Rome. . .

Paul understood that he was not called "to do as the Romans do" but as our Lord would have him do. He got off to a good start as Romans reveals. (Romans 1)

1. ROCATER
2. AHITF
3. SEGEKR
4. RLIDEOFIG
5. DORUNDOSTE
6. REVTNSA
7. SPEPIALSOHT
8. CGERA
9. SINLESOH

1. __ __ __ __ ◯ __ __
2. __ __ __ __ ◯
3. __ __ ◯ __ __ __
4. ◯ __ __ __ __ __ __ __ __
5. __ __ __ __ __ __ __ ◯ __ __
6. ◯ __ __ __ __ __ __
7. __ __ __ __ __ __ __ __ __ __ ◯
8. __ __ __ __ ◯
9. __ __ ◯ __ __ __ __ __

What Paul proposed to preach when in Rome.

Answer: __ __ __   __ __ __ __ __ __

159–Idiot's Domain

Perhaps these scrambled words will puzzle you. But you need not be baffled when our Lord calls your name. Just answer, "Yes, Lord. Yes!" (1 Corinthians 1)

1. TWENTIR
2. ISHORTNEGUSES
3. NREEHBTR
4. ENOILFSSSHO
5. UDONFOCN
6. RYLGO
7. TGYIHM

1. ◯ __ __ __ __ __ __
2. __ __ __ __ __ __ ◯ __ __ __ __ __ __
3. __ __ __ __ __ ◯ __ __
4. __ __ __ ◯ __ __ __ __ __ __ __
5. __ __ __ __ __ __ __ ◯
6. __ ◯ __ __ __
7. __ __ __ __ __ ◯

God made this kind of wisdom idiotic.

Answer: __ __ __ __ __ __ __ __

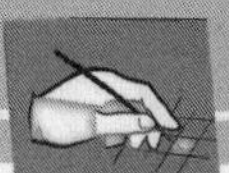

160–Yea Yea and Nay Nay

If you become discouraged in solving this puzzle, flip to the answers in the back of this book. If you become discouraged in life, look to God's Word. (2 Corinthians 1)

1. CLYIPITISM
2. GRIEFNUFSS
3. WLOEDAGKCEN
4. MOSTTYIEN
5. OLAVANTIS
6. TSHISGENL
7. DEREPAIDS
8. KAAPSTERR

1. ___ ___ ___ ◯ ___ ___ ___ ___ ___ ___
2. ___ ___ ___ ___ ___ ◯ ___ ___ ___ ___
3. ___ ___ ___ ___ ◯ ___ ___ ___ ___ ___ ___
4. ___ ___ ___ ___ ___ ◯ ___ ___ ___
5. ___ ___ ___ ___ ___ ___ ◯ ___ ___
6. ___ ___ ___ ___ ___ ___ ___ ◯ ___
7. ___ ◯ ___ ___ ___ ___ ___ ___ ___
8. ___ ___ ___ ___ ___ ___ ___ ___ ◯

We can rely on these when they come from God. Amen to that!

Answer: ___ ___ ___ ___ ___ ___ ___ ___

161–As Thou Hast Believed

Jesus found this in one man; would He find it in you, as well? (MATTHEW 8:5–13)

1. SSEAMEFL
2. MNTRETO
3. NSGGIAHN
4. VASTREN
5. LEEDEVIB
6. AMCPNREUA
7. RTYWOH
8. ODOWELLF
9. DEHLEA
10. GWENPIE
11. NOCTERNIU
12. AAMABHR

1. ◯ __ __ __ __ __ __ __

2. __ ◯ __ __ __ __ __

3. ◯ __ __ __ __ __ __ __

4. __ __ ◯ __ __ __ __

5. __ __ __ __ ◯ __ __ __

6. __ ◯ __ __ __ __ __ __ __

7. __ __ __ ◯ __ __

8. ◯ __ __ __ __ __ __ __

9. __ __ ◯ __ __ __

10. __ __ __ __ ◯ __ __

11. __ __ __ ◯ __ __ __ __ __

12. __ __ __ __ ◯ __ __

What did our Lord marvel at?

Answer: __ __   __ __ __ __ __   __ __ __ __ __

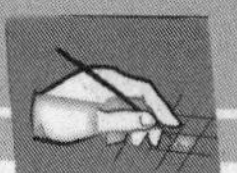

162–A Swine Time Was Had by All

It could be said that Jesus healed a man with "Legion-aires" disease. (MARK 5:1–20)

1. PETES
2. SISCOOPMAN
3. EDRSUAN
4. FFEEDUSR
5. HEDOCK
6. TSNOUDAH
7. HGUSTEBO
8. JRUDAE
9. CHEDOLT

1. ___ ___ ___ ___ ◯
2. ___ ◯ ___ ___ ___ ___ ___ ___ ___ ___
3. ___ ◯ ___ ___ ___ ___ ___
4. ◯ ___ ___ ___ ___ ___ ___ ___
5. ___ ___ ___ ___ ◯ ___
6. ___ ___ ___ ___ ◯ ___ ___ ___
7. ___ ___ ◯ ___ ___ ___ ___ ___
8. ___ ___ ___ ___ ___ ◯
9. ___ ___ ___ ___ ___ ___ ◯

What really ailed the man.

Answer: ___ ___ ___ ___ ___ ___ ___ ___ ___

163–An Offer You Can Refuse

Satan giveth and Satan taketh away. Give your best try at solving this puzzle in less than forty minutes. (LUKE 4)

1. PLETEM
2. SELAGN
3. AMNDOMC
4. RITSIP
5. NESTO
6. UMJARLESE
7. TNNOAIMU
8. EEVILREDD
9. ROWSPHI
10. SISLENDERW

1. ◯ __ __ __ __ __

2. __ __ __ ◯ __ __

3. __ __ __ ◯ __ __ __

4. __ ◯ __ __ __ __

5. __ ◯ __ __ __

6. __ __ __ __ __ ◯ __ __ __

7. __ __ __ __ ◯ __ __ __

8. __ __ __ ◯ __ __ __ __ __

9. __ ◯ __ __ __ __ __

10. __ __ __ __ __ __ ◯ __ __ __

What Satan offered to Jesus.

Answer: __ __ __ __ __ __ __ __ __ __

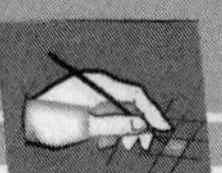

164–*Wheat or Rye?*

Unscramble these words to discover what you need to choose to satisfy your "soul hunger." (JOHN 6)

1. BAIIETSR
2. FMLSHIE
3. IBARB
4. CISLAMER
5. AANMN
6. ESSEAIDD
7. VOSALE
8. SSHEIF
9. EPSICISDL
10. RTHSTI
11. FIIUEFCNTS

1. ◯ __ __ __ __ __ __ __
2. ◯ __ __ __ ◯ __ __
3. __ __ ◯ __ __
4. __ __ ◯ __ __ __ ◯ __
5. __ ◯ __ __ __
6. __ __ __ __ __ __ __ ◯
7. __ ◯ __ __ __ __
8. ◯ __ __ __ __ __
9. __ __ __ __ __ __ ◯ __ __
10. __ __ ◯ __ __ __
11. __ __ ◯ __ __ __ __ ◯ __ __

What Jesus called Himself.

Answer: __ __ __ __ __ __ __ __ __ __ __ __ __ __ __ __ __

165–The Good, the Bad, and the Martyred

Unscramble the names of men and women who were either good, bad, or martyred. (Acts 1–7)

1. STATAIHM
2. JSEAM
3. SAUDJ
4. IVADD
5. RTPEE
6. NRCONIA
7. AAAPCHSI
8. RCSPOUROH
9. THENPES
10. AITLPE
11. WARDEN

1. ___ ___ ___ ___ ◯ ___ ___ ___

2. ___ ___ ___ ◯ ___

3. ___ ___ ___ ◯ ___

4. ___ ___ ◯ ___ ___

5. ___ ___ ___ ◯ ___

6. ◯ ___ ___ ___ ___ ___ ___

7. ___ ___ ___ ___ ___ ___ ___ ◯

8. ___ ___ ___ ___ ___ ◯ ___ ___ ___

9. ___ ___ ___ ◯ ___ ___ ___

10. ___ ___ ___ ___ ___ ◯

11. ___ ◯ ___ ___ ___ ___

What the first Christian martyr saw in Acts 7:56.

Answer: ___ ___ ___ ___ ___ ___ ___   ___ ___ ___ ___

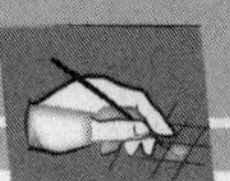

166–Walk This Way

Walking is a great way to shed unwanted pounds. Unscramble the clues, solve the puzzle, and you will no longer carry a weighty burden. (Romans 8)

1. HDLNRICE
2. NOJIT-ISHER
3. CRONENSIISTE
4. NTOOPAID
5. LDILFUEFL
6. TALOMR
7. STEADEEPNRIT
8. RBYETIL
9. GNBAEOD

1. ◯ __ __ __ __ __ __ __

2. __ ◯ __ __ __ - __ __ __ __ __

3. __ __ __ __ __ __ __ __ __ __ __ ◯

4. __ ◯ __ __ __ __ __ __

5. __ __ __ __ __ __ __ ◯ __

6. ◯ __ __ __ __ __

7. __ __ __ __ __ __ __ __ ◯ __ __ __

8. __ __ __ ◯ __ __ __

9. __ __ __ ◯ __ __ __

What we will no longer be when we walk in the Spirit.

Answer: __ __ __ __ __ __ __ __ __

167–Till Death Us Do Part

God wrote the instruction book on life and marriage. Unscramble the clues to discover His words of wisdom. (1 Corinthians 7)

1. EOPUPSS
2. RUDDEAF
3. GNATSFI
4. INGRVI
5. EENCOVEBLEN
6. IREDRAM
7. FISNADETCI
8. DAIBE
9. DEECLIRONC
10. SAFESTDT
11. ANDMTMSMOCNE

1. ___ ___ ___ ◯ ___ ___ ___
2. ___ ___ ___ ___ ___ ◯ ___
3. ___ ___ ___ ◯ ___ ___ ___
4. ___ ___ ___ ◯ ___ ___
5. ___ ___ ___ ___ ___ ◯ ___ ___ ___ ___ ___
6. ___ ___ ___ ___ ___ ___ ◯
7. ___ ___ ___ ___ ___ ___ ◯ ___ ___ ___
8. ___ ___ ◯ ___ ___
9. ◯ ___ ___ ___ ___ ___ ___ ___ ___ ___
10. ___ ___ ___ ___ ___ ___ ◯ ___
11. ___ ___ ___ ___ ___ ___ ___ ___ ___ ___ ◯ ___

What is the number one rule for a happy marriage?

Answer: ___ ___ ___ ___ ___ ___ ___ ___ ___ ___ ___

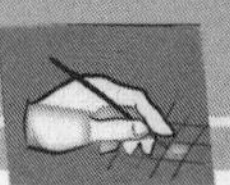

168–*Happy Birthday, Herod*

Herod tried to cover one sin with another and then another. Can you uncover the answer? (MATTHEW 14)

1. EDAHBDEE
2. THOPPER
3. RGHEARC
4. TBOHUGR
5. CANEDD
6. ORPINS
7. IPSTATB
8. SLEEDAP

1. __ __ ◯ __ __ __ __ __
2. __ __ __ __ __ ◯ __
3. __ __ __ ◯ __ __ __
4. __ __ ◯ __ __ __ __
5. ◯ __ __ __ __ __
6. __ __ ◯ __ __ __
7. __ ◯ __ __ __ __ __
8. __ __ __ __ ◯ __ __

In trying to please this person, Herod sinned.

Answer: __ __ __ __ __ __ __ __

169–Happy Birthday, Dear Jesus

Who knew that Christ Jesus' birth would be the most celebrated and important birthday ever? His Father did. (Luke 2)

1. HSTEIHG
2. EWEDDRON
3. EVYLENAH SHOT
4. NGDAWDLSI
5. LMEBHEETH
6. RYOGNIFILG
7. LIDREDEVE
8. SBINROTFR
9. RAGMEN
10. GSSUUUTA

1. ___ ___ ◯ ___ ___ ___ ___
2. ___ ◯ ___ ___ ___ ___ ___ ___
3. ___ ___ ___ ___ ___ ___ ___ ___   ___ ◯ ___ ___
4. ___ ___ ___ ◯ ___ ___ ___ ___ ___
5. ___ ___ ◯ ___ ___ ___ ___ ___ ___
6. ___ ___ ___ ___ ___ ___ ___ ◯ ___ ___
7. ◯ ___ ___ ___ ___ ___ ___ ___ ___
8. ___ ◯ ___ ___ ___ ___ ___ ___ ___
9. ___ ___ ◯ ___ ___ ___
10. ___ ___ ◯ ___ ◯ ___ ___ ___

What the angel of the Lord brought the shepherds in the fields.

Answer: ___ ___ ___ ___   ___ ___ ___ ___ ___ ___ ___

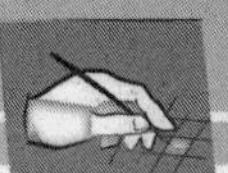

170–A Leopard Changes His Spots

Our "spots" can be changed in an instant by our heavenly Father whether we are willing or not. But it is for our good and His glory if we allow it. (Acts 9:1–30)

1. SABBANAR
2. AGUYSOSENG
3. LRGAHSTEU
4. FOODDNNCEU
5. BREHOTR
6. STEKAB
7. TRTHIGAS
8. AELCSS
9. ASCUDMAS
10. SELVES

1. ___ ___ ___ ___ ___ ___ ___ ◯
2. ___ ___ ___ ◯ ___ ___ ___ ◯ ___ ___
3. ___ ◯ ___ ___ ___ ___ ___ ___ ___
4. ___ ◯ ___ ◯ ___ ___ ___ ___ ___ ___ ___
5. ___ ___ ___ ◯ ___ ___ ___
6. ___ ◯ ___ ___ ___ ___
7. ___ ___ ◯ ___ ___ ___ ___ ___
8. ◯ ___ ___ ___ ___ ___
9. ___ ___ ___ ___ ___ ___ ◯ ___
10. ___ ___ ___ ◯ ___ ___

Ananias was sent by God to locate this man.

Answer: ___ ___ ___ ___   ___ ___   ___ ___ ___ ___ ___ ___

171–Present Gifts

God will bless us with many and varied gifts in exchange for one simple gift from us. (Romans 12)

1. BLEASARNOE
2. BYLOSER
3. USAMEER
4. MONDREFOC
5. REMMSBE
6. OJCIERE
7. VEFTNER
8. CIVERES
9. VECMOOER
10. TENPAIT

1. ___ ___ ◯ ___ ___ ___ ___ ___ ___ ___
2. ◯ ___ ___ ___ ___ ___ ___
3. ___ ___ ◯ ___ ___ ___ ___
4. ◯ ___ ___ ___ ___ ___ ___ ___ ___
5. ___ ___ ___ ___ ___ ◯ ___
6. ___ ___ ___ ___ ◯ ___ ___
7. ◯ ___ ___ ___ ___ ___ ___
8. ___ ___ ___ ___ ◯ ___ ___
9. ___ ___ ___ ___ ◯ ___ ___ ___
10. ___ ___ ___ ___ ◯ ___ ___

Paul said our bodies should be this.

Answer: ___ ___ ___ ___ ___ ___ ___ ___ ___ ___

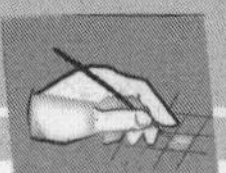

172–Love-eth

Here are some words gleaned directly from 1 Corinthians 13, often referred to as the "Love Chapter." See how many you can unscramble to solve the puzzle—we think you'll love-eth this one. (1 CORINTHIANS 13)

1. NEUTVHAT
2. EHHTOP
3. TOFHIPETR
4. HEFUSFRET
5. VIBLETHEE
6. RUEDHENT
7. HKITENHT
8. HERATEB
9. JTRHEEOIC
10. EKETSHE

1. ___ ___ ___ ___ ◯ ___ ___ ___

2. ___ ___ ___ ___ ___ ◯

3. ___ ___ ___ ___ ___ ___ ◯ ___ ___

4. ◯ ___ ___ ___ ___ ___ ___ ___ ___

5. ___ ___ ___ ___ ◯ ___ ___ ___ ___

6. ___ ___ ___ ___ ___ ___ ◯ ___

7. ___ ◯ ___ ___ ___ ___ ___ ___

8. ___ ___ ___ ◯ ___ ___ ___

9. ___ ◯ ___ ___ ___ ___ ___ ___ ___

10. ___ ___ ◯ ___ ___ ___ ___

"And now abideth. . ." (1 Corinthians 13:13)

Answer: . . . ___ ___ ___ ___ ___   ___ ___ ___ ___ ___

173–Paul: Man of Action

Paul was a man who worked tirelessly to proclaim Christ as Lord and Savior. Unscramble the verbs (words showing action) below to solve this puzzle. (2 CORINTHIANS 11)

1. PEACSDE
2. PUPDILES
3. STIGFAN
4. ROFEDMARTSN
5. DEAPHECR
6. BEDBOR
7. KNITH
8. TEPNESR
9. NGOISTAB
10. TDSOEN

1. __ ◯ __ __ __ __ __
2. __ ◯ __ __ __ __ __ __
3. ◯ __ __ __ __ __ __
4. __ __ __ __ __ ◯ __ __ __ __ __
5. __ __ ◯ __ __ __ __ __
6. ◯ __ __ __ __ __
7. __ __ ◯ __ __
8. __ __ __ __ __ ◯ __
9. __ __ __ __ __ __ __ ◯
10. ◯ __ __ __ __ __

His work for Christ brought Paul many of these.

Answer: __ __ __ __ __ __ __ __ __ __

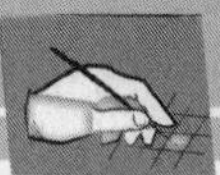

174–This Is My Body

The last meal Jesus enjoyed with His closest disciples was a Passover Seder. Unscramble the clues below to feed on this puzzle's answer. (Matthew 26:1–30)

1. SUADJ
2. NVEE
3. SDLEBES
4. AMTTTSEEN
5. YARTEB
6. ENVI
7. AFTES
8. NASTKH
9. VEWLET
10. RIKND

1. __ ◯ __ __ __
2. __ __ __ ◯
3. __ ◯ __ __ __ __ __
4. __ __ __ __ __ __ ◯ __ __
5. __ __ __ __ ◯ __
6. ◯ __ __ __
7. __ ◯ __ __ __
8. __ __ __ ◯ __ __
9. __ __ __ __ __ ◯
10. ◯ __ __ __ __

The bread that Jesus and His disciples ate was this.

Answer: __ __ __ __ __ __ __ __ __ __

175–Mission Possible

Jesus gave His original twelve disciples many duties and gifts. Even today we can receive these same duties and gifts as His chosen disciples did 2,000 years ago. (Luke 9:1–6)

1. ADEEISSS
2. SDUT
3. STWON
4. HESAK
5. SPEOLG
6. CHAPGERIN
7. EIANLHG
8. EVETLW
9. ONYJRUE

1. __ __ __ __ ◯ __ __ __
2. __ ◯ __ __
3. ◯ __ __ __ __
4. __ ◯ __ __ __
5. __ ◯ __ __ __ __
6. __ ◯ __ __ __ __ __ __ __
7. __ __ __ __ ◯ __ __
8. ◯ __ __ __ __ __
9. __ __ __ __ __ __ ◯

Jesus endowed this to His handpicked disciples.

Answer: __ __ __ __ __ __ __ __ __

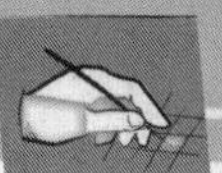

176–Here Comes the Bride

Christ Jesus used parables to teach His followers. Believe in Him and be prepared for His return as clues from His bridal parable instructs. (MATTHEW 25:1–13)

1. DGINKOM
2. OAERS
3. RIGSIVN
4. IMRTMDE
5. SHOLOFI
6. MASPL
7. GOBIMOEDRR
8. SSLEEVS

1. __ __ __ __ __ __ ◯
2. ◯ __ __ __ __
3. __ __ ◯ __ __ __ __
4. __ ◯ __ __ __ __ __
5. __ __ __ __ ◯ __ __
6. __ ◯ __ __ __
7. __ __ __ __ __ ◯ __ __ __ __
8. __ __ __ __ ◯ __ __

The wise young women arrived on time to this.

Answer: __ __ __ __ __ __ __ __

177–Share and Share Alike

God blesses those who give their very best with an honest and loving heart. Give this puzzle your very best—and don't hold back. (Acts 4:33–5:11)

1. SHOGT
2. RATHE
3. TTPEM
4. EROPSOSSSS
5. SHESUO
6. INNAAAS
7. RIUDEB
8. ALKDEC

1. ___ ___ ___ ◯ ___
2. ___ ___ ◯ ___ ___
3. ___ ___ ___ ◯ ___
4. ◯ ___ ___ ___ ___ ___ ___ ___ ___ ___
5. ◯ ___ ___ ___ ___ ___
6. ___ ___ ___ ___ ◯ ___ ___
7. ___ ___ ◯ ___ ___ ___
8. ___ ◯ ___ ___ ___ ___

This woman was true to her husband but not to God.

Answer: ___ ___ ___ ___ ___ ___ ___ ___

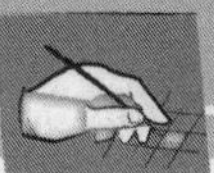

178–Follow the Leader (Part 1)

Christ was the first to die and arise from the grave but not the last. Those who believe in Him will get their turn someday, as well. (1 CORINTHIANS 15:1–8)

1. ESVAD
2. SPEACH
3. RYOEMM
4. DIRTH
5. SLOGPE
6. DNATS
7. DUBEIR
8. RTBNEEHR
9. EPHACERD
10. ESRPTNE

1. ◯ __ __ __ __

2. ◯ __ __ __ __ __

3. __ __ __ __ ◯ __

4. __ __ ◯ __ __

5. __ __ __ ◯ __ __

6. __ ◯ __ __ __

7. __ ◯ __ __ __ __

8. __ __ __ __ __ ◯ __ __

9. __ __ ◯ __ __ __ __ __

10. __ __ __ ◯ __ __ __

According to these, Christ died for our sins.

Answer: __ __ __ __ __ __ __ __ __ __ __

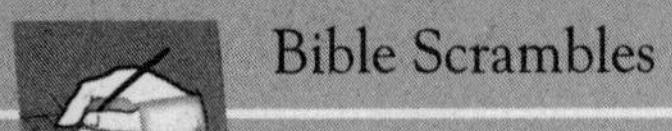

179–Follow the Leader (Part 2)

We are instructed to give our best to our Father God. He gave His best to us even though He knew what His Son would suffer in our stead. (1 Corinthians 15:9–24)

1. ITFHA
2. SIERN
3. ROLUDEAB
4. PSELEA
5. TDAHE
6. LFENAL
7. CAGER
8. RCHHUC
9. VEALI
10. HMEOTC
11. HRSPIEDE

1. ◯ ___ ___ ___ ___
2. ___ ◯ ___ ___ ___
3. ___ ___ ___ ___ ___ ◯ ___ ___
4. ___ ◯ ___ ___ ___ ___
5. ___ ___ ___ ◯ ___
6. ◯ ___ ___ ___ ___ ___
7. ___ ◯ ___ ___ ___
8. ___ ___ ◯ ___ ___ ___
9. ___ ___ ◯ ___ ___
10. ___ ___ ___ ___ ◯ ___
11. ___ ___ ___ ___ ◯ ___ ___ ___

Christ is the _____ of those who will rise from the dead.

Answer: ___ ___ ___ ___ ___ ___ ___ ___ ___ ___ ___

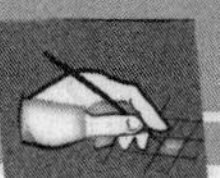

180–Follow the Leader (Part 3)

Paul writes that someday, like Christ, our perishable bodies will rise imperishable. How uplifting! (1 Corinthians 15:36–50)

1. SARST
2. UNROTPOCIR
3. LCSLEAITE
4. AHRTE
5. MGIEA
6. OWSSTE
7. RUNLATA
8. VENHAE
9. SFHLE

1. __ __ __ __ ◯
2. __ __ __ __ __ ◯ __ __ __ __
3. __ __ __ __ __ __ ◯ __ __
4. __ __ ◯ __ __
5. ◯ __ __ __ __
6. __ __ __ __ __ ◯
7. __ __ __ ◯ __ __ __
8. __ __ ◯ __ __ __
9. __ ◯ __ __ __

When Christ returns, those who believe in Him shall be resurrected with this kind of body.

Answer: __ __ __ __ __ __ __ __ __ __

181–Follow the Leader (Part 4)

Paul relates an once-popular adage that is not hard for believers to digest. (1 Corinthians 15:51–58)

1. NGIST
2. ETRIWTN
3. SESTFTDA
4. SLAT PRTUM
5. TOAMLR
6. DNUOS
7. NIKITGNLW
8. YYETRSM
9. DNNGUBOIA

1. ◯ ___ ___ ___ ___
2. ◯ ___ ___ ___ ___ ___ ___
3. ___ ___ ___ ___ ___ ◯ ___ ___
4. ◯ ___ ___ ___ ___ ___ ___ ___ ___
5. ___ ___ ___ ___ ___ ◯
6. ___ ◯ ___ ___ ___
7. ___ ◯ ___ ___ ___ ___ ___ ___ ___
8. ___ ___ ___ ___ ◯ ___ ___
9. ___ ___ ___ ___ ___ ◯ ___ ___ ___

"Death is _____ up in victory." (1 Corinthians 15:54)

Answer: ___ ___ ___ ___ ___ ___ ___ ___ ___

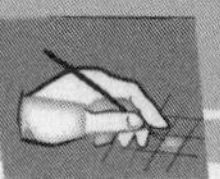

182–Judgment Day

We should make it our aim to please God, knowing that someday we will have to account for everything we've done. (2 Corinthians 5)

1. ROYLG
2. VISOELSDD
3. RRTREO
4. DEMOCMN
5. ROSBE
6. ITPSIR
7. HLOEBD
8. ARTLEEN
9. ADROASSSMBA

1. ◯ __ __ __ __
2. __ __ __ __ ◯ __ __ __ __
3. __ __ __ __ ◯ __
4. __ __ __ __ __ __ ◯
5. __ ◯ __ __ __
6. __ __ __ ◯ __ __
7. ◯ __ __ __ __ __
8. __ __ __ __ __ ◯ __
9. __ __ __ __ __ __ __ ◯ __ __ __

All our actions will be judged by the Lord.

Answer: __ __ __ __   __ __   __ __ __

183–Know Jesus, Know Peace; No Jesus, No Peace

Knowing Jesus means knowing or experiencing trials and tribulations at times. But have courage! A church sign once proclaimed: IF GOD HAS BROUGHT YOU TO IT, HE WILL GET YOU THROUGH IT. (ROMANS 5)

1. COREJIE
2. DYLOUNG
3. ENRSNIS
4. TREASH
5. EIPCEEERXN
6. RIFUEG
7. CEATPIEN
8. CPAEE
9. DOBLO

1. __ __ ◯ __ __ __ __
2. ◯ __ __ __ __ __ __
3. __ __ __ __ __ __ ◯
4. __ __ __ __ ◯ __
5. __ __ __ __ __ ◯ __ __ __ __
6. ◯ __ __ __ __ __
7. __ __ __ ◯ __ __ __ __
8. __ ◯ __ __ __
9. __ __ __ __ ◯

By faith, we are this in Jesus Christ.

Answer: __ __ __ __ __ __ __ __ __

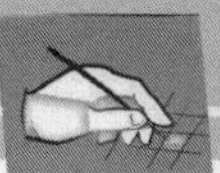

184–The End of the World (Part 1)

Jesus spoke of His return and the end times during His earthly ministry. You'll encounter some of the signs He foretold as you solve this puzzle. (MATTHEW 24:1–15)

1. DDFFEENO
2. CLIFFDATE
3. ROWRSSO
4. SLANDEOITO
5. ELPIESCSNET
6. ABYTER
7. RSUUROM
8. SCALPE
9. EDTAH
10. VEDCIEE
11. YQTIUINI
12. ESFMINA

1. _ ◯ _ _ _ _ _ _
2. ◯ _ _ ◯ _ _ _ _ _
3. ◯ _ _ _ _ _ _
4. _ ◯ _ _ _ _ _ _ _ _
5. ◯ _ _ _ _ _ _ _ _ _ _
6. _ _ _ ◯ _ _
7. _ _ _ ◯ _ _ _
8. ◯ _ _ _ _ _
9. ◯ _ _ _ _
10. _ _ _ _ _ _ ◯
11. _ _ _ _ _ _ ◯ _
12. _ _ _ _ _ _ ◯

This will be one of the signs of the end times.

Answer: _ _ _ _ _ _   _ _ _ _ _ _ _ _ _ _ _ _

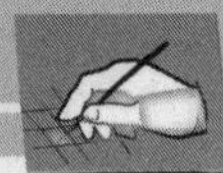

185–The End of the World (Part 2)

Jesus foretold the good news of His second coming. Here are more scrambled clues with an answer that may be things we'll see when He returns. (MATTHEW 24:9–31)

1. MRETTUP
2. NOSTAIN
3. SEWTINS
4. RGEHTA
5. KREENADD
6. GSEELA
7. CELTE
8. SENDOWR
9. REDENU
10. SYDA

1. __ __ __ __ ◯ __ __
2. __ __ __ __ ◯ __ __
3. ◯ __ __ __ ◯ __ __
4. __ __ __ __ __ ◯
5. __ ◯ __ __ __ ◯ __ ◯
6. __ __ ◯ __ __ __
7. __ ◯ __ __ __
8. __ ◯ __ __ __ __ __
9. __ __ __ __ ◯ __
10. __ __ ◯ __

Jesus will return with this.

Answer: __ __ __ __ __   __ __ __   __ __ __ __ __

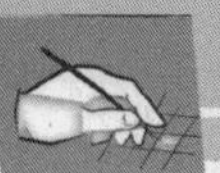

186–Trial by (Guilty) Jury

Jesus was questioned by an angry mob in the temple who wanted to convict a woman of a sinful crime. But Christ wouldn't let her "jury" off easy. (JOHN 8:1–11)

1. CESCAU
2. GNUROD
3. RINGEF
4. ETLYRUDA
5. TOWER
6. MTIGPNTE
7. DETONS
8. SREATM
9. DRHAE

1. __ __ ◯ __ __ __
2. __ __ ◯ __ __ __
3. __ __ ◯ __ __ __
4. __ ◯ __ __ __ __ __ __
5. __ __ __ __ ◯
6. __ __ ◯ __ __ __ __ __
7. __ __ __ ◯ __ __
8. __ __ __ __ ◯ __
9. __ __ __ __ ◯

The scribes and Pharisees were themselves this.

Answer: __ __ __ __ __ __ __ __ __

187–Amazing Talent

Each of us will be endowed with as many responsibilities as our Lord knows we can handle. Can you handle this puzzle without looking for the answers in the scripture referenced above? (Matthew 25:14–30)

1. TLLUOSHF
2. RELRU
3. ROEJYNU
4. VIENG
5. EDAGIN
6. EKTNA
7. LSATNET
8. ODGSO

1. ◯ ___ ___ ___ ___ ___ ___ ___
2. ___ ___ ___ ◯ ___
3. ___ ___ ___ ◯ ___ ___ ___
4. ___ ___ ◯ ___ ___
5. ___ ◯ ___ ___ ___ ___
6. ___ ___ ___ ___ ◯
7. ___ ___ ___ ___ ___ ◯ ___
8. ___ ___ ___ ___ ◯

As these, Jesus desires us to be good and faithful.

Answer: ___ ___ ___ ___ ___ ___ ___ ___

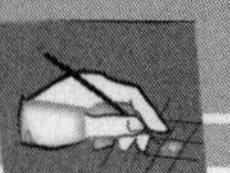

188–It Is Done

Jesus of Nazareth knew what He must suffer that fateful day on Calvary. He did it for us. Reflect on Christ's Passion as you solve the puzzle. (Matthew 27:1–50)

1. OSCRS
2. GRAVEIN
3. GUSEORDC
4. RTSAECL
5. MOSIN
6. KONESFAR
7. VEHSTEI
8. DEEDLIY
9. KEOMDC

1. ◯ ___ ___ ___ ___
2. ___ ___ ___ ___ ___ ___ ◯
3. ___ ___ ___ ◯ ___ ___ ___ ___
4. ___ ◯ ___ ___ ___ ___ ___
5. ___ ◯ ___ ___ ___
6. ◯ ___ ___ ___ ___ ___ ___ ___
7. ___ ___ ◯ ___ ___ ___ ___
8. ___ ___ ___ ___ ___ ◯ ___
9. ___ ___ ___ ___ ___ ◯

Our Lord was this for our sins, not His.

Answer: ___ ___ ___ ___ ___ ___ ___ ___ ___

189–Scrambled Word Pictures

Although Jesus never obtained a "masters" degree, He was a most effective teacher. Can you unscramble the words to learn what teaching aid He used in His sermons? (MATTHEW 5, 11, 13, 18, 20, 22)

1. LASPER
2. NESTLAT
3. RIEADYNV
4. ONGITAEENR
5. HBLEUS
6. EVANEL
7. DIWEGDN
8. EORWS

1. ○ __ __ __ __ __

2. __ ○ __ __ __ __ __

3. __ __ __ __ __ __ ○ __

4. __ __ __ __ __ ○ __ __ __ __

5. ○ __ __ __ __ __

6. ○ __ __ __ __ __

7. __ ○ __ __ __ __ __

8. ○ __ __ __ __

Jesus often used these in His ministry.

Answer: __ __ __ __ __ __ __ __

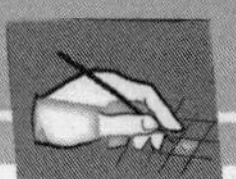

190–It's a Miracle! (Part 1)

During His earthly ministry Jesus performed many miracles. Unscramble these words and work the puzzle to see what Jesus did and said to the deaf and dumb man. (Mark 7:31–37)

1. ISGNEFR
2. SITP
3. NISDHTSAOE
4. SHPECE
5. REGHDCA
6. NILPA
7. GOUTEN
8. RAHE
9. KEPAS

1. ___ ___ ___ ___ ◯ ___ ___
2. ___ ◯ ___ ___
3. ___ ___ ___ ___ ___ ___ ___ ◯ ___ ___
4. ___ ◯ ___ ___ ___ ___
5. ___ ◯ ___ ___ ___ ___ ___
6. ___ ___ ◯ ___ ___
7. ◯ ___ ___ ___ ___ ___
8. ◯ ___ ___ ___
9. ___ ___ ◯ ___ ___

Christ spoke this word, which means "be opened," to the man who was deaf and dumb.

Answer: ___ ___ ___ ___ ___ ___ ___ ___ ___

191–It's a Miracle! (Part 2)

Because of this man's great faith he was rewarded with seeing his employee healed and whole again. Have faith that you can solve this word scramble with a little help from Jesus. (MATTHEW 8:5–13)

1. HEMOTC
2. AEEDHL
3. DOFUN
4. GHOTE
5. ORUYHTTIA
6. TYOWHR
7. THIFA
8. ELOSSRID
9. VESTNRA

1. ○ __ __ __ __ __

2. __ ○ __ __ __ __

3. __ __ __ ○ __

4. __ __ __ ○ __

5. __ ○ __ __ __ __ __ __ __

6. __ __ ○ __ __ __

7. __ __ ○ __ __

8. __ ○ __ __ __ __ __ __

9. __ __ __ __ __ ○ __

The sick and dying man was employed by this man.

Answer: __ __ __ __ __ __ __ __ __ __

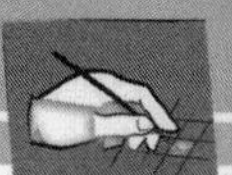

192–It's a Miracle! (Part 3)

Jesus performed His first miracle in public in Cana of Galilee at a wedding celebration. You'll have cause to celebrate, too, if you can solve this puzzle without looking up the story. (JOHN 2:1–11)

1. ESORW
2. AFTSE
3. HOMTRE
4. RAGAMEIR
5. RROONGEV
6. IPSIDELCS
7. MIGDOROREB
8. SDTTEA
9. ONSET

1. ○ ___ ___ ___ ___
2. ___ ___ ○ ___ ___
3. ___ ___ ○ ___ ___ ___
4. ___ ___ ___ ___ ___ ___ ___ ○
5. ___ ___ ___ ___ ○ ___ ___ ___
6. ___ ___ ___ ___ ___ ○ ___ ___ ___
7. ___ ___ ___ ___ ___ ___ ___ ___ ○ ___
8. ___ ___ ___ ○ ___ ___
9. ○ ___ ___ ___ ___

Jesus changed the contents of these into wine.

Answer: ___ ___ ___ ___ ___ ___ ___ ___ ___

193–It's a Miracle! (Part 4)

Jesus felt an obligation to fill the stomachs as well as the spirits of His followers. As our Good Shepherd, He continues to meet both our physical and spiritual needs. (JOHN 6:1–13)

1. HEFSIS
2. MINERA
3. VEIF DAUHTSON
4. HEGRTA
5. ANTUNMOI
6. VAOSEL
7. WHYNONPRTE
8. SKHNTA
9. EVAPORSS

1. ◯ __ __ __ __ __
2. ◯ __ __ __ __ __
3. __ __ __ __   __ __ __ __ __ ◯ __ __
4. ◯ __ __ __ __ __
5. ◯ __ __ __ __ __ __ __
6. __ __ __ __ ◯ __
7. __ __ ◯ __ __ __ __ __ __ __
8. ◯ __ __ __ __ __
9. __ __ __ ◯ __ __ __ __

These filled twelve baskets after all had eaten.

Answer: __ __ __ __ __ __ __ __ __

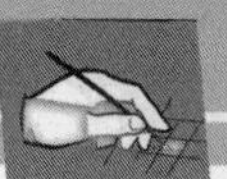

194–It's a Miracle! (Part 5)

The answers to these word scrambles are not always easy to see. God's answers to our spiritual "blindnesses" can be seen clearly in the Light of the World. (John 9)

1. GISHT
2. IMOLAS
3. GESNIE
4. DEEPON
5. HATBASB
6. SRKOW
7. DEGBGE
8. ENDINS
9. ETITPLS
10. HSDAEW

1. ___ ___ ___ ◯ ___
2. ___ ◯ ___ ___ ___ ___
3. ◯ ___ ___ ___ ___ ___
4. ___ ◯ ___ ___ ___ ___
5. ___ ___ ___ ___ ◯ ___ ___
6. ___ ___ ◯ ___ ___
7. ___ ___ ___ ___ ◯ ___
8. ___ ___ ___ ◯ ___ ___
9. ___ ___ ___ ◯ ___ ___ ___
10. ___ ___ ◯ ___ ___ ___

They confirmed to the Pharisees that this was indeed the man who was born blind.

Answer: ___ ___ ___   ___ ___ ___ ___ ___ ___ ___ ___

195–Our Eyes Can Deceive Us

The crucifixion death of the Christ left many sorrowers behind. Try to imagine their shock and wonder at what followed three days later as you work this word scramble. (John 20:1–18)

1. GASLEN
2. RYMA ALENDGAME
3. PHEUSCLER
4. ETNKA
5. WYAA
6. STEEEPW
7. NETSO
8. NOWMA
9. NEBOR

1. ___ ___ ___ ◯ ___ ___
2. ___ ___ ___ ___ ◯ ___ ___ ___ ___ ___ ___ ___ ___
3. ___ ___ ◯ ___ ___ ___ ___ ___ ___
4. ◯ ___ ___ ___ ___
5. ___ ___ ___ ◯
6. ___ ___ ___ ___ ___ ___ ◯
7. ___ ___ ◯ ___ ___
8. ___ ___ ◯ ___ ___
9. ◯ ___ ___ ___ ___

What His loved ones *didn't* expect to see.

Answer: ___ ___ ___ ___ ___ ___ ___ ___ ___

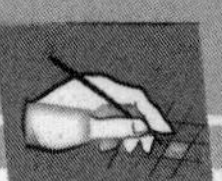

196–A Job Well Done

His earthly ministry lasted a mere three years or so, but His message will last for eternity. Unscramble the words to find out what Jesus' basic mission was all about. (John 17)

1. VNIGE
2. EWROP
3. DLROW
4. RWDOS
5. FLIE NETLAER
6. YITSCANF
7. SADEFMTIEN
8. ETFPCER

1. ◯ __ __ __ __
2. __ ◯ __ __ __
3. __ __ __ __ ◯
4. __ __ __ __ ◯
5. __ __ __ __ __ __ __ __ ◯ __ __
6. __ ◯ __ __ __ __ __ __
7. ◯ __ __ __ __ __ __ __ __ __
8. __ __ __ __ ◯ __ __

Jesus declared and glorified this.

Answer: __ __ __ ' __ __ __ __ __

197–All That and a Bag of Chips

When others are full of themselves, we may say that they believe they're "all that and a bag of chips." One man who never bragged about Himself or His deeds was, is, and forever truly will be "all that and a bag of chips." (JOHN 1–2, 4, 6, 10, 14)

1. IGLTH
2. ETH YAW
3. SAESIMS
4. ALIMECR OKREWR
5. OGDO REDPHEHS
6. ADERB
7. HET IFLE
8. AVISURO
9. TEH BALM

1. ___ ___ ___ ___ ◯
2. ___ ◯ ___ ___ ___ ___
3. ___ ◯ ___ ___ ___ ___ ___
4. ___ ___ ___ ___ ◯ ___ ___ ___ ___ ___ ___ ___ ___
5. ___ ___ ___ ___ ___ ◯ ___ ___ ___ ___ ___ ___
6. ___ ◯ ___ ___ ___
7. ___ ___ ___ ___ ◯ ___ ___
8. ◯ ___ ___ ___ ___ ___ ___
9. ◯ ___ ___ ___ ___ ___ ___

He is "all that and more."

Answer: ___ ___ ___ ___ ___ ___ ___ ___ ___ ___ ___

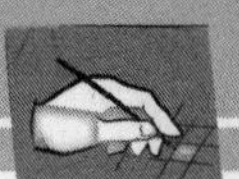

198–A Great Day's Catch

Some men called to one vocation in life were called away from it by Jesus. See who these men were, what they did for a living, and where they first encountered our Lord and Savior. (LUKE 5:1–11)

1. GUTHADR
2. FSIHSE
3. HNJO
4. SPETRRAN
5. ESMJA
6. NOSMI
7. CLUNAH
8. RNESFEIHM
9. DBEEEEZ
10. DUTUITMEL

1. __ __ __ __ ◯ __ __
2. __ __ __ __ ◯ __
3. __ __ __ ◯
4. __ __ __ __ ◯ __ __ __
5. __ __ __ ◯ __
6. ◯ __ __ __ __
7. __ ◯ __ __ __ __
8. __ __ __ __ __ ◯ __ __ __
9. __ __ __ ◯ __ __ __
10. __ __ __ __ __ ◯ __ __ __

Jesus "caught" His first disciples on this lake.

Answer: __ __ __ __ __ __ __ __ __ __

199–Yet Shall He Live

Our Lord had His reasons for His slow response to hearing the sad news about a sick loved one. His delayed trip was a lesson in love and patience for his disciples. The solutions to this word scramble tell who Jesus loved and what happened when He arrived at His loved ones' hometown. (JOHN 11:1–45)

1. WSJE
2. AVERG
3. SITSSRE
4. UZALSAR
5. SSCNIESK
6. KWAEA
7. TNYBAEH
8. SHPLETEE
9. EMCO TFROH

1. ◯ __ __ __
2. __ __ __ __ ◯
3. __ __ ◯ __ __ __ __
4. __ __ __ __ __ ◯ __
5. ◯ __ __ __ __ __ __ __
6. __ ◯ __ __ __
7. __ ◯ __ __ __ __ __
8. __ __ __ __ ◯ __ __ __
9. __ __ __ __ __ __ __ ◯ __

What "the resurrection and the life" did with Mary and Martha.

Answer: __ __ __ __ __ __ __ __ __ __

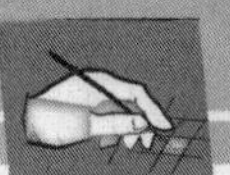

200–How Does Your Garden Grow?

It's important that farmers and gardeners know how to get the most out of their crops for optimum results at harvesttime. Our heavenly Father passed His knowledge down to His Son. What will you pass down to your children about "crop production"? (John 15:1–16)

1. HONEATR
2. RUBDEN
3. RTIFU
4. ANRIEM
5. VODEL
6. TREDIHEW
7. ASBHECNR
8. SHNOCE

1. __ __ __ ◯ __ __ __
2. __ __ ◯ __ __ __
3. __ __ ◯ __ __
4. __ ◯ __ __ __ __
5. __ __ ◯ __ __
6. __ ◯ __ __ __ __ __ __
7. __ __ __ ◯ __ __ __ __
8. __ __ __ __ ◯ __

God is the husbandman of this.

Answer: __ __ __ __ __ __ __ __

201–Waste Not, Want Not

How easily money can slip through our fingers if we're not diligent. Jesus told a parable of a young man who wasn't careful with his money or his life, but God turned his life around and still loved him unconditionally just like his earthly father. (LUKE 15:11–32)

1. ROOPITN
2. THREAF
3. EROHTBR
4. DEWATS
5. INEWS
6. GUNYORE
7. TDTEAF FALC
8. NVGILI

1. ◯ ___ ___ ___ ___ ___ ___

2. ___ ___ ___ ___ ___ ◯

3. ___ ___ ◯ ___ ___ ___ ___

4. ___ ___ ___ ___ ___ ◯

5. ___ ___ ◯ ___ ___

6. ___ ___ ___ ___ ◯ ___ ___

7. ___ ◯ ___ ___ ___ ___ ___ ___ ___ ___

8. ◯ ___ ___ ___ ___ ___

Another term for "foolishly extravagant."

Answer: ___ ___ ___ ___ ___ ___ ___ ___

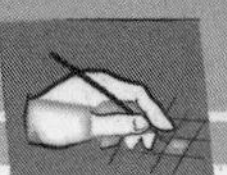

202–The Reading of Father's Will

We have been adopted into God's family according to Paul's epistle to the Romans. Therefore we are entitled to all that Christ Jesus inherited from God, including eternal life. Amen. (Romans 8)

1. USJSE
2. OPPESUR
3. RTPISI
4. ABDEGNO
5. RBYETIL
6. NEHLDCIR
7. ELFRYE
8. PAONOITD
9. RSOUNCQERO
10. FGIERSFUN

1. ◯ _ _ _ _
2. _ _ _ _ ◯ _ _
3. _ _ _ _ ◯ _
4. _ _ ◯ _ _ _ _
5. _ _ _ _ _ ◯ _
6. _ ◯ _ _ _ _ _ _
7. _ _ _ ◯ _ _
8. _ _ _ _ _ ◯ _ _
9. _ _ _ _ _ _ ◯ _ _ _
10. ◯ _ _ _ _ _ _ _ _

We are this with Christ.

Answer: _ _ _ _ _ – _ _ _ _ _ _ _

SECRET MESSAGE BIBLE WORD SEARCHES

1

Trouble between Brothers

Genesis 4:6–10

And the **LORD** **said unto** **Cain**, Why art **thou wroth**? and why is thy **countenance fallen**? If thou **doest well**, **shalt** thou not be **accepted**? and if thou doest not well, sin lieth at **the door**. And unto **thee shall** be his **desire**, and thou shalt **rule** over him. And Cain **talked** with **Abel** his brother: and it **came to pass**, **when they** were in the **field**, that Cain **rose** up **against** Abel his brother, and **slew him**. And the LORD said unto Cain, **Where** is Abel thy brother? And he said, I **know** not: **Am I my** **brother's keeper**? And he said, **What** **hast thou** done? the **voice** of thy brother's **blood crieth** **unto me** from **the ground**.

E E I N W H I D C E H P L A U
A C C E P T E D E M O T N U O
T S N I A G A H C K C E I D H
K L D A O L T S H A L L A R T
I E D C N V L Y M I M A C O T
S W E T A E N E L L A F T L S
B H I P H N T L W H E N H R A
L I A I E O V N E T U W E A H
O M F L P R U F U D S H G R T
O E R A T C I W I O T E R O B
D E S I R E O A R O C R O O E
T S I I L N S U R O N E U D G
D A E D K E L B R O T I N E V
E T H E Y E B N F R S H D H O
H M H W I S G A A R D E E T N

Secret Message

____

____

____

____

____

____

2

Sarah's Laughter

Genesis 21:1–6

And the **Lord visited Sarah** as he had said, and the Lord did unto Sarah as he had **spoken**. For Sarah **conceived**, and **bare** Abraham a **son** in his **old age**, at the **set time** of which **God had spoken** to him. And **Abraham** called the **name** of his son that was **born** unto him, whom Sarah bare to him, **Isaac**. And Abraham **circumcised** his son Isaac being **eight** days old, as God had **commanded** him. And Abraham was an **hundred** years old, when his son Isaac was born unto him. And Sarah said, God **hath made** me to **laugh**, **so that** all that **hear** will laugh **with me**.

W	H	G	U	A	L	H	E	R	C	E	D	I	S	D
V	H	A	T	H	M	A	D	E	O	N	G	P	W	O
I	D	C	O	D	M	M	A	N	N	E	O	A	I	D
S	D	A	B	O	R	N	B	R	C	K	A	B	T	E
I	E	G	A	D	L	O	H	A	E	O	M	R	H	S
T	M	C	T	O	D	T	L	N	I	P	A	A	M	I
E	I	O	K	E	I	E	S	O	V	S	S	H	E	C
D	T	M	H	E	A	R	R	S	E	D	E	A	A	M
A	C	M	A	N	D	E	T	D	D	A	T	M	H	U
E	N	A	O	F	M	F	E	R	N	H	H	I	M	C
H	A	N	C	A	A	S	I	S	A	U	T	B	U	R
A	R	D	N	N	T	O	F	F	E	R	H	I	N	I
R	G	E	X	X	M	A	D	D	V	I	G	A	B	C
A	E	D	T	A	H	T	O	S	A	B	I	R	I	C
S	O	H	P	Q	U	G	S	D	A	H	E	R	A	B

Secret Message

____

____

____

____

____

____

3

Promise to Abraham

Genesis 22:15–18

And **the angel** of the LORD **called unto Abraham** out of **heaven** the **second time**, **and said**, By **myself** have I **sworn**, saith the LORD, for **because** **thou hast** **done this thing**, and hast not **withheld** thy son, **thine** **only son**: That in **blessing** I will bless thee, and in **multiplying** I will multiply **thy seed** as the **stars** of the heaven, and as the **sand** which is upon the **sea shore**; and thy seed **shall possess** the **gate** of **his enemies**; and in thy seed shall **all the nations** of the **earth** be **blessed**; because thou hast **obeyed** **my voice**.

E	N	I	H	T	C	M	A	H	A	R	B	A	W	H
O	E	R	O	H	S	A	E	S	G	W	A	L	S	T
H	D	E	M	O	E	R	L	S	M	N	S	L	O	N
B	E	C	A	U	S	E	A	L	E	Y	I	T	T	H
L	E	I	A	H	L	T	A	T	E	C	S	H	B	O
E	S	O	R	A	S	T	H	S	S	D	O	E	T	A
S	Y	V	H	S	H	E	I	D	A	A	O	N	L	M
S	H	Y	D	T	A	H	I	P	D	N	U	A	D	F
E	T	M	R	N	T	A	P	M	L	D	D	T	I	D
D	N	A	G	E	S	O	O	Y	E	Y	R	I	T	N
W	E	E	N	D	I	B	S	T	H	N	I	O	H	E
G	L	O	N	H	E	O	S	O	H	L	E	N	L	V
A	D	A	D	Y	N	F	E	R	T	O	M	S	G	A
T	I	M	E	B	L	E	S	S	I	N	G	G	I	E
E	O	D	L	L	A	H	S	S	W	O	R	N	D	H

Secret Message

____

____

____

____

____

____

4

Baby in an Ark

Exodus 2:1–5

And there went **a man of** the **house of Levi**, and took to **wife** a **daughter** of Levi. And the **woman conceived**, and **bare a son**: and when **she saw him** that he was a **goodly child**, she hid him **three months**. And when she could not **longer hide** him, she took for him an **ark of bulrushes**, and **daubed** it with **slime** and **with pitch**, and put the child **therein**; and she laid it in the **flags** by the **river's brink**. And his **sister stood afar off**, to wit what would be **done to him**. And the daughter of **Pharaoh** came down to **wash herself** at the river; and her **maidens walked** along by the **river's side**; and when she saw the ark among the flags, she sent her maid **to fetch** it.

F	N	W	H	D	A	U	G	H	T	E	R	T	S	O
L	A	F	D	R	E	I	D	R	E	P	H	E	H	R
A	M	F	A	R	I	V	A	I	O	R	H	H	E	S
G	O	O	D	L	Y	V	I	V	E	S	S	T	D	A
S	W	R	U	G	H	V	E	E	U	F	S	E	H	T
P	D	A	U	B	E	D	M	R	C	I	I	O	L	O
T	H	F	E	L	I	O	L	S	S	N	U	W	N	F
S	C	A	F	H	N	U	H	B	R	S	O	P	O	E
L	T	O	R	T	B	E	A	R	E	L	I	C	S	T
I	I	O	H	A	S	Y	A	I	T	O	O	D	A	C
M	P	S	O	A	O	W	M	N	N	N	U	D	E	H
E	H	R	W	D	S	H	A	K	E	G	T	L	R	H
E	T	H	E	R	E	I	N	S	N	E	D	I	A	M
M	I	H	O	T	E	N	O	D	H	R	B	H	B	A
M	W	A	L	K	E	D	F	O	K	R	A	C	B	Y

Secret Message

____

____

____

____

____

____

5

Food from Heaven

Exodus 16:2–4

And the whole **congregation** of the **children** of **Israel** **murmured** against **Moses** and **Aaron** in the **wilderness**: And the children of Israel **said unto** them, **Would to God** we **had died** **by the hand** of the LORD in the **land of Egypt**, when we sat by the **flesh pots**, and when we did **eat bread** to **the full**; for ye have **brought** us **forth** into this wilderness, to **kill this** whole **assembly** with **hunger**. Then said the LORD unto Moses, Behold, **I will rain** bread from **heaven** for you; and the **people** shall go out and **gather** a certain **rate** **every day**, that I may **prove** them, **whether** they **will walk** in **my law**, or no.

W	W	I	L	L	W	A	L	K	H	A	T	L	F	C
E	V	O	R	P	A	O	M	O	U	N	T	A	O	O
V	D	E	R	U	M	R	U	M	F	F	H	N	R	F
E	A	A	S	S	E	M	B	L	Y	A	G	D	T	O
R	E	H	T	E	H	W	E	O	D	R	D	O	H	S
Y	R	W	H	T	D	S	A	D	E	T	S	F	S	G
D	B	A	G	T	H	N	I	G	H	R	O	E	P	N
A	T	M	U	P	I	E	A	H	E	E	N	G	E	E
Y	A	R	O	S	D	T	F	H	T	R	E	Y	O	R
D	E	T	R	S	I	R	T	U	E	L	A	P	P	D
W	S	A	B	O	E	A	N	D	L	H	L	T	L	L
A	E	O	N	G	G	S	L	O	N	L	T	I	E	I
L	O	T	N	U	D	I	A	S	R	T	H	Y	K	H
Y	E	U	S	I	W	I	L	L	R	A	I	N	B	C
M	H	E	A	V	E	N	I	X	T	H	A	D	A	Y

Secret Message

____

____

____

____

____

____

6

Year of Liberty

Leviticus 25:10–13

And ye shall **hallow** the **fiftieth year**, and **proclaim liberty throughout** all **the land** unto all the **inhabitants thereof**: it shall be **a jubile unto you**; and ye shall **return every man** unto his **possession**, and ye shall return every man unto his **family**. A jubile shall **that** fiftieth year be unto you: ye **shall not sow**, **neither reap** that **which groweth** of **itself** in it, **nor gather** the **grapes** in it of thy **vine undressed**. For it is **the jubile**; it shall be **holy** unto you: ye shall eat the **increase** thereof **out of the field**. In the year of **this jubile** ye shall return every man unto his possession.

W H A U E S A E R C N I T S H
W N O O U H T E W O R G N T C
O O D Y T U N D R E S S E D I
L I S O T H D G F A M I L Y H
L S I T E R A Y C L T T I A W
A S R N O T E T E F H H B E D
H E T U H N H B I A E R U E Y
O S D E N A L F I Y R O J E A
U S R L D E B L R L E U S F G
T O E I E N I I A O O G I L R
O P A B O I A T T H F H H E A
F F P U J V F L H A S O T S P
T H E J U B I L E E N U U T E
H M I A L C O R P H R T B I S
E V E R Y M A N I N T L S E E

Secret Message

____

____

____

____

____

____

7

Brave Spies, Fearful Spies

Numbers 13:27–30

And **they** told him, and **said**, We came unto **the land** whither **thou sentest** us, and **surely it floweth** with milk and **honey**; and this is the **fruit of it**. **Nevertheless** the **people** be **strong** that dwell in the land, and the **cities** are **walled**, and very **great**: and **moreover** we saw the **children** of Anak there. The **Amalekites dwell in** the land of the **south**: and the **Hittites**, and the **Jebusites**, and the **Amorites**, dwell in the **mountains**: and the **Canaanites** dwell by the sea, and by the coast of **Jordan**. And **Caleb stilled** the people before **Moses**, and said, **Let us go** up at once, and **possess** it; for we are well able to **overcome** it.

F	D	E	L	L	A	W	L	E	T	U	S	G	O	G
J	O	R	D	A	N	M	O	M	O	S	E	S	N	R
H	V	N	O	W	M	A	A	T	E	L	P	O	E	P
S	E	T	I	T	T	I	H	L	N	S	R	Y	D	A
Y	R	S	S	L	Y	E	E	D	E	T	O	I	D	T
H	C	E	C	E	L	H	D	T	S	K	M	U	J	E
S	O	N	H	A	T	E	I	S	G	F	I	E	T	P
N	M	T	N	R	L	N	W	R	Y	R	B	T	N	H
I	E	D	E	L	A	E	E	D	O	U	Y	F	E	U
A	T	V	I	A	T	A	B	S	S	I	E	L	R	S
T	E	T	N	H	T	E	L	I	U	T	N	O	D	E
N	S	A	M	O	R	I	T	E	S	O	O	W	L	I
U	C	R	E	V	O	E	R	O	M	F	H	E	I	T
O	S	S	E	S	S	O	P	S	A	I	D	T	H	I
M	A	N	S	U	R	E	L	Y	I	T	D	H	C	C

Secret Message

8

Forty Years of Wandering

Deuteronomy 29:1–4

<u>These are</u> the **words** of the **covenant**, which **<u>the LORD</u>** **commanded Moses** **<u>to make</u>** with the **children** of Israel in the **<u>land of Moab</u>**, beside the covenant which **<u>he made</u>** with **<u>them in</u>** **Horeb**. And Moses **called** unto **<u>all Israel</u>**, and **said** unto them, Ye **<u>have seen</u>** all that the LORD did before **<u>your eyes</u>** **<u>in the land</u>** of **Egypt** unto **Pharaoh**, and unto all his **servants**, and unto all his land; the **great temptations** which thine **<u>eyes have</u>** seen, the **signs**, and those great **miracles**: Yet the LORD hath **<u>not given</u>** you an **heart** to **perceive**, and **<u>eyes to see</u>**, and **<u>ears to hear</u>**, unto this day.

W H E A S E R V A N T S T D I
D N D G D T N A N E V O C T S
O N R E Y N H E M A D E O N T
M O O T L P A P W D V M G E G
I T L H L L T L E I A I A R E
R G E E E A A D E K S R E D A
A I H M T A N C E H S A A L R
C V T I N A R D S T T O L I U
L E O N M E T T O W M N L H H
E N I M P L E H T F W O I C D
S H O R E B E S S E M O S I I
N C T E V A H S E Y E O R E A
S E Y E R U O Y Y V H E A D S
W T H E S E A R E I A L E B S
D E R N E P H A R A O H L S S

Secret Message

____

____

____

____

____

____

9

Hidden from Sight

Joshua 2:3–6

And the **king** of **Jericho** sent unto **Rahab, saying, Bring forth** the men that are come to thee, which are **entered** into **thine house**: for they **be come** to **search** out all the **country**. And the **woman took** the **two men**, and hid them, and **said thus, There** came **men unto** me, but I **wist not whence** they were: And it **came to pass** about the **time** of shutting of the **gate**, when it was **dark**, that the **men went out**: whither the men went **I wot not**: **pursue** after them **quickly**; for ye shall **overtake** them. But she had **brought** them up to the **roof of the house**, and **hid them** with the stalks of **flax**, which she had **laid** in **order** upon the **roof**.

S	R	P	U	R	S	U	E	N	W	E	N	I	H	T
S	H	O	E	A	E	K	A	T	R	E	V	O	O	O
A	B	D	O	T	M	M	G	E	T	E	H	N	C	O
P	R	O	D	F	O	F	D	A	M	I	T	D	O	K
O	I	A	I	W	O	T	N	O	T	S	T	H	U	M
T	N	S	H	O	H	F	C	B	I	E	C	O	N	E
E	G	E	R	A	E	E	T	W	R	I	S	U	T	N
M	F	A	P	I	B	E	M	H	R	O	Y	S	R	U
A	O	R	S	U	G	E	E	E	E	L	U	E	Y	N
C	R	C	S	N	H	T	J	N	K	H	X	G	E	T
E	T	H	I	T	T	O	H	C	T	A	O	M	H	O
G	H	Y	D	I	A	L	I	E	L	E	O	U	G	T
S	A	I	D	T	H	U	S	F	R	W	R	N	S	E
S	H	T	A	W	Q	E	M	I	T	E	I	E	A	E
M	E	N	W	E	N	T	O	U	T	K	R	A	D	Y

Secret Message

10

One Great Shout

Joshua 6:20–23

The people shouted with a **great shout**, that the **wall fell** down **flat**, so that the **people went up** into the **city, every** man **straight** before him, and they **took** the city. And they **utterly destroyed** all that was in the city, **both man** and woman, **young and old**, and **ox, and sheep**, and ass, with the **edge** of the **sword**. But **Joshua** had said unto the **two men** that had **spied out** the **country**, Go into the **harlot's house**, and **bring out** thence the **woman**, and all that she hath, as ye sware unto her. And the **young men** that were **spies** went in, and **brought** out **Rahab**, and her **father**, and her **mother**, and her **brethren**, and **all that she had**.

N	W	Y	O	U	N	G	A	N	D	O	L	D	E	S
A	H	B	K	X	L	L	E	F	L	L	A	W	V	E
M	C	R	O	N	A	M	O	W	A	H	T	S	E	I
H	I	I	O	G	G	N	N	P	E	T	D	S	R	P
T	I	N	T	N	R	D	D	H	E	U	U	R	Y	S
O	M	G	U	Y	A	A	S	S	P	O	H	A	T	E
B	R	O	U	G	H	T	B	U	H	D	P	R	B	D
U	Y	U	T	L	A	E	T	S	E	E	A	L	R	G
A	T	T	V	H	B	N	T	S	E	I	E	O	E	E
G	T	T	T	O	E	O	T	F	G	P	W	P	T	A
R	S	L	E	W	L	R	H	H	A	S	O	U	H	U
E	L	W	T	R	O	H	T	E	R	T	O	L	R	H
A	O	A	A	Y	L	M	Y	A	L	H	H	T	E	S
T	L	H	E	Y	T	Y	E	O	S	I	S	E	N	O
F	R	D	A	E	Y	R	T	N	U	O	C	L	R	J

Secret Message

____

____

____

____

____

____

11

Celestial Standstill

Joshua 10:11–12, 14

And it **came to pass**, as they **fled** from before **Israel**, and were in the **going** down to **Bethhoron**, that the LORD **cast down** great **stones** from **heaven** upon them unto **Azekah**, and they **died**: they were more which died with **hailstones** than they whom the **children** of Israel **slew** with the **sword**. Then **spake Joshua** to the LORD **in the day** when the LORD **delivered** up the **Amorites** before the children of Israel, and he said in the **sight** of Israel, **Sun, stand** thou **still** upon **Gibeon**; and thou, **Moon**, in the **valley of Ajalon**. . . . And there was **no day** like that **before** it or **after** it, that the LORD **hearkened** unto the **voice** of a man: for the LORD **fought** for Israel.

W	H	I	B	C	H	I	L	D	R	E	N	C	T	G
S	V	H	D	E	K	A	I	W	N	N	G	H	H	O
T	C	A	E	O	F	D	I	E	D	F	G	J	G	I
O	A	E	L	R	U	O	V	L	S	I	A	L	U	N
N	M	D	I	L	B	A	R	S	S	E	M	L	O	G
E	E	E	V	E	E	D	S	E	T	T	H	E	F	C
S	T	N	E	H	T	Y	W	A	M	N	O	D	A	Y
E	O	E	R	P	H	J	O	S	H	U	A	N	A	I
T	P	K	E	G	H	N	R	F	A	G	I	A	E	I
I	A	R	D	A	O	N	D	N	A	T	S	N	U	S
R	S	A	K	R	R	E	T	F	A	J	R	D	E	P
O	S	E	S	N	O	E	B	I	G	T	A	E	C	A
M	Z	H	O	I	N	L	L	I	T	S	E	L	I	K
A	S	O	C	A	S	T	D	O	W	N	L	F	O	E
R	M	A	E	I	N	T	H	E	D	A	Y	L	V	N

Secret Message

12

Deadly Nap

Judges 4:17–18, 21

Howbeit Sisera **fled away** on his **feet** to the tent of **Jael** the wife of **Heber the Kenite**: for there was **peace between Jabin** the **king** of **Hazor** and the **house** of Heber the Kenite. And Jael went out to **meet Sisera**, and **said unto** him, Turn in, **my lord**, **turn in to me**; **fear not**. And when he had **turned** in unto her into the **tent**, she **covered** him with a **mantle**. . . . Then Jael Heber's **wife** took a **nail** of the tent, and **took** an **hammer** in her **hand**, and went **softly** unto him, and **smote** the nail into **his temples**, and **fastened** it into the **ground**: for he was **fast asleep** and **weary**. **So he died**.

W	H	I	S	T	E	M	P	L	E	S	T	E	E	F
E	W	D	N	F	L	E	D	A	W	A	Y	H	E	J
A	I	E	P	C	H	E	L	K	P	R	O	T	F	A
R	T	N	S	E	P	T	I	T	I	H	I	E	A	B
Y	T	R	O	M	E	R	A	P	N	N	D	E	S	I
E	S	U	O	H	O	L	N	R	E	A	G	E	T	N
T	D	T	B	S	E	T	S	K	H	A	M	M	E	R
I	R	D	E	I	T	L	E	A	J	O	C	H	N	E
E	O	A	T	S	T	H	N	T	T	A	K	E	E	C
B	L	K	W	E	T	D	O	N	N	S	S	O	D	I
W	Y	S	E	R	E	R	I	A	S	H	A	Z	O	R
O	M	F	E	A	R	N	O	T	A	R	M	F	Y	T
H	I	B	N	X	R	X	O	T	N	U	D	I	A	S
W	E	D	N	U	O	R	G	C	O	V	E	R	E	D
H	Y	L	T	F	O	S	S	O	H	E	D	I	E	D

Secret Message

____

____

____

____

____

____

13

The Chosen Ones

Judges 7:4–5

And the **LORD** said unto **Gideon,** The **people** are yet **too many**; **bring** them down unto the **water**, and **I will try them for thee there**: and **it shall be**, that of **whom I say** unto thee, This shall **go with thee**, the same shall go **with thee**; and of **whomsoever** I say unto thee, This **shall not go** with thee, the same shall not go. So he **brought down** the people unto the water: and the LORD **said unto** Gideon, **Every one** that **lappeth** of the **water with his tongue**, as a **dog lappeth**, him **shalt thou set** by **himself; likewise** every one that **boweth down upon** his **knees** to **drink.**

L	I	K	E	W	I	S	E	T	E	S	U	O	H	T
H	O	N	D	O	W	N	U	P	O	N	W	T	T	M
A	N	I	Y	O	I	T	F	G	K	I	D	N	H	E
O	O	R	N	D	L	L	W	S	N	E	M	U	E	B
G	B	D	R	I	L	A	P	P	E	T	H	D	R	R
T	G	O	W	I	T	H	T	H	E	E	E	I	E	O
O	L	G	W	E	R	S	T	N	S	O	N	A	L	U
N	E	L	R	E	Y	H	H	A	Y	G	P	S	E	G
L	U	A	P	P	T	E	F	A	G	D	U	L	V	H
L	G	P	P	I	H	H	S	O	L	I	T	H	E	T
A	N	P	W	E	E	I	W	A	R	L	D	T	R	D
H	O	E	H	I	M	S	E	L	F	T	B	E	Y	O
S	T	T	O	O	M	A	N	Y	E	R	H	E	O	W
S	I	H	H	T	I	W	R	E	T	A	W	E	N	N
X	X	W	H	O	M	S	O	E	V	E	R	J	E	V

Secret Message

____

____

____

____

____

____

14

Ultimate Sacrifice

Judges 11:34–36

And **Jephthah** came to **Mizpeh** unto his house, and, **behold**, his daughter came out to **meet him** with **timbrels** and with **dances**: and she was his only **child**; beside her he had **neither** son nor daughter. And it **came to pass**, when **he saw her**, that he rent his **clothes**, and said, **Alas**, my daughter! thou hast **brought** me **very low**, and **thou art one** of them that **trouble** me: for I have **opened** my **mouth** unto the LORD, and I cannot **go back**. And she said unto him, My **father**, if thou hast opened thy mouth **unto the LORD**, do to me **according** to that which hath **proceeded** out of thy mouth; **forasmuch** as the LORD hath taken **vengeance** for **thee of thine** **enemies**.

C	B	W	N	E	N	I	H	T	F	O	E	E	H	T
L	R	E	M	E	V	E	R	Y	L	O	W	S	J	H
O	O	H	H	O	I	E	O	P	E	N	E	D	E	O
T	U	P	E	O	U	T	N	N	D	I	I	D	P	U
H	G	R	E	J	L	T	H	G	M	E	P	S	H	A
E	H	O	L	H	A	D	H	E	E	T	S	C	T	R
S	T	C	B	M	H	C	N	E	R	A	U	A	H	T
H	L	E	U	S	E	E	C	U	P	M	N	R	A	O
R	R	E	O	E	N	E	D	O	S	Z	E	C	H	N
E	R	D	R	H	I	S	T	A	R	H	I	D	E	E
A	U	E	T	B	G	E	R	H	W	D	H	M	S	T
E	R	D	T	O	M	O	T	A	I	H	I	A	E	L
R	E	H	T	A	F	I	S	O	R	M	L	N	D	X
D	A	N	C	E	S	E	T	K	C	A	B	O	G	X
U	N	T	O	T	H	E	L	O	R	D	L	I	H	C

Secret Message

____

____

____

____

____

____

15

A Wedding Banquet

Judges 14:10–14

So his **father went down** unto the **woman**: and **Samson** made **there** a **feast**. . . . They **brought** thirty **companions** to be with him. And Samson **said unto them**, I will now put forth a **riddle** unto you: if ye can **certainly declare** it me **within** the **seven days** of the feast, and **find it out**, then I will give you **thirty sheets** and thirty **change** of garments: But if ye cannot declare it me, then **shall** ye **give me** thirty sheets and thirty change of **garments**. And they **said unto him**, Put **forth** thy riddle, that **we may hear it**. And he said unto them, Out of the **eater came forth meat**, and out of the **strong** came forth **sweetness**. And they **could** not in **three days expound** the riddle.

M	E	A	T	W	H	T	R	O	F	E	M	A	C	S
H	S	W	E	E	T	N	E	S	S	E	W	C	R	A
T	H	I	R	T	Y	E	R	E	H	T	I	E	A	M
E	T	T	W	O	R	E	H	T	A	F	T	R	T	S
G	X	W	E	N	T	D	O	W	N	A	H	T	H	O
A	S	P	C	I	N	T	G	E	E	B	I	A	S	N
R	N	C	O	H	N	D	I	M	D	R	N	I	E	S
M	O	T	O	U	A	H	N	A	M	O	W	N	L	Y
E	I	E	D	U	N	N	R	Y	I	U	D	L	D	A
N	N	I	D	L	L	D	G	H	S	G	A	Y	D	D
T	A	E	S	Y	A	D	E	E	R	H	T	S	I	N
S	P	H	T	R	O	F	E	A	S	T	E	T	R	E
E	M	E	V	I	G	A	E	R	A	L	C	E	D	V
N	O	D	F	F	I	N	D	I	T	O	U	T	T	E
O	C	R	X	M	I	H	O	T	N	U	D	I	A	S

Secret Message

____

____

____

____

____

____

16

A Fool for Love

Judges 16:18–19

And when **Delilah** saw that he **had told** her **all his heart**, **she sent** and **called** for the **lords** of the **Philistines, saying, Come up** this once, for he **hath shewed** me all his **heart**. Then the lords of the **Philistines came** up **unto her**, and **brought money** in their **hand**. And she **made him sleep upon her knees**; and she **called for a man**, and she **caused** him to **shave** off the **seven locks** of his **head**; and she **began** to **afflict** him, and his **strength went from him**.

P	W	D	E	W	E	H	S	H	T	A	H	H	O	P
U	H	W	E	N	T	F	R	O	M	H	I	M	N	H
E	A	I	A	L	S	A	Y	I	N	G	R	A	W	I
M	N	A	L	S	L	T	H	E	I	E	M	S	D	L
O	D	E	L	I	L	A	H	R	H	A	A	E	A	I
C	L	S	H	L	S	K	C	O	L	N	E	V	E	S
M	O	H	I	I	T	T	T	E	H	J	U	N	H	T
I	T	E	S	D	G	N	I	T	E	W	A	A	D	I
H	D	S	H	Y	U	I	G	N	T	G	V	H	E	N
E	A	E	E	U	N	N	S	L	E	E	P	U	S	E
D	H	N	A	T	E	S	O	B	U	S	A	L	U	S
A	O	T	R	R	S	R	O	F	D	E	L	L	A	C
M	T	A	T	R	D	B	R	O	U	G	H	T	C	A
E	E	S	N	S	T	C	I	L	F	F	A	G	T	M
H	U	P	O	N	H	E	R	K	N	E	E	S	H	E

Secret Message

____

____

____

____

____

____

17

One Fell Swoop

Judges 16:28–30

Samson called unto the LORD, and said, O **Lord GOD**, **remember** me, I pray thee, and **strengthen** me, **I pray thee**, only **this once**, O God, that **I may be** at once **avenged** of the **Philistines** for my **two eyes**. And Samson **took hold** of the two **middle pillars** upon which the **house stood**, and on which it was **borne up**, of the one with his **right hand**, and of the **other** with his **left**. And Samson said, **Let me die** with the Philistines. And he **bowed himself** with all his **might**; and the **house fell** upon the **lords**, and upon all the **people** that were **therein**. So the **dead** which he **slew** at his **death** were more than they which he slew in **his life**.

H	T	W	H	A	N	T	T	H	I	S	O	N	C	E
L	O	R	D	G	O	D	F	L	E	S	M	I	H	S
P	O	U	E	C	S	I	D	N	A	H	L	A	L	A
C	K	T	S	O	M	H	I	S	L	I	F	E	M	V
S	H	H	D	E	A	T	H	M	E	I	T	M	W	E
R	O	E	E	N	S	T	R	E	N	G	T	H	E	N
A	L	R	T	I	O	T	H	E	R	I	G	H	T	G
L	D	E	L	D	I	T	O	D	M	S	A	M	C	E
L	S	I	O	E	Y	N	B	O	W	E	D	E	A	D
I	H	N	T	A	T	E	L	D	D	I	M	S	L	E
P	S	F	R	T	R	M	I	G	H	T	E	B	L	S
N	E	P	G	S	E	Y	E	O	W	T	T	P	E	D
L	I	M	A	Y	B	E	H	D	C	O	O	M	D	R
H	O	U	S	E	F	E	L	L	I	E	E	F	R	O
O	M	X	B	O	R	N	E	U	P	E	X	Z	J	L

Secret Message

____

____

____

____

____

____

18

Ruth's Dedication

Ruth 1:16–19

And **Ruth** said, **Intreat** me not to **leave** thee, or to **return** from **following** after **thee**: for **whither** thou **goest**, I will go; and where thou **lodgest**, I will lodge: thy **people** shall be my people, and thy **God** my God: Where thou **diest**, will I die, and there will I be **buried**: the LORD do so to me, and **more** also, if **ought** but **death part** thee and me. When she saw that she was **stedfastly minded** to go with her, then she **left speaking** unto her. So they **two** went until <u>**they came**</u> to **Bethlehem**.

T	F	E	L	W	H	B	E	R	E	L	E	A	V	E
D	I	D	N	A	O	U	M	I	A	Y	N	D	R	U
L	T	H	L	I	T	R	A	P	E	L	P	O	E	P
V	O	E	B	E	F	I	O	R	E	T	T	H	E	S
Y	T	R	R	T	S	E	I	D	A	S	T	V	E	P
M	L	E	D	D	T	D	O	G	H	A	H	E	T	E
E	T	S	E	O	G	H	E	T	R	F	E	T	O	A
H	A	T	H	E	O	L	U	A	S	D	E	N	T	K
E	E	D	D	O	D	R	F	D	J	E	U	D	H	I
L	R	A	E	H	E	E	X	E	X	T	G	Y	G	N
H	T	K	A	H	E	T	W	D	L	S	E	D	U	G
T	N	S	T	I	J	U	E	N	V	R	O	L	O	G
E	I	I	H	E	U	R	R	I	O	B	E	T	N	L
B	H	U	W	E	I	N	E	M	A	C	Y	E	H	T
W	M	T	W	O	N	G	N	I	W	O	L	L	O	F

Secret Message

19

A Need Met

Ruth 2:15–19

And when she was **risen up** to glean, Boaz **commanded** his **young** men, **saying**, Let her glean even **among** the **sheaves**, and **reproach** her not: And let **fall** also some of the **handfuls** of **purpose** for her, and **leave** them, that she may **glean** them, and **rebuke** her not. **So she** gleaned in the **field** until even, and **beat** out that she had **gleaned**: and it was about an **ephah** of **barley**. And she **took** it up, and went into the **city**: and her **mother in law** saw what she had gleaned: and she **brought** forth, and gave to her that she had **reserved** after she was **sufficed**. And her mother in law said unto her, **Where hast** thou gleaned to day? and **where wroughtest thou**? **blessed** be he that did take **knowledge** of thee. And she **shewed her** mother in law **with whom** she had wrought, and said, The man's **name** with whom I wrought **to day** is **Boaz**.

T T O O K G L E A N E D W H A
S O T C N O R E H D E W E H S
A D S U F F I C E D U N E S L
H A O E T R E D L E I F G A U
E Y S Y V K N E P H A H D Y F
R D H I U A T D U U R U E I D
E T E B M H E M N H R O L N N
H R E M G I O H E G Y P W G A
W R O U G H T E S T T H O U H
I C O L W Y N L I A T E N S F
R R E H E Z L C R O W M K X E
B A T L W A L N I R E H T O M
N I R X F O V B L E S S E D A
W A T A E B D E V R E S E R N
B A M O N G R E P R O A C H E

Secret Message

____

____

____

____

____

____

20

A Voice in the Night

1 Samuel 3:8–11

And the LORD called Samuel **again** the **third** time. And he **arose** and **went to Eli**, and said, **Here am I**; for thou **didst** call me. And Eli **perceived** that the **LORD** had called the **child. Therefore Eli said** unto Samuel, **Go, lie down**: and **it shall be**, if he **call thee**, that thou **shalt say**, Speak, LORD; for thy **servant** heareth. So Samuel went and lay down in his **place**. And the LORD **came**, and **stood**, and **called** as at **other times**, Samuel, **Samuel**. Then Samuel **answered**, **Speak**; for thy servant heareth. And the LORD said to Samuel, **Behold**, **I will do** a **thing** in **Israel**, at which both the **ears** of **every one** that **heareth** it shall **tingle**.

S E E H T L L A C B W H O W I
T E R S E E I S R A E L E T W
O H D U E H T E R A E H R E I
O I M P A R O S E I A R O E L
D A N T S O V H M F T D F L L
S H G I T S H A L L B E E D D
P C S A I S E L N M I R R I O
L R H P I R A T C T L E E A E
A O E I E N C S H I M W H S V
C L R H L A D A T A N S T I E
E A A D M D K Y C H E N D L R
G O L I E D O W N S I A G E Y
A M I L E O T T N E W N H U O
P E R C E I V E D E I T G L N
S E M I T D R I H T O S R A E

Secret Message

____

____

____

____

____

____

21

Prostrate before the Lord

1 Samuel 5:1–4

And the **Philistines** **took the ark** of God, and brought it from **Ebenezer** unto Ashdod. When the Philistines took the **ark of God**, they **brought** it into the **house** of **Dagon**, and set it by Dagon. And when they of **Ashdod** **arose early** on the **morrow**, behold, Dagon was **fallen** **upon his face** to the **earth** before the **ark of the LORD**. And they **took** Dagon, and set him in his **place again**. And when **they arose** early **on the morrow** **morning**, **behold**, Dagon was fallen upon his face to the **ground** **before the ark** of the LORD; and the **head of Dagon** and both the **palms** of his **hands** were **cut off** upon the **threshold**; only the stump of Dagon was left to him.

R	T	D	A	G	A	I	N	D	O	D	H	S	A	B
E	O	N	W	T	H	R	L	A	A	A	D	T	H	E
Z	O	U	C	A	H	O	K	G	R	R	R	W	O	F
E	K	O	N	T	H	E	M	O	R	R	O	W	U	O
N	R	R	N	S	M	C	Y	N	F	R	L	S	S	R
E	A	G	E	R	O	A	I	A	R	G	M	E	E	E
B	E	R	L	E	R	F	D	O	R	L	O	T	N	T
E	H	B	L	A	N	S	M	H	A	O	E	D	I	H
T	T	R	A	R	I	I	A	P	C	D	S	R	T	E
K	K	O	F	T	N	H	H	U	O	L	D	E	S	A
M	O	U	E	H	G	N	T	T	O	O	N	A	I	R
N	O	G	A	D	F	O	D	A	E	H	A	R	L	K
T	T	H	H	E	F	P	L	A	C	E	H	L	I	I
S	R	T	A	F	E	U	L	I	T	B	E	Y	H	S
X	A	R	K	O	F	T	H	E	L	O	R	D	P	X

Secret Message

____

____

____

____

____

____

22

A Giant Challenge

1 Samuel 17:43, 46, 49–51

And the **Philistine said** unto **David**, **Am I a dog**, that thou **comest** to me with **staves**? And the Philistine **cursed** David by **his gods**. . . . **This day** will the LORD **deliver** thee into **mine hand**; and I will **smite** thee. . . . David put **his hand** in **his bag**, and **took thence** a stone, and **slang** it, and smote the Philistine in his **forehead**, that the stone **sunk into** his forehead; and he **fell upon his face** to the **earth**. So David **prevailed** over the Philistine with a **sling** and with a **stone**, and **smote** the Philistine, and **slew him**; but there was no **sword** in the **hand of David**. . . . When the Philistines saw their **champion** was **dead**, **they fled**.

E	C	N	E	H	T	S	U	N	K	I	N	T	O	N
C	O	H	D	R	O	W	S	W	H	L	D	E	O	R
A	M	G	A	E	W	E	H	A	S	I	O	P	T	D
F	E	N	H	M	V	E	A	P	V	L	U	R	A	A
S	S	A	C	A	P	E	N	A	I	L	S	A	D	E
I	T	L	T	S	A	I	D	S	L	R	M	M	N	H
H	I	S	B	A	G	D	O	E	A	E	O	I	M	E
D	L	T	L	F	A	A	F	N	S	C	T	A	I	R
E	D	O	E	E	D	T	D	H	M	S	E	D	N	O
L	N	N	D	H	W	E	A	E	I	S	P	O	E	F
F	A	E	H	T	S	H	V	L	T	I	L	G	H	L
Y	H	I	S	R	E	V	I	L	E	D	T	I	A	I
E	S	N	U	A	E	H	D	M	K	O	O	T	N	S
H	I	C	X	E	P	R	E	V	A	I	L	E	D	G
T	H	I	S	D	A	Y	X	S	D	O	G	S	I	H

Secret Message

____

____

____

____

____

____

23

Can't Touch This

2 Samuel 6:5–9

And **David** and all the **house** of **Israel played** before the LORD on all **manner** of **instruments** made of fir **wood**, even on **harps**, and on **psalteries**, and on **timbrels**, and on **cornets**, and on **cymbals**. And when they came to **Nachon's threshingfloor**, **Uzzah** put forth his hand to the **ark of God**, and **took hold** of it; for the **oxen shook** it. And the **anger** of the LORD was **kindled** against Uzzah; and God **smote** him there for his **error**; and there he **died** by the ark of God. And David was **displeased**, **because** the LORD had made a **breach** upon Uzzah: and he **called** the **name** of the **place Perezuzzah** to **this day**. And David was **afraid** of the LORD that day.

A	T	W	S	H	D	O	T	O	O	K	H	O	L	D
N	S	H	P	C	E	I	L	H	S	E	D	R	O	L
G	T	H	R	M	Y	E	S	E	I	I	O	B	X	H
E	I	U	A	E	A	M	I	P	A	S	S	E	E	C
R	M	N	H	R	S	R	B	R	L	H	D	C	N	A
D	B	D	S	E	E	H	F	A	A	E	A	A	H	E
E	R	I	E	T	L	A	I	Z	L	L	A	U	Y	R
Y	E	V	L	D	R	S	Z	N	P	S	D	S	D	B
A	L	A	T	E	N	U	D	H	G	E	E	E	E	A
L	S	D	N	O	Z	Z	M	E	R	F	L	K	F	D
P	O	N	H	E	R	Z	T	E	I	D	L	H	K	R
R	A	C	R	D	E	A	E	M	N	D	A	O	O	O
M	A	E	S	U	O	H	O	I	N	T	C	T	O	R
N	P	D	O	G	F	O	K	R	A	H	S	S	H	R
S	T	E	N	R	O	C	W	X	E	T	O	M	S	E

Secret Message

____

____

____

____

____

____

24

Dancing in the Streets

2 Samuel 6:14–17

And **David danced** before the LORD with all his **might**; and David was **girded** with a **linen ephod**. So David and all the **house of Israel** brought up the **ark of the LORD** with shouting, and with the **sound** of the **trumpet**. And as the ark of the LORD **came** into the **city of David**, **Michal** Saul's **daughter looked through** a **window**, and saw **king** David **leaping** and **dancing** **before the LORD**; and she despised him in her **heart**. And they **brought** in the ark of the LORD, and set it in his **place**, in the **midst** of the **tabernacle** that David had **pitched** for it: and David **offered burnt offerings** and **peace** offerings **before** the LORD.

D W H D I V A D F O Y T I C C
L A H C I M E T R U M P E T A
A T U R E K D T H R O U G H M
S S U G O E R O F E B L N G E
E G T O H L O R D E D F I I C
L N L R O T L M P M I C P M A
C I H O U S E O F I S R A E L
A R N E H A H R E D T D E D P
N E L E P G T D N C I C L E S
R F B A N H F U A V A D H R D
E F B I G A O D A N C E D E E
B O K U T S K D T I C T P F D
A U O D R E R W O D N I W F R
T R A E H N A T S D I M N O I
B E F O R E T H E L O R D G G

Secret Message

____

____

____

____

____

____

25

Tempting Vision

2 Samuel 11:2–6

And it came to pass in an **eveningtide**, that **David arose** from **off his bed**, and **walked upon the roof** of the **king's house**: and from the **roof** he saw a woman **washing herself**; and the woman was very **beautiful** to **look** upon. And David sent and **enquired** after the woman. And **one said**, Is not this **Bathsheba**, the **daughter** of **Eliam**, the **wife** of **Uriah** the **Hittite**? And David sent **messengers**, and **took** her; and she came in unto him, and he **lay with her**; for she was **purified** from her **uncleanness**: and she **returned** unto her **house**. And the **woman conceived**, and sent and **told** David, and said, I am with **child**. And David sent to **Joab**, saying, Send me Uriah the Hittite.

U	N	C	L	E	A	N	N	E	S	S	E	F	I	W
P	W	H	A	T	P	U	R	I	F	I	E	D	A	R
O	E	L	I	A	M	D	E	N	R	U	T	E	R	D
N	D	N	A	M	O	W	U	D	M	Y	I	E	L	K
T	E	I	L	Y	L	F	I	R	E	E	T	O	E	A
H	R	D	D	U	W	V	F	S	I	H	T	D	B	E
E	I	E	H	R	A	I	U	H	G	A	I	E	S	S
R	U	V	E	D	S	O	T	U	I	T	H	O	C	U
O	Q	I	R	B	H	I	A	H	G	S	R	A	H	O
O	N	E	S	A	I	D	H	N	H	A	B	K	I	H
F	E	C	E	O	N	D	I	T	U	E	O	E	L	S
R	I	N	L	J	G	N	A	F	O	O	R	N	D	G
G	A	O	F	B	E	B	W	A	L	K	E	D	A	N
T	T	C	L	V	L	U	F	I	T	U	A	E	B	I
E	S	R	E	G	N	E	S	S	E	M	T	O	O	K

Secret Message

____

____

____

____

____

____

26

Solomon's Wise Request

1 Kings 3:11–14

Because thou hast asked this **thing**, and hast not **asked** for thyself **long life**; neither hast asked **riches** for thyself, nor hast asked the **life** of thine enemies; but hast asked for thyself understanding to **discern judgment**; **behold**, I have done **according** to thy **words**: lo, I have **given** thee a **wise** and an understanding **heart**; so that there was none like thee before thee, **neither** after thee shall any **arise** like unto thee. And I have also given thee that which thou hast not asked, both riches, and **honour**: so that there shall not be any among the **kings** like unto thee **all thy days**. And if thou **wilt walk** in my **ways**, to **keep** my **statutes** and my **commandments**. . .then I will **lengthen** thy days.

W C H I C H Q S E T U T A T S
D O L O N G L I F E D U E Y Y
I M E N W T T R A V L E A L A
S M E D I T H O J E O W R R D
C A K U S S I A L T H S I E Y
E N M I E T N O N S E E S E H
R D E S N O G E L H B O E M T
N M O H N G M S C W I S D O L
K E E P T G S I M W O R D S L
F N I R D G R U O N O H S G A
D T T U H A N N D T X X F I A
E S J P L N T E R L O N L V Y
K O W I L T W A L K H E A E A
S L F O M N E I T H E R S N D
A E E E R H A C C O R D I N G

Secret Message

____

____

____

____

____

____

27

The House of the Lord

1 Kings 7:48–51

And **Solomon** made all the **vessels** that pertained unto the **house** of the **LORD**: the **altar** of gold, and the **table** of **gold**, whereupon the **shewbread** was, and the **candlesticks** of **pure** gold, **five** on the **right** side, and five on the **left**, before the **oracle**, with the **flowers**, and the **lamps**, and the **tongs** of gold, and the **bowls**, and the **snuffers**, and the **basons**, and the **spoons**, and the **censers** of pure gold; and the **hinges** of gold, both for the **doors** of the **inner** house, the most **holy** place, and for the doors of the house, to **wit**, of the **temple**. So was **ended** all the **work** that **king** Solomon **made** for the house of the LORD.

H O W C E N S E R S E G N I H

D M A N Y Y F E A R S T O T A

L O H D I S I E D I T S T G A

R K O E S H V L O L K O O S O

I M L R O E E B N C T L P O S

G B Y U S W I A I L D O D L T

H H I S S B O T W K O M W N F

T P E E R R S S I N H O U S E

O L N A E E L N S H B N P E L

S R A T L A G O U M E I U L A

L O R D C D X S X F I N R P M

R I N M A P G W I T F N E M P

I A A F R N E N D E D E R E S

C D F L O W E R S N E R R T O

E S L T W O R K B A S O N S W

Secret Message

28

Solomon and Sheba

1 Kings 10:4–8

And when the **queen** of **Sheba** had seen all **Solomon's** wisdom, and the house that he had **built**, and the meat of his **table**, and the **sitting** of his **servants**, and the **attendance** of his **ministers**, and their **apparel**, and his **cupbearers**, and his **ascent** by which he went up unto the **house of the LORD**; there was no more **spirit** in her. And she said to the king, It was a **true report** that I heard in mine **own land** of thy acts and of thy wisdom. **Howbeit** I **believed** not the **words**, until I came, and **mine eyes** had seen it: and, behold, **the half was not told me**: thy wisdom and **prosperity exceedeth** the fame which I heard. **Happy** are thy men, happy are these thy servants, which **stand continually** before thee, and **that hear thy wisdom**.

H	O	W	M	O	D	S	I	W	Y	H	T	D	I	D
H	A	P	P	A	R	E	L	D	N	A	T	S	T	H
A	E	Q	S	N	O	M	O	L	O	S	U	R	E	T
P	B	C	E	T	L	E	X	C	E	E	D	E	T	H
P	B	E	O	O	E	F	L	A	H	E	H	T	P	A
Y	U	E	H	N	H	C	N	B	C	O	R	S	R	T
Q	I	D	F	S	T	S	N	U	A	O	H	I	O	H
M	L	E	E	A	F	I	P	A	P	T	T	N	S	E
I	T	V	S	W	O	B	N	E	D	I	B	I	P	A
N	A	E	P	A	E	W	R	U	E	N	T	M	E	R
E	T	I	I	A	S	E	N	B	A	T	E	M	R	E
E	S	L	R	T	U	C	W	L	I	L	D	T	I	S
Y	O	E	I	R	O	O	E	N	A	L	L	L	T	O
E	R	B	T	M	H	O	G	N	O	N	N	Y	Y	A
S	E	R	V	A	N	T	S	T	T	S	D	R	O	W

Secret Message

____

____

____

____

____

____

29

Voice of God

1 Kings 19:10–12

And he said, I have been very **jealous** for the **Lord God** of **hosts**: for the **children** of **Israel** have **forsaken** thy **covenant, thrown** down **thine altars**, and **slain** thy **prophets** with the sword; and I, **even I only**, **am left**; and they **seek my life**, to take **it away**. And he said, Go **forth**, and **stand** upon the mount before the Lord. And, behold, the Lord **passed** by, and a **great** and **strong wind rent** the **mountains**, and **brake** in pieces the **rocks** before the Lord; but the Lord was **not in the wind**: and after the wind an **earthquake**; but the Lord was not in the earthquake: And after the earthquake **a fire**; but the Lord was not **in the fire**: and after the fire a **still small voice**.

W	N	O	T	I	N	T	H	E	W	I	N	D	H	E
G	T	N	A	N	E	V	O	C	L	R	E	O	E	Y
R	O	C	K	S	M	Y	L	I	F	E	K	G	P	A
E	E	E	S	T	E	H	P	O	R	P	A	D	A	W
A	W	V	N	W	S	A	S	V	E	L	R	R	S	A
T	L	I	E	I	J	N	A	L	H	E	B	O	S	T
H	I	T	K	N	H	I	I	L	K	D	I	L	E	I
N	N	G	A	D	I	T	W	A	H	S	C	E	D	N
T	T	H	S	R	E	O	U	M	T	H	W	O	R	J
D	H	E	R	E	S	Q	N	S	I	N	O	F	E	N
T	E	R	O	N	H	H	O	L	F	S	U	A	W	S
K	F	I	F	T	E	H	D	L	Y	O	L	O	T	L
O	I	F	R	R	D	R	C	I	A	O	R	A	M	M
E	R	A	M	L	E	F	T	T	U	H	N	T	I	T
O	E	H	G	N	O	R	T	S	T	D	I	M	H	N

Secret Message

30

The Captain and the Slave Girl

2 Kings 5:1–4

Now Naaman, **captain** of the **host** of the **king** of Syria, was a **great** man with his **master**, and **honourable, because** by him the Lord had **given deliverance** unto Syria: he was also a **mighty** man in **valour**, but he was a **leper**. And the **Syrians** had gone out by **companies**, and had **brought away captive** out of the **land** of Israel a **little maid**; and she **waited** on **Naaman's wife**. And she said unto her **mistress**, **Would** God my lord **were** with the **prophet** that is in **Samaria**! for he would **recover** him of his **leprosy**. And **one went** in, and told his lord, **saying**, **Thus and** thus said the maid that is of the land **of Israel**.

D W H Y O P S E M E S S E N G
L E M E S R E P E L R H T O L
U V L I D O T H G U O R B N A
O I C I G P R A S N A I R Y S
W T O R V H M P O V A L O U R
R P M D E E T U E I E A O A N
E A P I I T R Y R L S N D R A
C C A T S A S A E O U D N W D
O G N W B T M A N A A M A N S
V N I L A A R E M C C Y S S H
E I E I S S G E L N E N U T H
R Y S W I R H O S T B E H W K
E A J F E R E W O S T V T I R
D S O A A N C A P T A I N F N
R I T V D E T I A W E G L E R

Secret Message

____

____

____

____

____

____

31

A Leper Healed

2 Kings 5:13–15

And his **servants** came **near**, and **spake** unto him, and said, My **father**, if the **prophet** had **bid** thee do some **great thing**, wouldest thou not have done it? how much **rather** then, when he **saith** to thee, **Wash**, and be **clean**? Then went he **down**, and **dipped** himself **seven times** in **Jordan**, according to the **saying** of the **man of God**: and his **flesh** came **again** like unto the flesh of a **little child**, and he was clean. And he **returned** to the man of God, he and all his **company**, and **came**, and **stood before** him: and he said, **Behold**, now I **know** that there is no God in all the **earth**, but in **Israel**: now therefore, I **pray** thee, take a **blessing** of thy servant.

```
N L I T T L E R E H T A R B R
S E V E N T I M E S W H A E T
Y N A P M O C W A S T H T F E
T A E R G B E H O L D U D O L
E G N I Y A S N A D R O J R P
E A R N S T O O D N G A A E M
A I E K A P S N E F H T R A E
D N P S I P T D O C A M E O S
E I R T T I N N O N U K N O W
P N A D H E A R T H T E W K I
P N Y G O M V F T E H P O R P
I S Y L E A R S I R I I D A H
D L I H C L E A N X N X O A S
I D E B L E S S I N G L J F A
B E L F H S E L F A T H E R W
```

Secret Message

32

The Missing Enemy

2 Kings 7:5–7

And they **rose up** in the **twilight**, to go unto the camp of the **Syrians**: and **when** they were **come** to the **uttermost part** of the **camp of Syria**, **behold**, there was **no man there**. For the LORD had **made** the host of the Syrians to **hear** a **noise** of **chariots**, and a noise of **horses**, **even** the noise of a **great host**: and they said one to **another**, Lo, the **king of Israel** hath **hired against** us the **kings** of the **Hittites**, and the kings of the **Egyptians**, to come upon us. **Wherefore they arose and fled** in the twilight, and **left their tents**, and their horses, and their asses, even the camp as it was, and **fled for their life**.

W H K I N G S O R O F D E L F
K T F I L O R D R S C T E E P
D I R T S N I A G A R F V U I
S S N A I R Y S M A T E E T C
O D S G P H V P E T N S S H E
R L E E O D O H H A O O N E T
W O T R T F H E N R M R A I A
T H S S S I I O T R A A I R H
E E E Y O R T S E S N Y T L A
S B R N T H D T R Y T E P I N
E I R E E E T M I A H H Y F D
A M N R R U I A A H E T G E F
S T O I R A H C E D R L E A L
S N H C S H W H E R E F O R E
A D F L E T W I L I G H T D D

Secret Message

33

Getting Ready to Build

1 Chronicles 22:14–16

Now, behold, in my **trouble I have prepared for the house** of the LORD an **hundred thousand talents of gold**, and a thousand thousand talents **of silver**; and of **brass and iron** without **weight**; for it is in **abundance**: timber also and stone have I prepared; and thou mayest add thereto. **Moreover there are workmen** with thee in abundance, **hewers** and **workers of stone and timber**, and all **manner of cunning men for every** manner of work. Of the gold, the silver, and the brass, and the iron, there **is no number. Arise therefore, and be doing**, and the LORD **be with thee**.

E B D N A W H P Y F G N I O D
S S A R B W M O R E O V E R R
U E R A E R E H T E N R O A O
O T R O U B L E S O P L T D F
H S A B V I M D R N D A O H N
T A R L E L R I O W E B R C E
E D E E T W D E T O R U U E M
E B V U K N I H B D D N I V D
O S L T A R E T N M N D W A L
F L I I A R O A H I U A O H O
S D S R E L S W N T H N R I G
T N F F A U E G A H H C K O F
O U O F O R E N N A M E M S O
N R T H G I E W T E E V E R Y
E F T O H E W E R S R G N O D

Secret Message

34

Promise of Healing

2 Chronicles 7:14–16

If **my people**, **which** are **called** by **my name**, **shall humble themselves**, **and pray**, **and seek my face**, and **turn from** their **wicked ways**; **then will I hear** from **heaven**, and will **forgive their sin**, and **will heal their land**. Now **mine eyes** shall be **open**, and mine **ears attent unto** the **prayer** that is **made** in this **place**. For now have I **chosen** and **sanctified** this **house**, that my name may be there for ever: and mine eyes and mine **heart** shall **be there perpetually**.

P	R	A	Y	E	R	W	H	O	B	D	N	E	H	T
U	E	I	F	O	R	G	I	V	E	H	L	L	O	T
Y	A	R	P	D	N	A	T	I	U	H	L	P	E	T
H	P	O	P	O	U	S	F	M	C	L	E	O	H	E
T	H	L	T	E	A	I	B	T	A	N	S	E	Y	E
G	M	N	A	H	T	L	O	H	L	E	M	P	W	N
E	U	Y	I	C	E	U	S	W	L	S	A	Y	I	E
A	D	K	N	S	E	I	A	I	E	O	D	M	C	V
R	T	A	E	A	R	H	R	L	D	H	E	A	K	A
S	S	T	R	E	M	I	V	L	L	C	F	A	E	E
E	D	C	E	W	S	E	E	I	A	Y	S	H	D	H
S	O	S	H	N	S	D	E	H	M	N	E	Y	N	T
U	O	I	T	S	T	A	N	E	T	N	D	N	A	C
O	C	H	E	A	R	T	L	A	E	H	L	L	I	W
H	T	I	B	F	Y	T	U	R	N	F	R	O	M	M

Secret Message

____

____

____

____

____

____

35

Hand of God

Ezra 8:21–23

Then I **proclaimed** a fast there, at the **river** of **Ahava**, that we might **afflict ourselves before** our God, to seek of him a **right** way for us, and for our **little ones**, and for all our **substance**. For I was **ashamed** to **require** of the **king a band** of **soldiers** and **horsemen** to help us against the **enemy** in the way: **because** we had **spoken** unto the king, **saying, The hand of our God is upon all them for good that seek him**; but his **power** and his **wrath** is against all them that **forsake** him. So we **fasted** and **besought** our God for this: and he was **intreated** of us.

L	K	W	D	O	G	R	U	O	F	O	H	E	A	D
M	I	H	K	E	E	S	T	A	H	T	R	E	F	E
W	N	T	N	E	M	E	S	R	O	H	H	S	F	T
A	G	N	T	E	S	I	E	D	Z	R	P	G	L	A
A	A	O	G	L	N	R	A	O	N	O	I	O	I	E
B	B	P	N	G	E	E	F	L	K	A	U	W	C	R
E	A	U	H	Q	S	O	M	E	C	R	H	N	T	T
F	N	S	U	U	R	E	N	Y	S	O	A	E	T	N
O	D	I	A	S	H	A	M	E	D	T	R	E	H	I
R	R	C	A	T	V	W	L	N	S	H	E	P	G	T
E	E	K	L	A	R	V	A	B	S	K	E	D	U	F
B	E	L	H	A	E	O	U	F	O	R	G	O	O	D
R	A	A	T	S	V	S	O	L	D	I	E	R	S	A
S	A	H	G	N	I	Y	A	S	F	A	S	T	E	D
F	E	J	O	U	R	E	W	O	P	R	N	E	B	Y

Secret Message

36

City in Ruins

Nehemiah 2:2–5

Wherefore the **king said** unto me, Why is thy **countenance** sad, seeing thou **art not sick**? this is **nothing** else but **sorrow of heart**. Then I was very sore **afraid**, and said unto the king, Let the **king live** for ever: why should not my countenance **be sad**, when **the city**, the place of my **fathers' sepulchres**, lieth **waste**, and the **gates thereof** are **consumed with fire**? Then the king said unto me, For what dost thou make **request**? So I **prayed** to the **God of heaven**. And I said unto the king, If it **please** the king, and if thy **servant** have **found favour** in **thy sight**, that thou **wouldest** send me unto **Judah**, unto the **city of my** fathers' sepulchres, that I **may build it**.

E T S A W W W I T H F I R E A
N S H H F A S O R R O W O F F
T E P T E A O S T S E U Q E R
T D V C H A T D I A R D N E A
H L E A O G R H R M E I A H I
D U M H E U I T E N H A Y S D
I O A F V H N S O R T S M E E
A W Y W A O F T Y B S E F P I
S T B D T V H O E H E R O U H
G K U S F I O S D N T V Y L I
N J I N N O A U G O A A T C A
I C L G R D U T R A G N I H X
K E D E M U S N O C R T C R X
E V I L G N I K D P R A Y E D
E S T H E C I T Y P L E A S E

Secret Message

37

Courageous Queen

Esther 4:14–16

For if thou **altogether holdest** thy **peace** at **this time**, then **shall** there **enlargement** and **deliverance arise** to the Jews from **another place**; but thou and thy **father's house** shall be **destroyed**: and who **knoweth whether** thou art come to the **kingdom** for such a time as this? Then **Esther** bade them **return Mordecai** this **answer**, Go, **gather** together all the Jews that are **present** in **Shushan**, and **fast ye for** me, and **neither eat nor drink three days, night** or day: I also and my **maidens** will fast **likewise**; and so will I go in unto the king, which is not **according** to the law: and if I perish, **I perish**.

A	D	K	N	O	W	E	T	H	H	O	W	W	W	A
D	N	E	N	R	E	S	U	O	H	S	E	H	S	H
E	T	S	L	I	U	E	H	F	A	T	H	E	R	S
S	P	I	W	I	R	T	R	U	H	E	A	T	E	I
T	R	W	R	E	V	D	E	H	S	L	E	H	H	R
R	E	E	R	E	R	E	R	R	T	H	C	E	T	E
O	S	K	G	N	I	D	R	O	C	C	A	R	O	P
Y	E	I	L	A	T	E	G	A	N	D	E	N	N	I
E	N	L	A	R	G	E	M	E	N	T	P	G	A	T
D	T	H	I	S	T	I	M	E	T	C	A	C	S	H
A	O	R	E	H	T	I	E	N	M	T	E	E	H	G
R	O	F	E	Y	T	S	A	F	H	D	D	C	A	I
I	O	R	E	H	T	S	E	E	R	L	A	A	L	N
S	N	E	D	I	A	M	R	O	O	R	Y	L	L	D
E	K	I	N	G	D	O	M	H	E	C	S	P	A	I

Secret Message

____

____

____

____

____

____

38

Esther Approaches the King

Esther 7:1–4

So the **king** and **Haman** came to **banquet** with **Esther** the **queen**. And the king said again unto Esther on the **second day** at the banquet of **wine**, What is thy **petition**, queen Esther? and it shall be **granted** thee: and what is thy **request**? and it shall be **performed**, even to the **half** of the **kingdom**. Then Esther the queen **answered** and said, If I have found **favour** in thy **sight**, O king, and if it **please** the king, let my **life** be **given** me at my petition, and my **people** at my request: For we are **sold**, I and my people, to be **destroyed**, to be **slain**, and to **perish**. But if we had been sold for **bondmen** and **bondwomen**, I had held my **tongue**, although the **enemy** could not countervail the king's **damage**.

W H A A N S W E R E D T P N P
P E T I T I O N E R S E O E E
T E U Q N A B E F I L S N E R
A B O N D W O M E N L A P U F
D N O C E S O Y S I S E D Q O
E A S F S V I O G A N L E R R
D M L I D K I I N L O P T E M
N A G A H A S G I S U E N Q E
H H M O D G N I K R U S A U D
S G R E H T S E P I V E R E T
I E D E Y O R T S E D U G S T
R O N B O N D M E N O M O T H
E R D I E G C A I V Y P X X G
P H A M W U L I A S A C L A I
D A M A G E A F O T D R D E S

Secret Message

39

Job Is Blessed

Job 42:12–16

So the Lord **blessed** the **latter end** of **Job** more than his **beginning**: for he had **fourteen** thousand **sheep**, and **six** thousand **camels**, and a **thousand yoke** of **oxen**, and a thousand she **asses**. He had also **seven sons** and **three daughters**. And he **called** the **name** of the first, **Jemima**; and the name of the second, **Kezia**; and the name of the third, Kerenhappuch. And in **all** the **land** were no **women found** so **fair** as the daughters of Job: and their **father** gave them inheritance among their brethren. After this lived Job an hundred and **forty years**, and **saw** his sons, and his sons' sons, even **four** generations.

J	E	M	I	M	A	W	H	A	T	D	S	I	D	F
Y	S	A	T	S	A	W	A	N	C	L	L	A	D	O
S	E	S	S	A	I	M	O	W	E	O	D	U	A	R
D	L	A	D	I	J	O	B	M	B	E	N	J	U	T
E	O	B	R	S	X	N	A	R	E	E	U	S	G	Y
L	P	D	O	S	E	C	N	S	E	N	O	I	H	F
L	T	N	H	V	E	L	O	R	I	A	F	R	T	D
A	T	A	E	E	R	H	T	O	O	K	O	X	E	N
C	E	S	V	D	E	R	F	D	L	Y	U	T	R	P
H	I	U	R	N	N	O	E	E	A	A	R	G	S	E
Y	F	O	R	E	U	M	O	S	I	M	T	H	I	E
O	L	H	M	R	A	X	X	S	Z	A	E	T	J	H
K	J	T	S	N	O	S	A	E	E	L	E	S	E	S
E	L	O	A	C	D	N	A	L	K	L	N	K	A	R
G	N	I	N	N	I	G	E	B	F	A	T	H	E	R

Secret Message

____

____

____

____

____

____

40

Rooted in Righteousness

Psalm 1:1–5

Blessed is the man that **walketh** not in the **counsel** of the **ungodly**, nor **standeth** in the way of **sinners**, nor **sitteth** in the **seat** of the **scornful**. But his **delight** is in the law of the LORD; and in his law doth he **meditate** day and **night**. And he **shall** be like a **tree planted** by the **rivers** of **water**, that **bringeth forth** his **fruit** in his **season**; his **leaf** also shall not **wither**; and **whatsoever** he doeth shall **prosper**. The ungodly are not so: but are like the **chaff** which the **wind driveth away**. **Therefore** the ungodly shall not stand in the **judgment**, nor sinners in the **congregation** of the **righteous**.

S C W B R I N G E T H H A T D
C O N G R E G A T I O N H O E
O U I C W S V H P L A N T E D
R N G H H I E E W I T H E R T
N S H A T R N S O H L I K S P
F E T F E E I D E S S E L B S
U L N F V T T G A A T A A L M
L S O A I A R T H Y T A W F S
S R S H R T E T I T A P H A L
E R A L D I E H A S E R L W Y
T N E M G D U J U N G O D L Y
I P S N N E R I V E R S U P E
U N T A N M O T H D E P U S N
R G T H G I L E D O R E T A W
F S L L A H S D L H T R O F Y

Secret Message

41

Despair

Psalm 22:1–6

My God, my God, why hast thou **forsaken me**? why art **thou so** far from **helping me**, and from the **words** of my **roaring**? O my God, **I cry in** the day **time**, but thou **hearest** not; and in the **night season**, and **am not silent**. But thou **art holy**, O thou that **inhabitest** the **praises** of **Israel**. Our **fathers trusted in thee**: they trusted, and **thou didst** deliver them. They **cried unto thee**, and were **delivered**: they trusted in thee, and **were not confounded**. But **I am a worm**, and no man; a **reproach** of men, and **despised** of the **people**.

W	F	A	T	H	E	R	S	H	O	I	N	T	H	E
T	H	O	U	D	I	D	S	T	N	E	T	W	S	T
E	D	E	R	E	V	I	L	E	D	H	S	I	I	S
R	T	E	A	S	S	E	A	S	O	N	L	N	N	D
O	M	M	I	Y	A	E	N	U	T	E	T	I	T	R
A	U	G	R	R	L	K	S	S	N	C	D	Y	H	O
R	S	N	A	O	C	O	E	T	O	N	E	R	E	W
I	E	I	T	I	W	T	H	N	D	T	T	C	E	H
N	E	P	O	O	I	A	F	T	M	H	S	I	P	E
G	N	L	R	B	T	O	M	Y	R	E	U	I	P	L
T	N	E	A	O	U	H	G	A	S	A	R	G	E	W
H	I	H	N	N	A	O	E	I	I	R	T	A	O	O
G	N	M	D	R	D	C	A	E	D	E	R	S	P	O
I	A	E	E	F	T	R	H	H	I	S	S	P	L	S
N	D	E	S	I	P	S	E	D	I	T	A	L	E	M

Secret Message

____

____

____

____

____

____

42

Praise the Lord!

Psalm 95:3–9

For the LORD is a **great God**, and a **great King** **above all** gods. In his **hand are** the deep **places** of the **earth**: the **strength** of the **hills** is his also. The **sea is his**, and **he made it**: and his **hands formed** the **dry land**. O **come**, let us **worship** and **bow down**: let us **kneel** before the LORD our **maker**. For **he is our God**; and we are the **people** of his **pasture**, and the **sheep** of his hand. To day if ye will hear his **voice**, **harden** not your **heart**, as in the **provocation**, and as in the day of **temptation** in the **wilderness**: When your **fathers tempted** me, **proved** me, and **saw my work**.

T	H	D	R	Y	L	A	N	D	G	A	I	N	S	E
P	S	P	I	H	S	R	O	W	R	B	A	W	M	L
M	S	D	N	A	H	D	I	G	E	O	S	O	A	A
S	H	E	E	P	Y	E	T	N	A	V	C	D	K	P
S	N	E	C	P	T	V	A	I	T	E	O	W	E	M
A	S	O	I	A	K	O	C	K	G	A	I	O	R	N
E	I	W	I	S	L	R	O	T	O	L	P	B	K	E
H	H	A	T	T	O	P	V	A	D	L	K	R	I	D
F	S	K	N	U	A	U	O	E	E	E	O	D	E	R
A	I	O	N	R	H	T	R	R	R	W	M	T	C	A
T	A	F	N	E	O	N	P	G	Y	A	P	R	I	H
H	E	M	A	D	E	I	T	M	O	M	D	I	O	S
E	S	R	E	S	T	L	W	O	E	D	T	N	V	F
R	T	H	S	E	E	A	R	T	H	T	L	O	A	R
S	L	L	I	H	S	T	R	E	N	G	T	H	D	H

Secret Message

____

____

____

____

____

____

43

Prosperous Woman

Proverbs 31:11–17

The **heart** of her **husband** doth **safely trust in her**, so that he **shall have no need** of **spoil**. She will do **him good** and **not evil** all the days of her life. She **seeketh wool**, and **flax**, and **worketh willingly** with her **hands**. She is like the **merchants' ships**; she **bringeth** her food from afar. She **riseth** also while it is yet **night**, and **giveth** meat to her **household**, and a **portion** to her **maidens**. She **considereth** a **field**, and **buyeth** it: with the **fruit** of her hands she **planteth** a **vineyard**. She **girdeth** her **loins** with strength, and **strengtheneth** her arms.

T N I G H T D N A B S U H H S
F E P M T T R L I V E T O N S
F L S E E K E T H I E N I D W
R I A C Y R F R I N O O N I O
U O F X U H C I E N L A L H O
I P E H B T T H E D H L E T L
T S L O O E T E A L I E F E A
S R Y U V G D I D N D S R K R
T P A S N N U M G R T O N R D
H O I E U I S L A R I S W O O
T R R H H R Y Y U I M G O W C
E T A O S B E S N I D G S F A
S I P L A N T E T H M E V A H
I O R D I H T E V I G A N B O
R N V V E W H S H A L L A S T

Secret Message

____

____

____

____

____

____

44

Poor but Wise

Ecclesiastes 9:13–18

This **wisdom** have I **seen also under the sun**, and it **seemed** great unto me: There was a **little city**, and **few men** within it; and there came a **great king against** it, and **besieged** it, and built great **bulwarks** against it: Now there was **found** in it a **poor wise** man, and he by his wisdom **delivered** the city; yet no man **remembered** that same poor man. Then said I, Wisdom is **better** than **strength**: **nevertheless** the poor man's wisdom is **despised**, and his **words** are **not heard**. The words of **wise men** are heard in **quiet more** than the **cry of him** that **ruleth** among **fools**. Wisdom is better than **weapons** of war: but one **sinner destroyeth** much **good**.

W H A P O O R W I S E H T T I
Q U I E T M O R E T T R N D R
Y G N I K T A E R G L U E E E
A T O D E D M E N S C L M S T
G C I O E E N E R R I E W T T
A N D C D R R O Y B M T E R E
I W E E E T T O T B S H F O B
N I R M S L F H E H T H E Y D
S S E L E H T R E V E N W E E
T D V R I S E T S S I A G T S
T O I M E D I R I O U E R H I
F M L S D R O W N L I N T D P
S E E N A L S O N S L O O F S
H I D S N O P A E W S B O O E
S K R A W L U B R K F O U N D

Secret Message

45

Sheltered by Love

Song of Songs 2:3–7

As the **apple tree** among the **trees** of the **wood,** so is my **beloved** among the sons. I **sat down** under his **shadow** with **great delight**, and **his fruit** was **sweet** to **my taste**. **He brought** me to the **banqueting house, and his banner** over me was love. Stay me with **flagons, comfort** me with **apples**: for I am **sick of love**. His **left hand** is under **my head**, and his **right hand** doth **embrace** me. I **charge** you, O ye **daughters** of **Jerusalem**, by the **roes**, and by the **hinds** of the **field**, that ye **stir** not up, nor **awake** my love, till he **please.**

J S A T D O W N W S T I R S H
E E G I E S A E L P D T I A T
R E R U M W O O D A R C G E R
U R E R B E O S E O K S H M E
S T A F R E I H F O R E T R S
A E T S A T Y M F E M L H E E
L P T I C M O L T N E P A V W
E T P H E C O H S I S P N O O
M N E L G V G B D N U A D T C
G N I T E U Q N A B O A I H D
N H T H A T O E I N H G A G L
S I H D N A R R K S N R A I E
S N D E V O L E B A G E O L I
C D W A S L O V E E W H R E F
A S P T E R L E F T H A N D S

Secret Message

____

____

____

____

____

____

46

Advance Man

Isaiah 40:1–5

Comfort ye, comfort ye my **people**, saith **your** God. **Speak** ye **comfortably** to **Jerusalem**, and cry unto her, that her **warfare** is **accomplished**, that her **iniquity** is **pardoned**: for she hath **received** of the LORD's **hand double** for all her sins. The **voice** of him that **crieth** in the **wilderness**, **Prepare** ye the way of the LORD, make **straight** in the **desert** a **highway** for our God. **Every valley shall** be **exalted**, and every **mountain** and hill shall be made low: and the **crooked** shall be made straight, and the **rough places** plain: And the **glory** of the LORD shall be **revealed**, and all **flesh** shall see it **together**: for the **mouth** of the LORD hath **spoken** it.

F W H H O S V I N T R O U G H
H L A E N H M O U T H N H D T
Y N E W Y A E W I T E I I E E
D E H S I L P M O C C A G S I
S T L A H L B T O G E T H E R
E X A L T E D A M Y J N W R C
P R E P A R E E T E E U A T E
S P E A K V C I R R U O Y R D
E Y N R T R U U F N O M A U E
L L R D O Q S P F I E F L P V
B L E O I A D I L Y R S M E I
U S K N L T H G I A R T S O E
O E I E A G I A W H C E S P C
D P M D E L A E V E R E V L E
R O P H E C Y N E K O P S E R

Secret Message

47

Trust God

Jeremiah 17:7–10

Blessed is the man that **trusteth** in the **Lord**, and **whose hope** the Lord is. For **he shall** be as a **tree planted** by the **waters**, and that **spreadeth** out **her roots** by the **river**, and **shall not** see **when heat cometh**, but **her leaf** shall be **green**; and shall not be **careful** in the **year** of **drought**, **neither** shall **cease from yielding fruit**. The **heart** is **deceitful** above all **things**, and **desperately wicked**: who can know it? I the Lord **search** the heart, I try the **reins**, even to give **every** man **according to his ways**, and according to the fruit of his **doings**.

T W R H E A R T M H Y R E V E
H O P E C D A T O N L L A H S
I R E V I R R F R E T H T P O
N C D Y D N A O F E K T R I H
G N E G L E S E L R C E E O W
S A S A L U S U S G A T E N Q
R R S R S U F P E D G S P H T
W H E N H E A T E N D U L E O
R H L T R E I T I R N R A S H
C D B A A U H D O E A T N H I
D O C J R W R U I U C T T A S
D I M F A O G T H I N E E L W
T N H E C H H W I C K E D L A
I G S C T E B G N I D L E I Y
O S A O R H K H E R R O O T S

Secret Message

48

Time of Despair

Lamentations 5:1–8

Remember, O Lord, what is come upon us: **consider**, and behold our **reproach**. Our **inheritance** is **turned** to **strangers**, our **houses** to **aliens**. We are **orphans** and **fatherless**, our **mothers** are as widows. We have **drunken** our **water** for **money**; our **wood** is sold unto us. Our **necks** are under **persecution**: we **labour**, and have no rest. We have **given** the hand to the **Egyptians**, and to the **Assyrians**, to be **satisfied** with **bread**. Our **fathers** have **sinned**, and are not; and we have **borne** their **iniquities**. **Servants** have **ruled** over us: there is none that doth **deliver** us out of their hand.

T D E N N I S H E F A S R D E
S E R V A N T S A H N M O D G
Y L E O F W H T O A M O N E Y
A I P T P S H U H C W O U L P
N V R T R E S P Y D E N R U T
S E O B R E R E B M E M E R I
N R A S S O E S L R O U S N A
A G C H T G H O E R D R I S N
I N H E R I T A N C E Q J U S
R E D I S N O C L G U H D G M
Y K E W D N M A N I I T T T O
S N N A J E B A T R E V I A U
S U E T S O R I B O R N E O F
A R A E U T E L N E C K S N N
B D E R S S A T I S F I E D M

Secret Message

____

____

____

____

____

____

49

Precious and Perfect

Ezekiel 28:13–15

Thou hast been in **Eden** the **garden** of God; **every precious** stone was thy **covering**, the **sardius**, **topaz**, and the **diamond**, the **beryl**, the **onyx**, and the **jasper**, the **sapphire**, the **emerald**, and the **carbuncle**, and **gold**: the **workmanship** of thy **tabrets** and of thy **pipes** was **prepared** in thee in the day that thou wast **created**. Thou art the **anointed cherub** that **covereth**; and I have set thee so: thou wast upon the **holy mountain** of God; thou hast **walked** up and **down** in the **midst** of the **stones** of **fire**. Thou wast **perfect** in thy **ways** from the day that thou wast created, **till iniquity** was **found** **in thee**.

J	D	P	T	A	B	R	E	T	S	W	H	A	T	R
A	N	O	I	N	T	E	D	I	S	M	I	D	S	T
S	O	V	L	H	E	R	W	T	A	S	N	S	A	E
P	M	Z	L	E	S	G	O	L	D	A	E	E	R	K
E	A	N	I	A	T	N	U	O	M	P	I	P	D	E
R	I	E	N	P	E	I	A	L	B	P	Y	W	I	E
H	D	D	I	S	R	R	C	M	E	H	N	C	U	P
H	E	R	Q	X	S	E	I	O	K	I	A	C	S	A
F	W	A	U	Y	I	V	P	F	V	R	H	U	Z	W
O	A	G	I	N	H	O	I	A	B	E	O	Y	A	S
U	L	F	T	O	S	C	I	U	R	I	R	W	P	R
N	K	H	Y	Y	S	T	N	U	C	E	N	E	O	V
D	E	T	A	E	R	C	B	E	V	I	D	W	T	S
E	D	W	I	D	L	A	R	E	M	E	Y	L	O	H
O	L	Y	R	E	B	P	E	R	F	E	C	T	N	D

Secret Message

____

____

____

____

____

____

50

Heart of Stone

Ezekiel 36:25–28

Then will I **sprinkle** clean **water** upon you, and **ye shall be clean**: **from all** your **filthiness**, and from all your **idols**, will I **cleanse** you. **A new heart** also **will I give** you, and a **new spirit will I put** within you: and I **will take away** the **stony** heart **out of your** flesh, and I will give **you an heart of flesh**. And I will **put my** spirit within you, and **cause** you to **walk** in my **statutes**, and ye shall **keep** my **judgments**, and **do them**. And ye shall **dwell in the land** that I **gave to** your **fathers**; and ye shall **be my people**, and I will be **your God**.

I	R	E	T	A	W	I	N	T	H	E	L	A	N	D
D	B	Y	W	R	H	W	I	L	L	T	A	K	E	L
O	Y	A	T	U	A	T	U	P	I	L	L	I	W	L
L	M	E	X	O	P	E	L	K	N	I	R	P	S	E
S	T	O	N	Y	Y	F	H	R	E	S	S	S	P	W
I	U	O	A	F	R	O	N	W	T	S	S	D	I	D
O	P	W	E	O	E	Y	U	N	E	E	K	L	R	L
S	A	P	M	T	O	S	E	A	T	N	L	Y	I	L
G	E	A	E	U	H	M	N	U	N	I	A	E	T	I
D	L	S	R	O	G	S	T	A	G	H	W	S	O	W
L	O	G	U	D	P	A	E	I	E	T	E	H	D	N
A	O	T	U	A	T	L	V	L	K	L	D	A	D	E
D	R	J	H	S	C	E	E	E	F	I	C	L	R	H
F	A	T	H	E	R	S	E	E	T	F	S	L	S	T
Y	M	E	B	E	M	P	Z	E	K	O	O	I	E	L

Secret Message

51

Safe from Harm

Daniel 3:26–27

Then **Nebuchadnezzar** came near to the **mouth** of the **burning** fiery furnace, and **spake**, and said, **Shadrach, Meshach**, and **Abednego**, ye **servants** of the **most high God**, come forth, and **come hither**. Then Shadrach, Meshach, and Abednego, **came forth** of the **midst** of the **fire**. And the **princes**, **governors**, and **captains**, and the king's **counsellors**, being gathered **together**, saw these men, upon whose **bodies** the fire had **no power**, nor was an **hair** of their head **singed**, neither were their **coats** changed, nor the **smell of fire** had **passed** on them.

A	B	E	D	N	E	G	O	M	I	D	S	T	W	H
A	P	T	W	E	R	I	F	F	O	L	L	E	M	S
A	R	S	T	B	G	N	I	N	R	U	B	H	R	E
N	I	T	A	U	M	E	O	F	T	H	T	I	E	C
S	N	O	O	C	S	I	N	G	E	D	A	H	U	N
R	C	G	S	H	A	D	R	A	C	H	T	R	Y	C
O	E	E	T	A	S	T	N	A	V	R	E	S	G	O
L	S	T	H	D	O	G	H	G	I	H	T	S	O	M
L	C	H	E	N	O	P	O	W	E	R	K	I	V	E
E	O	E	M	E	S	H	A	C	H	N	G	S	E	H
S	A	R	R	Z	R	U	D	E	S	S	A	P	R	I
N	T	L	E	Z	D	I	O	V	E	R	X	A	N	T
U	S	X	C	A	M	E	F	O	R	T	H	K	O	H
O	F	I	E	R	Y	F	U	R	N	A	C	E	R	E
C	A	P	T	A	I	N	S	B	O	D	I	E	S	R

Secret Message

____

____

____

____

____

____

52

Den of Lions

Daniel 6:18–22

Then the king went to his **palace**, and **passed** the **night fasting**: **neither** were **instruments** of **musick brought before him**: and his **sleep** went from him. Then the king arose very **early** in the **morning**, and went in **haste** unto the **den of lions**. And when he came to the den, he **cried** with a **lamentable voice** unto **Daniel**: and the king **spake** and said to Daniel, O Daniel, **servant** of the **living** God, is thy God, whom thou **servest continually**, able to **deliver** thee from the **lions**? Then said Daniel **unto the king**, **O king**, live **for ever**. **My God** hath sent his **angel**, and hath shut the lions' **mouths**, that they have **not hurt me**.

P	A	S	S	E	D	Y	W	T	S	E	V	R	E	S
T	H	L	A	T	L	E	K	K	C	I	S	U	M	I
H	D	E	I	R	C	N	N	A	G	T	D	M	T	F
G	B	S	A	V	L	I	L	O	N	D	D	Y	R	O
U	L	E	E	A	I	A	N	E	F	I	L	G	U	R
O	N	I	F	R	P	N	M	D	G	L	E	O	H	E
R	N	T	O	O	V	U	G	E	A	N	I	D	T	V
B	L	I	O	N	R	A	N	U	N	N	A	O	O	E
G	R	S	G	T	S	E	N	E	E	T	I	R	N	R
N	E	V	S	H	H	I	H	T	I	E	A	E	E	S
I	V	N	U	N	T	E	E	I	T	T	C	B	L	L
N	I	D	E	N	U	R	K	S	M	I	H	A	L	E
R	L	F	O	T	O	E	A	I	O	R	D	E	A	E
O	E	C	R	I	M	H	P	V	N	U	S	X	R	P
M	D	X	G	N	I	T	S	A	F	G	N	I	K	O

Secret Message

____

____

____

____

____

____

53

Faithful Husband

Hosea 11:1–4

When **Israel** was a **child**, then **I loved him**, and **called** my **son** out of **Egypt**. As they called them, so **they went** from them: they **sacrificed** unto **Baalim**, and **burned incense** to **graven images**. I **taught Ephraim** also to go, taking them by their **arms**; but they **knew not** that I **healed** them. I **drew** them with **cords** of a **man**, with **bands of love**: and **I was to them** as they that **take off** the **yoke** on their **jaws**.

C	W	S	H	A	T	O	N	W	E	N	K	T	P	R
H	O	S	M	T	S	A	C	R	I	F	I	C	E	D
I	I	E	T	R	Y	O	K	E	U	T	W	S	E	D
L	I	D	S	W	A	J	T	E	H	E	P	E	R	O
D	P	H	E	N	T	S	D	R	O	C	H	G	R	O
S	I	L	O	V	E	D	H	I	M	F	E	A	A	D
M	S	A	R	R	Y	C	T	T	O	H	F	M	M	P
I	R	C	T	U	R	E	N	G	O	E	D	I	I	S
T	A	C	A	L	L	E	D	I	R	A	E	N	L	L
P	E	A	T	I	W	O	N	S	D	L	H	E	A	I
Y	L	P	W	Y	I	M	A	N	T	E	H	V	A	F
G	A	I	E	V	O	L	F	O	S	D	N	A	B	T
E	P	H	R	A	I	M	H	O	L	E	S	R	S	I
S	T	A	U	G	H	T	N	R	A	E	L	G	U	X
X	Q	M	E	H	T	O	T	S	A	W	I	G	K	B

Secret Message

____

____

____

____

____

____

54

Call to Repentance

Joel 2:11–14

And the LORD shall **utter** his **voice** before his **army**: for his camp is **very great**: for he is **strong** that **executeth his word**: for **the day of the LORD** is great and very terrible; and who can **abide** it? Therefore also now, saith the LORD, **turn ye even to me** with **all your heart**, and with **fasting**, and with **weeping**, and with **mourning**: And **rend your heart**, and not your garments, and turn unto the LORD your God: for he is gracious and merciful, **slow to anger**, and of great kindness, and **repenteth** him of **the evil**. Who knoweth if he will return and repent, and leave a **blessing** behind him; even a **meat offering** and a **drink** offering unto **the LORD your God**?

W	M	H	U	T	T	E	R	I	G	N	O	R	T	S
D	O	G	R	U	O	Y	D	R	O	L	E	H	T	L
C	U	T	G	R	H	F	L	E	Y	T	X	T	V	O
I	R	H	N	N	G	B	U	P	G	R	E	R	E	W
G	N	E	D	Y	I	O	E	E	S	A	C	A	R	T
N	I	E	J	E	B	P	O	N	D	E	U	E	Y	O
I	N	V	D	E	L	E	E	T	R	H	T	H	G	A
T	G	I	L	V	E	S	A	E	O	R	E	R	R	N
S	B	L	K	E	S	Y	E	T	W	U	T	U	E	G
A	R	M	Y	N	S	C	I	H	S	O	H	O	A	E
F	S	P	A	T	I	R	T	O	I	Y	F	Y	T	R
G	O	D	S	O	N	R	J	U	H	L	D	D	G	M
E	N	T	V	M	G	O	D	N	I	L	S	N	R	A
D	R	O	L	E	H	T	F	O	Y	A	D	E	H	T
M	E	A	T	O	F	F	E	R	I	N	G	R	E	L

Secret Message

____

____

____

____

____

____

55

Prepare to Meet Thy God

Amos 4:11–13

I have overthrown some of you, as God overthrew **Sodom** and **Gomorrah**, and ye were as a **firebrand plucked** out of the **burning**: yet have ye **not returned** unto me, saith **the LORD**. Therefore thus will I do unto thee, **O Israel**: and because I will do this unto thee, prepare to **meet thy God**, O Israel. For, lo, **he that formeth** the **mountains**, and **createth** the **wind**, and **declareth** unto man what is his **thought**, that **maketh** the **morning darkness**, and **treadeth** upon the **high places** of the **earth**, The LORD, The **God of hosts**, is **his name**.

M	B	M	A	K	E	T	H	E	S	I	D	D	D	E
O	S	H	O	V	E	R	T	H	R	O	W	N	B	E
R	I	S	T	U	D	R	O	L	E	H	T	A	I	N
N	P	E	G	E	N	A	P	B	L	H	C	R	R	W
I	L	C	O	E	M	T	U	E	G	P	R	B	D	H
N	U	A	H	E	A	R	A	U	T	W	E	E	O	T
G	C	L	H	A	N	R	O	I	T	V	A	R	G	E
D	K	P	O	I	S	H	T	F	N	C	T	I	Y	R
A	E	H	N	I	T	A	T	H	T	S	E	F	H	A
R	D	G	O	I	O	N	D	M	I	A	T	D	T	L
K	A	I	M	G	O	M	O	R	R	A	H	O	T	C
N	S	H	H	T	E	D	A	E	R	T	E	T	E	E
E	N	G	A	N	O	T	R	E	T	U	R	N	E	D
S	G	H	I	S	N	A	M	E	E	I	N	X	M	H
S	T	S	O	H	F	O	D	O	G	I	H	A	V	E

Secret Message

____

____

____

____

____

____

56

Upon Mount Zion. . .

Obadiah 15–17

For the **day of the LORD** is **near** upon all the **heathen**: as **thou hast done**, it shall be done unto **thee**: **thy reward** shall **return** upon thine **own head**. For as **ye have drunk** upon my **holy mountain**, so shall all the heathen **drink continually**, yea, they shall drink, and they shall **swallow down**, and they **shall** be as though they **had not been**. But upon **mount Zion** shall be **deliverance**, and there shall be **holiness**; and the **house** of **Jacob** **shall possess** their **possessions**.

H	H	D	E	L	I	V	E	R	A	N	C	E	E	O
W	A	M	R	A	S	W	A	L	L	O	W	E	P	H
N	D	D	Y	E	D	H	V	E	N	R	H	S	O	O
S	N	E	A	R	T	R	A	T	E	T	S	D	S	L
S	O	O	E	Y	H	U	I	L	S	T	H	E	S	Y
E	T	O	L	D	O	N	R	N	L	T	O	T	E	M
S	B	E	S	J	U	F	T	N	K	W	S	H	S	O
S	E	A	M	A	H	E	T	H	N	S	A	Y	S	U
O	E	N	L	C	A	T	E	H	E	V	S	R	I	N
P	N	L	S	O	S	A	E	N	E	H	O	E	O	T
L	Y	D	R	B	T	A	I	D	T	L	E	W	N	A
L	S	O	T	H	D	L	R	B	O	O	O	A	S	I
A	K	W	E	H	O	U	S	E	O	B	A	R	D	N
H	I	N	A	H	N	H	C	O	N	T	A	D	D	I
S	N	X	X	K	E	M	O	U	N	T	Z	I	O	N

Secret Message

57

Bad Choice

Jonah 1:1–4

Now the **word of the LORD came** unto **Jonah** the **son of Amittai**, saying, **Arise**, go to **Nineveh**, that **great city**, and **cry against it**; for **their wickedness** is come up **before me**. But Jonah **rose** up to **flee unto Tarshish** from the **presence** of the LORD, and went **down to Joppa**; and he **found** a **ship going** to Tarshish: so he **paid the fare** thereof, and **went** down into it, to go with them unto Tarshish from the presence of the LORD. But the LORD sent out a **great wind** into **the sea**, and there was a **mighty tempest** in the sea, so that the ship was **like** to be **broken**.

F	L	E	E	U	N	T	O	H	R	O	W	L	A	M
O	T	H	E	I	R	A	C	N	P	O	Y	I	P	P
U	E	C	N	E	S	E	R	P	E	I	S	K	P	O
N	T	M	I	G	H	T	Y	P	T	L	H	E	O	W
D	I	A	T	I	M	M	A	F	O	N	O	S	J	I
N	E	N	R	L	I	V	G	R	E	D	E	I	O	C
I	N	T	E	S	H	E	A	C	I	I	T	W	T	K
W	Y	H	O	V	H	C	I	T	Y	S	F	H	N	E
T	C	A	M	E	E	I	N	N	I	N	E	E	W	D
A	V	N	E	H	W	H	S	H	N	S	G	G	O	N
E	W	O	R	D	O	F	T	H	E	L	O	R	D	E
R	E	J	N	J	O	N	I	A	K	A	I	E	H	S
G	T	E	M	P	E	S	T	P	O	R	N	A	E	S
P	A	I	D	T	H	E	F	A	R	E	G	T	A	C
H	E	E	M	E	R	O	F	E	B	D	I	N	I	T

Secret Message

____

____

____

____

____

____

58

What God Wants

Micah 6:6–8

Wherewith shall I **come before** the LORD, and **bow myself** before the **high God**? shall I come before him with **burnt offerings**, with **calves** of **a year old**? Will the LORD be **pleased** with **thousands** of **rams**, or with ten thousands of **rivers of oil**? shall I give my **firstborn** for my **transgression**, the **fruit** of my **body** for the **sin of my soul**? He **hath shewed** thee, **O man**, what is **good**; and what doth the LORD **require** of thee, but to do **justly**, and to love **mercy**, and to **walk humbly** with thy God?

C A Y E A R O L D E S A E L P
B A W E R I U Q E R H I L C H
V U L E M V R S E I N U O M I
F C R V A E H N A M O S R P R
I O A N E R R G P S H E D C C
R Y M N T S O C Y A M Y E O W
S S S B B O W M Y S E L F M H
T E T H D F F B L D E B H E E
B J E M R O A F O S T M H B R
O U E U N I B G E D I U R E E
R S I I T L H H P R Y H L F W
N T S A C G E O F J I E S O I
U L N O I S S E R G S N A R T
S Y S H E W E D H A T H G E H
X K L A W T H O U S A N D S X

Secret Message

____

____

____

____

____

____

59

One Scary God

Nahum 1:2–6

<u>God is jealous</u>, and the LORD **revengeth**; the LORD revengeth, and is **furious**; the LORD will **<u>take vengeance</u>** on his **adversaries**, and he **<u>reserveth wrath</u>** for **<u>his enemies</u>**. The LORD is slow to **anger**, and **<u>great in power</u>**, and will not at all **acquit** the **wicked**: the LORD hath his way in the **whirlwind** and in the **storm**, and the **clouds** are the **dust** of his **feet**. He rebuketh the sea, and **<u>maketh it dry</u>**, and **drieth** up all the **rivers**: **Bashan** languisheth, and **Carmel**, and the **flower** of Lebanon languisheth. The **mountains quake** at him, and the hills **melt**, and the earth is burned at his **presence**, yea, the **world**, and all that dwell therein. **<u>Who can stand</u>** before his indignation?

G	R	E	A	T	I	N	P	O	W	E	R	R	W	H
R	A	W	H	I	R	L	W	I	N	D	T	E	D	S
E	I	S	D	N	A	D	C	O	U	H	C	G	G	D
S	Y	N	E	U	P	K	R	S	R	N	M	N	O	U
E	R	I	N	I	E	R	T	I	A	L	C	A	D	O
R	D	A	A	D	M	O	E	E	E	A	D	L	I	L
V	T	T	H	L	R	E	G	S	H	T	I	S	S	C
E	I	N	S	M	P	N	N	R	E	O	H	P	J	A
T	H	U	A	R	E	H	T	E	G	N	E	V	E	R
H	T	O	B	V	E	L	F	H	S	E	C	E	A	M
W	E	M	E	C	Y	V	T	O	F	I	K	E	L	E
R	K	K	A	C	Q	U	I	T	N	I	H	A	O	L
A	A	D	V	E	R	S	A	R	I	E	S	N	U	E
T	M	R	E	W	O	L	F	U	R	I	O	U	S	Q
H	V	E	H	D	N	A	T	S	N	A	C	O	H	W

Secret Message

____

____

____

____

____

____

60

Idols Are Dumb

Habakkuk 2:18–20

What **profiteth** the **graven image** that the **maker** thereof hath graven it; the **molten** image, and a **teacher of lies**, that the maker of his **work trusteth therein**, to make **dumb idols**? **Woe unto him** that **saith** to the **wood, Awake**; to the dumb **stone, Arise, it shall teach**! **Behold**, it is **laid over** with **gold** and **silver**, and there is **no breath** at all in the **midst** of it. But **the LORD** is in his **holy temple**: **let all** the **earth keep silence before** him.

H	T	R	A	E	H	T	O	S	I	L	E	N	C	E
W	M	H	A	N	S	N	E	T	L	O	M	Y	L	C
H	B	A	E	D	P	P	R	T	E	I	R	S	E	D
O	S	E	I	L	F	O	R	E	H	C	A	E	T	T
G	E	M	F	W	O	R	K	O	V	S	T	A	A	R
D	R	H	E	O	B	R	T	B	F	L	O	R	L	U
U	M	A	K	E	R	N	D	H	E	I	I	I	L	S
M	O	K	V	O	U	E	F	T	E	H	T	S	H	T
B	E	G	P	E	R	E	E	P	O	R	O	E	P	E
I	H	E	O	T	N	K	N	H	E	A	E	L	T	T
D	B	W	A	L	A	I	D	O	V	E	R	I	D	H
O	D	O	O	W	D	K	M	K	T	U	K	K	N	T
L	H	C	A	E	T	L	L	A	H	S	T	I	C	I
S	N	O	B	R	E	A	T	H	G	O	N	T	A	A
I	H	O	L	Y	T	E	M	P	L	E	N	X	X	S

Secret Message

____

____

____

____

____

____

61

A God Who Sings

Zephaniah 3:14–17

Sing, O **daughter of Zion**; **shout**, O **Israel**; be **glad** and **rejoice** with all the **heart**, O daughter of **Jerusalem**. The **Lord** hath **taken away** thy **judgments**, he hath **cast out** thine **enemy**: the **king of Israel**, even the LORD, is **in the midst** of thee: thou shalt **not see evil** any more. **In that day** it shall **be said** to Jerusalem, **Fear thou not**: and to Zion, Let not thine **hands** be **slack**. The LORD **thy God** in the midst of thee is **mighty**; he will **save**, he will rejoice over thee **with joy**; he will **rest in his love**, he will joy over thee with singing.

H E A R T O N U O H T R A E F
I K I N G O F I S R A E L J G
N N J E R U S A L E M S W U L
T D O G Y H T H A T A T S D A
H W I T H J O Y T H G I M G D
A G N I S S L O R D Y N R M I
T S D I M E H T N I A H N E R
D A U G H T E R O F Z I O N E
A C K C A L S E S C A S P T J
Y A Y E E I L D V T D L A S O
L S W M N V N E E I L O L K I
N T O W E A A N A T L V O J C
O O N A H N W S H R I E S D E
O U O M E D E A B Y S H O U T
Z T E P H B A N Y I A I H X X

Secret Message

62

Rebuilding Project

Haggai 1:3–8

Then came the **word of the Lord** by **Haggai** the **prophet**, saying, **Is it time** for you, O ye, to dwell in your **cieled houses**, and this house **lie waste**? Now therefore **thus saith** the Lord of hosts; **Consider your ways**. Ye have **sown much**, and **bring** in **little**; ye eat, but ye have **not enough**; ye **drink**, but ye are not **filled** with drink; ye **clothe** you, but there is **none warm**; and he that **earneth wages** earneth wages to put it into a **bag with holes**. Thus saith the Lord of hosts; Consider your ways. **Go up** to the **mountain**, and **bring wood**, and build the house; and I will take **pleasure** in it, and I will be glorified, saith the Lord.

C	B	W	H	O	W	N	I	S	I	T	T	I	M	E
A	O	R	S	G	O	V	O	E	R	H	N	D	O	A
E	B	N	I	R	O	F	J	N	U	S	R	R	U	R
D	R	A	S	N	E	A	H	S	E	O	W	I	H	N
S	I	U	G	I	G	H	S	E	L	W	H	N	N	E
Y	N	H	S	W	D	A	T	E	A	N	A	K	G	T
A	G	O	G	A	I	E	H	O	A	M	G	R	I	H
W	W	U	T	T	E	T	R	R	L	U	G	G	M	W
R	O	E	H	E	F	L	H	L	D	C	A	T	H	A
U	O	E	R	O	N	E	P	H	I	H	I	B	F	G
O	D	U	D	I	G	O	U	P	O	T	L	D	I	E
Y	I	R	N	G	O	F	U	T	H	L	T	E	L	S
M	O	U	N	T	A	I	N	G	T	E	E	L	L	M
W	P	L	C	I	E	L	E	D	H	O	U	S	E	S
P	R	O	P	H	E	T	S	A	W	E	I	L	D	E

Secret Message

____

____

____

____

____

____

63

Comforting Zion

Zechariah 1:14–17

So the **angel** that **communed** with me said unto me, **Cry thou**, saying, Thus saith the **LORD of hosts**; I am **jealous** for **Jerusalem** and for **Zion** with a great jealousy. And I am very **sore displeased** with the **heathen** that are **at ease**: for I was but a little displeased, and they **helped** forward the **affliction**. Therefore thus saith the LORD; I am **returned** to Jerusalem with **mercies**: **my house** shall be **built** in it, saith the LORD of hosts, and a **line** shall be **stretched** forth upon Jerusalem. Cry yet, saying, **Thus saith** the LORD of hosts; My **cities** through **prosperity** shall yet be **spread** abroad; and the LORD shall yet **comfort** Zion, and shall yet **choose** Jerusalem.

E	S	O	O	H	C	J	E	A	L	O	U	S	W	H
S	L	A	T	K	D	E	S	A	E	L	P	S	I	D
A	I	I	N	S	D	R	O	C	O	M	F	O	R	T
E	H	F	N	T	T	U	R	E	E	Y	S	D	E	I
T	E	D	D	E	T	S	H	E	T	P	R	D	T	O
A	L	C	E	P	H	A	O	I	E	T	Z	E	U	E
F	P	I	N	C	H	L	R	H	A	Z	R	H	R	I
F	E	T	U	A	H	E	S	A	F	I	U	C	N	N
L	D	I	M	B	P	M	H	E	G	O	E	T	E	A
I	L	E	M	S	I	E	S	C	H	N	D	E	D	N
C	M	S	O	E	A	U	S	T	S	A	E	R	N	G
T	G	R	C	T	O	E	Y	R	E	S	T	T	O	E
I	P	A	H	H	N	R	D	R	E	R	O	S	A	L
O	M	E	Y	O	C	N	P	M	E	R	C	I	E	S
N	N	M	T	H	U	S	S	A	I	T	H	G	X	X

Secret Message

____

____

____

____

____

____

64

Proving God

Malachi 3:10–12

Bring ye all the **tithes** into the **storehouse**, that there may be **meat** in **mine house**, and **prove me** now herewith, saith the **LORD of hosts**, if I will not open you the **windows** of **heaven**, and **pour** you out a **blessing**, that there shall not be **room enough** to **receive** it. And I will **rebuke** the **devourer** for **your sakes**, and he shall not **destroy** the **fruits** of your **ground**; neither shall your **vine cast** her fruit before **the time** in the **field**, saith the LORD of hosts. And all **nations** shall call you **blessed**: for ye shall be a **delightsome land**, saith the LORD of hosts.

W T W B C H P R O V E M E A S
I A H L A N D E T F W A S T G
N E E E S O D R R S C Y S H R
D M S S T A R U G E A O Y G O
O A U S I I I O E N H U O S O
W R O E T T M V M F R R R I M
S E H D S S R E O A E S T H E
E C E R E L I D S N B A S E N
H E R M U A R L T A U K E A O
T I O C H O I C H H K E D V U
I V T A L P P T G E E S F E G
T E S U O H E N I M V I R N H
N A T I O N S T L H E I I R E
E V E G N I S S E L B R N R S
E E I G R O U N D G B H T E X

Secret Message

65

Prayer

Matthew 6:5–8

And when **thou prayest**, thou **shalt** not be as the **hypocrites** are: for they **love** to pray **standing** in the **synagogues** and in the **corners** of the **streets**, that they may be **seen** of men. **Verily** I say unto you, They have their **reward**. But thou, when thou prayest, **enter** into thy **closet**, and when thou hast **shut** thy **door**, pray to thy Father which is in **secret**; and thy Father which **seeth** in secret shall reward thee **openly**. But when ye pray, use not **vain repetitions**, as the **heathen** do: for they **think** that they shall be **heard** for their much **speaking**. Be not ye **therefore** like unto them: for your **Father knoweth** what things ye have **need** of, **before** ye **ask** him.

S W H T L A H S E D R R S S V
Y E C L O S E T I R E N R E A
N H M A V T T H E A T W E T I
A S T G E O S P E W N T N I N
G S P E A K I N G E E E R R R
O Y L A W R E S P R E R O C E
G L B E F O R E C C I O C O P
U N F U I C N E I N D F S P E
E E T O R A S K U D R E C Y T
S P T H I N K T R E A R N H I
I O S T R E E T S E E E E O T
N H E A T H E N S N H H E O I
N H E O W G N I D N A T S T O
O P T R Y L I R E V A Y A X N
X S H U T N T S E Y A R P F S

Secret Message

____

____

____

____

____

____

66

The Lost Sheep

Matthew 18:10–13

Take **heed** that ye **despise** not one of these **little ones**; for I say unto you, That in **heaven** their **angels** do **always behold** the **face** of my **Father** which is in heaven. For the **Son of man** is **come** to **save** that which was **lost**. How **think** ye? if a man have an **hundred sheep**, and one of them be gone **astray**, doth he not **leave** the ninety and nine, and **goeth** into the **mountains**, and **seeketh** that which is **gone** astray? And if so be that he **find** it, **verily** I **say** unto you, he **rejoiceth** more of that sheep, than of the **ninety and nine** which **went not** astray.

H	U	N	D	R	E	D	S	H	E	E	P	W	H	L
E	A	A	T	H	T	E	C	I	O	J	E	R	O	E
A	N	R	M	O	U	N	T	A	I	N	S	S	E	A
T	G	I	H	D	L	O	H	E	B	E	T	S	T	V
O	E	R	N	I	E	I	S	C	A	N	L	H	L	E
E	L	D	T	D	W	H	T	A	R	E	H	T	A	F
T	S	G	J	S	N	E	E	T	S	V	U	E	S	U
N	S	O	Y	S	E	A	N	E	L	A	D	O	T	C
A	Y	N	A	O	T	E	Y	T	E	E	A	G	C	O
M	A	E	R	H	V	E	K	T	N	H	O	R	Y	M
F	W	I	T	H	I	N	K	E	E	O	M	N	P	E
O	L	E	S	I	P	S	E	D	T	N	T	O	E	R
N	A	T	A	A	N	T	V	L	Y	H	I	E	C	S
O	V	E	R	I	L	Y	A	A	S	S	O	N	A	N
S	S	H	E	E	D	X	S	X	V	D	N	I	F	Y

Secret Message

67

The Greatest Commandment

Matthew 22:34–40

But when the **Pharisees** had **heard** that he had put the **Sadducees** to **silence**, they were **gathered together**. Then one of them, which was a **lawyer**, asked him a **question**, **tempting** him, and **saying**, **Master**, which is the **great commandment** in the **law**? **Jesus** said unto him, Thou **shalt love** the **Lord thy God** with all thy **heart**, and with all thy **soul**, and with all thy **mind**. This is the **first** and great commandment. And the **second** is like unto it, Thou shalt love thy **neighbour** as **thyself**. On these two commandments **hang** all the law and the **prophets**.

T	H	Y	S	E	L	F	T	A	E	R	G	W	H	E
R	U	O	B	H	G	I	E	N	R	N	D	E	W	E
R	D	N	I	M	E	R	T	H	I	O	E	I	S	L
R	A	O	R	E	L	S	I	T	G	T	E	S	E	U
N	S	I	E	C	A	T	P	Y	H	A	N	G	M	O
P	A	T	H	E	D	M	H	E	C	N	E	L	I	S
W	Y	S	T	H	E	T	A	J	E	S	U	S	E	A
S	I	E	E	T	D	R	R	E	N	T	H	C	E	D
T	N	U	G	R	T	S	I	Y	W	E	O	R	E	D
E	G	Q	O	E	G	H	S	I	D	N	V	E	N	U
H	T	L	T	T	H	A	E	W	D	R	E	T	E	C
P	N	C	E	S	O	L	E	A	M	M	A	A	N	E
O	D	M	V	A	E	T	S	L	A	W	Y	E	R	E
R	N	C	O	M	M	A	N	D	M	E	N	T	H	S
P	T	S	L	X	X	D	E	R	E	H	T	A	G	N

Secret Message

____

____

____

____

____

____

68

The Resurrection

Matthew 28:5–10

I know that ye **seek** Jesus, which was **crucified**. He is not here: for he is **risen**. . . . **Come**, see the **place** where the **Lord** lay. And go **quickly**, and tell his **disciples** that he is risen from the dead; and, **behold**, he **goeth** before you into **Galilee**; there shall ye see him: lo, I have told you. And they **departed** quickly from the **sepulchre** with **fear** and **great joy**; and did **run** to bring his disciples **word**. And as they went to **tell** his disciples, behold, Jesus met them, saying, **All hail**. And they came and held him by the **feet**, and **worshipped** him. Then said **Jesus** unto them, Be not **afraid**: go tell my **brethren** that they go into Galilee, and there shall they see me.

N	W	W	H	E	N	N	Q	U	I	C	K	L	Y	G
T	U	O	H	E	E	A	N	G	A	E	M	O	C	O
E	L	R	O	S	D	F	D	T	H	F	E	L	R	E
E	S	D	I	O	R	E	E	D	R	O	R	L	U	T
L	E	R	H	C	L	U	P	E	S	E	L	A	C	H
D	E	L	B	A	C	K	P	A	T	O	H	E	I	S
T	K	O	I	N	E	W	I	H	R	Y	D	I	F	D
L	D	T	Y	L	H	E	H	D	N	T	G	R	I	L
I	A	V	O	E	A	K	S	E	E	E	E	P	E	O
A	E	R	J	S	S	G	R	H	A	K	E	D	D	H
H	T	A	T	N	D	H	O	B	E	S	L	E	C	E
L	O	E	A	M	T	E	W	L	C	I	U	L	K	B
L	E	D	E	E	E	A	D	R	A	E	F	S	E	M
A	E	N	R	F	X	X	G	J	L	Y	C	E	E	T
F	N	B	G	D	I	S	C	I	P	L	E	S	Y	J

Secret Message

____

____

____

____

____

____

69

Crowds Follow Jesus

Mark 3:7–12

But **Jesus withdrew** himself with his **disciples** to the **sea**: and a **great multitude** from **Galilee followed** him, and from **Judaea**, and from **Jerusalem**, and from **Idumaea**, and from beyond **Jordan**; and they about **Tyre** and **Sidon**, a great multitude, when they had heard what great things he did, came unto him. And he spake to his disciples, that a **small ship** should **wait** on him because of the multitude, lest they should **throng** him. For he had **healed** many; **insomuch** that they **pressed** upon him for to **touch** him, as many as had **plagues**. And **unclean spirits**, when they saw him, fell down before him, and **cried**, saying, Thou art the **Son of God**. And he **straitly** charged them that they should not make him **known**.

W	H	Y	J	E	R	U	S	A	L	E	M	P	Y	C
S	O	L	O	E	U	L	D	C	J	E	S	L	P	E
M	F	T	R	U	S	S	N	R	D	O	L	A	R	D
A	O	I	D	O	P	U	N	I	G	E	R	G	E	U
L	L	A	A	E	I	N	S	E	A	T	N	U	S	T
L	L	R	N	E	R	C	R	D	A	O	A	E	S	I
S	O	T	T	O	I	W	N	O	R	P	E	S	E	T
H	W	S	E	P	T	N	L	H	E	A	L	E	D	L
I	E	E	L	Y	S	A	T	Y	R	E	C	F	O	U
P	D	E	R	T	T	E	R	H	E	A	N	K	G	M
H	S	E	I	D	U	M	A	E	A	D	U	N	F	T
A	L	A	E	D	H	A	M	A	N	U	W	O	O	A
I	W	H	C	U	O	T	T	H	L	J	E	W	N	E
P	R	O	S	G	A	L	I	L	E	E	Y	N	O	R
I	N	S	O	M	U	C	H	W	N	O	D	I	S	G

Secret Message

____

70

The Day or Hour

Mark 13:32–37

But of that **day** and that **hour** knoweth no **man**, no, not the **angels** which are in **heaven**, neither the **Son**, but the **Father**. Take ye **heed**, **watch** and **pray**: for ye know not when the **time** is. For the Son of Man is as a man taking a far **journey**, who left his **house**, and gave **authority** to his **servants**, and to every man his **work**, and **commanded** the **porter** to watch. Watch ye therefore: for ye know not when the **master** of the house **cometh**, at **even**, or at **midnight**, or at the **cockcrowing**, or in the **morning**: **Lest** coming **suddenly** he find you **sleeping**. And what I say unto you I say unto all, Watch.

M W H S A T D O E R E T S A M
I S H O U S E T M H E L L O R
D D P N R V K O O M E E Y A I
N R S E E W R I L G M L L U N
I E C N E N O Y N I V C N T C
G T E O I S W A T C H O E H O
H R R N C P T D E E H M D O M
T O G A S K S N A W A E D R M
Y P R E V E C N A T H T U I A
O R U E G H H R E V A H S T N
V A U E H N A J O U R N E Y D
N Y D O E T N A R W T E H W E
I L L X H E A V E N I X S Q D
M I L E S T M F J I M N P H O
A Y L P R S L E E P I N G T Y

Secret Message

71

Good News

Mark 16:15–20

And he said unto them, **Go** ye into all the **world**, and **preach** the **gospel** to every **creature**. He that **believeth** and is **baptized** shall be **saved**; but he that believeth not shall be **damned**. And these **signs** shall **follow** them that believe; In my name shall they cast out **devils**; they shall speak with **new tongues**; they shall take up **serpents**; and if they **drink** any **deadly thing**, it shall not **hurt** them; they shall lay **hands** on the **sick**, and they shall **recover**. So then after the **Lord** had **spoken** unto them, he was **received** up into **heaven**, and sat on the **right hand** of **God**. And they went **forth**, and preached **every where**.

B	W	H	Y	D	S	E	U	G	N	O	T	W	E	N
A	I	D	J	E	E	R	E	V	O	C	E	R	S	S
P	N	U	W	O	R	L	D	S	R	E	B	A	E	U
T	E	G	O	S	P	E	L	K	E	H	V	T	R	H
I	K	E	D	B	E	L	I	E	V	E	T	H	E	I
Z	O	D	A	M	N	E	D	R	D	A	S	E	H	C
E	P	I	P	L	T	E	S	I	B	V	E	R	W	F
D	S	I	G	N	S	O	R	G	E	E	H	U	Y	E
T	O	W	O	L	L	O	F	H	L	N	D	T	R	S
P	D	T	H	G	N	I	H	T	Y	L	D	A	E	D
E	R	R	M	T	O	P	R	H	U	R	T	E	V	N
E	A	E	I	L	C	H	T	A	H	E	G	R	E	A
O	S	D	A	N	O	P	E	N	L	X	X	C	E	H
L	O	S	I	C	K	R	X	D	E	V	I	L	S	X
G	F	O	R	T	H	O	D	E	V	I	E	C	E	R

Secret Message

____

____

____

____

____

____

72

Mary's Song

Luke 1:46–54

My **soul** doth **magnify** the **Lord**, and my **spirit** hath **rejoiced** in **God** my **Saviour**. For he hath **regarded** the **low estate** of his **handmaiden**: for, behold, from henceforth all **generations** shall call me **blessed**. For he that is **mighty** hath done to me **great things**; and **holy** is his **name**. And his **mercy** is on them that **fear** him from generation to generation. He hath shewed **strength** with his arm; he hath **scattered** the **proud** in the imagination of their **hearts**. He hath put down the mighty from their seats, and **exalted** them of low degree. He hath **filled** the **hungry** with good things; and the **rich** he hath sent **empty** away. He hath **helped** his servant **Israel**, in remembrance of his mercy.

S	C	A	T	T	E	R	E	D	Y	T	H	G	I	M
G	O	W	H	D	E	T	L	A	X	E	O	T	O	P
N	L	U	L	O	R	D	D	S	M	H	C	I	R	A
I	R	Y	L	O	W	E	S	T	A	T	E	O	T	H
H	O	L	Y	A	I	T	J	N	H	V	U	E	M	G
T	R	R	E	T	S	L	D	O	G	D	I	E	A	E
T	T	!	V	I	R	M	B	E	I	E	R	O	H	N
A	L	I	S	R	A	A	L	B	E	C	T	R	U	E
E	M	H	W	I	E	A	E	S	Y	E	E	X	N	R
R	A	D	D	P	L	S	S	P	E	G	Y	D	G	A
G	G	E	C	S	T	T	S	I	A	N	T	G	R	T
A	N	L	C	R	H	R	E	R	I	L	P	D	Y	I
X	I	L	X	A	A	A	D	D	E	L	M	A	R	O
C	F	I	S	T	R	E	N	G	T	H	E	M	A	N
S	Y	F	S	H	D	H	F	D	E	P	L	E	H	S

Secret Message

____

____

____

____

____

____

73

Jesus' Birth

Luke 2:4–7

And **Joseph** also went up from **Galilee**, out of the city of **Nazareth**, into **Judaea**, unto the **city of David**, which is called **Bethlehem**; (because he was of the **house** and **lineage** of David:) To be **taxed** with **Mary** his espoused **wife**, being great **with child**. And so it was, that, while they were there, the **days** were **accomplished** that she should be **delivered**. And she brought forth her **firstborn son**, and **wrapped** him in **swaddling clothes**, and **laid** him in a **manger**; because there was no **room** for them in the **inn**.

A	W	H	S	A	T	R	E	G	N	A	M	W	A	S
C	M	A	W	R	H	Y	G	D	E	P	P	A	R	W
C	S	R	A	E	P	A	A	C	T	I	S	O	N	D
O	F	W	D	M	E	H	E	L	H	T	E	B	H	E
M	I	E	D	N	S	T	N	H	E	E	H	A	N	R
P	R	D	L	G	O	E	I	W	L	L	T	F	I	E
L	S	L	I	R	J	S	L	I	T	R	O	O	M	V
I	T	I	N	N	L	N	L	F	A	A	L	P	P	I
S	B	H	G	E	A	A	R	E	E	E	C	D	T	L
H	O	C	O	G	G	Z	I	I	D	A	Y	S	V	E
E	R	H	E	Y	R	A	M	D	H	D	E	R	N	D
D	N	T	E	W	S	R	A	H	O	U	S	E	E	B
O	U	I	T	J	E	E	S	U	S	J	B	X	I	R
T	H	W	X	C	I	T	Y	O	F	D	A	V	I	D
S	O	N	X	C	C	H	A	R	D	T	O	N	X	B

Secret Message

____

____

____

____

____

____

74

Shepherds in the Field

Luke 2:8–12

And there were in the same **country shepherds abiding** in the **field**, keeping **watch** over their **flock** by **night**. And, **lo**, the **angel of the Lord** came **upon** them, and the **glory** of the Lord **shone** round **about** them: and they were **sore afraid**. And the angel said unto them, **Fear not**: for, **behold**, I bring you good **tidings** of great **joy**, which shall be to **all people**. For unto you is **born** this day in the **city** of **David** a **Saviour**, which is **Christ** the **Lord**. And this shall be a **sign** unto you; Ye shall find the **babe** wrapped in swaddling clothes, **lying** in a **manger**.

Y	T	I	D	I	N	G	S	W	H	S	I	G	N	D
N	R	O	B	D	A	T	D	A	B	O	U	T	I	D
H	C	T	A	W	R	I	R	D	T	H	E	V	G	S
H	E	B	N	P	H	O	O	E	R	D	A	S	H	D
A	O	E	A	U	F	T	L	E	R	D	C	I	T	Y
L	K	H	R	G	O	T	E	R	H	E	E	Y	F	O
L	C	O	S	N	U	C	H	U	N	D	G	N	F	M
P	O	L	D	I	A	R	T	O	S	H	O	N	E	Y
E	L	D	R	Y	J	O	F	I	S	P	E	P	A	H
O	F	I	E	L	D	A	O	V	U	N	D	T	R	M
P	H	E	H	B	A	B	L	A	B	I	D	I	N	G
L	Y	J	P	E	S	U	E	S	S	O	L	I	O	L
E	N	Y	E	B	A	B	G	C	H	R	I	S	T	O
T	O	H	H	E	M	A	N	N	G	E	R	X	X	R
J	T	I	S	O	R	E	A	F	R	A	I	D	O	Y

Secret Message

____

____

____

____

____

____

75

Jesus Calms the Storm

Luke 8:22–25

[Jesus] went into a **ship** with his **disciples**: and he said unto them, Let us go over unto the other **side** of the **lake**. And they **launched** forth. But as they **sailed** he <u>**fell asleep**</u>: and there came down a <u>**storm of wind**</u> on the lake; and they were filled with **water**, and were in **jeopardy**. And they came to him, and **awoke** him, saying, **Master**, master, we **perish**. Then he **arose**, and **rebuked** the **wind** and the **raging** of the water: and they **ceased**, and there was a **calm**. And he said unto them, Where is your **faith**? And they being **afraid** wondered, saying one to another, What **manner** of man is this! for he **commandeth** even the winds and water, and they **obey** him.

C O M M A N D E T H W H A T A
C S O U N T R Y G W E D N I W
R E I J E P R S U N S A N D O
T L H D E D E P I S I C I B K
M A S T E R T E P D L G E Y E
E U R S T R A R L E A Y A D V
E N E O L I W I N S G T O R W
A C B H S E N S J A A E K A L
F H U E S E U H S E C L A P L
R E K M I D N G O C F T L O H
A D E E E S D I S C I P L E S
I T D L O R M T H A O O K J F
D P I L A C E X I L X E O K C
E A S H T I A F P M A N N E R
S T O R M O F W I N D X M O C

Secret Message

____

76

Raising Lazarus

John 11:41–44

Then they **took** away the **stone** from the **place** where the **dead** was **laid**. And **Jesus lifted** up his **eyes**, and said, **Father**, I **thank** thee that thou hast heard me. And I knew that thou **hearest** me **always**: but because of the **people** which **stand** by I said it, that they may **believe** that thou hast **sent** me. And when he thus had **spoken**, he **cried** with a loud **voice**, **Lazarus**, <u>**come forth**</u>. And he that was dead came forth, bound **hand** and **foot** with **graveclothes**: and his face was **bound** about with a **napkin**. Jesus saith unto them, <u>**Loose him**</u>, and let him go.

E C I O V A S D E A D F T S G

E Y P F O O T R J M E S Y T R

L U E S R N O A I I S A E A A

I D O S E L N H A Z W A R N V

F U P S U S E F R L O M C D E

T T L H E S D F A T H E R E C

E A E D O W E H A N T D I A L

D W A O S T H J E R E E E S O

B E L I E V E P P O N K D S T

N E S U R A Z A L O D F O M H

I A N Y O K F T A H N E J P E

K K E W N S X X C A U M E Y S

P O V A S C O M E F O R T H A

A O H V O I C N D E B H A N D

N T O N A T S E R A E H C N G

Secret Message

77

Paul Sees the Light

Acts 9:3–7

And as he **journeyed**, **he came** near **Damascus**: and **suddenly** there **shined round** about him a **light** from **heaven**: And **he fell** to the **earth**, and **heard** a **voice saying** unto him, **Saul**, Saul, why **persecutest** thou me? And he said, Who **art thou**, **Lord**? And the Lord said, I am **Jesus** whom thou persecutest: it is **hard for thee to kick against** the **pricks**. And he **trembling** and **astonished** said, Lord, what wilt thou have **me to do**? And the Lord said unto him, **Arise**, and **go into the city**, and it **shall** be **told thee** what thou must do. And the **men which** journeyed with **him stood speechless**, **hearing** a voice, but **seeing** no man.

J K G N I E E S T H G I L W N
G O I N T O T H E C I T Y H E
Y S U C I S D F A A D I D S V
A U A R K R E R S R O U N D A
H H S U N L A T O L D T H E E
I C U S L E O E U L T F S S H
M I S U L N Y J H C R S O I S
S H E C I O V E O U E R N R K
T W J S H A L L D L M S A A C
O N H A D E N I H S B E R M I
O E E M E M A C E H L Y T E R
D M A A T H E E T O I T T T P
O D R D A E S A Y I N G H O M
A T D S P T S N I A G A O D C
H U S S U D D E N L Y X U O X

Secret Message

78

Who Can Be against Us?

Romans 8:35–39

Who **shall separate** us from the love of **Christ**? shall **tribulation**, or **distress**, or **persecution**, or **famine**, or **nakedness**, or **peril**, or **sword**? As it is **written**, For thy sake we are **killed** all the day long; we are **accounted** as **sheep** for the **slaughter**. Nay, in all these things we are more than **conquerors through** him that **loved** us. For I am **persuaded**, that **neither death**, nor life, nor **angels**, nor **principalities**, nor **powers**, nor things **present**, nor things to come, nor **height**, nor **depth**, nor any other **creature**, shall be able to separate us from the **love of God**, which is in Christ **Jesus** our **Lord**.

S S C W S L A U G H T E R H J
F E R O E R S S E R T S I D E
L A I E N E D I I A N G E L S
D O M T W Q P B R A D A R L U
N P R I I O U A U O T E L L S
N O R D N L P E G H H I H A C
A T I E A E A F R T P E E H S
K H N T S T O P I O I E R S N
E R I N U E D E I G R I U D T
D O K U V C N E H C S S T O G
N U I O O A E T V T N F A T H
E G L C E R V S I O S I E I T
S H L C T S W O R D L I R E P
S I E A W R I T T E N N C P E
G R D E D A U S R E P O M E D

Secret Message

____

____

____

____

____

____

79

Embrace Hope

Romans 15:13–16

Now the God of **hope** fill you with all joy and **peace** in **believing**, that ye may **abound** in hope, **through** the **power** of the **Holy Ghost**. And I **myself** also am **persuaded** of you, my **brethren**, that ye also are **full** of **goodness**, **filled** with all **knowledge**, able also to **admonish** one **another**. **Nevertheless**, brethren, I **have written** the **more boldly** unto you in some sort, as **putting** you in mind, because of the **grace** that is **given** to me of God, that I **should** be the minister of **Jesus Christ** to the **Gentiles**, **ministering** the **gospel** of God, that the **offering** up of the Gentiles **might** be **acceptable**, being **sanctified** by the Holy Ghost.

S W H A A D M O N I S H H R M
T S I R H C T F W E O A E I S
G N E G R A C E L R V H N H S
O S E L I T N E G E T I O K E
S A D T E R O M P O S U G D N
P B R E T H R E N T L Y I B D
E O D G I I T A E D A P M E O
L U W D O F R R T D E B D L O
E N R E G F I W E A E A L I G
T D P L R N F T C V U L Y E L
G O S W G T I E C S E I L V L
H G U O R H T T R N U N D I U
O S S N F G O E T I A U L N F
S L E K F I P L I U N S O G L
T L J F O M R P Y A P G B U L

Secret Message

____

____

____

____

____

____

80

First Importance

1 Corinthians 15:3–8

For I **delivered** unto you **first** of all that which I also **received**, how that **Christ died for our sins according** to the **scriptures**; and that **he was buried**, and that **he rose again** the **third day** according to the scriptures: and that he **was seen** of **Cephas, then** of the **twelve**: After that, he was seen of **above five hundred brethren** at **once**; of **whom** the **greater part remain** unto this **present**, but **some** are **fallen asleep**. After that, he was seen of **James**; then **of all the apostles**. And last of all he was seen of me also, as of **one born** out of **due time**.

D N E L L A F W H J A M E S P
E E H T L L A F O F S Y O R D
I R R O E E E S O G L P E H A
R H U D L M M R N E E S S A W
U T S D N H O I O N E B O R N
B E S C E U D S T N P A T Y H
S R E W R R H R T E C W H A S
E B A S O I E E E D U E I R A
L S I C T T P V V V I D R E G
T N C H A C L T I I O E D C A
S A E E E E H L U L F B D E I
O T R P W P A R T R E M A I N
P G H T E T S R I F E D Y V A
A A S E T H E R O S E S O E F
S T H E N A P O S T T L E D S

Secret Message

____

____

____

____

____

____

81

Herald of Hope

2 Corinthians 5:17–20

Therefore if any man **be in Christ**, he is a new **creature**: old **things are passed away**; **behold**, **all things** are **become new**. And all things **are of** God, who hath **reconciled us** to **himself** by **Jesus** Christ, and hath **given** to us the **ministry** of **reconciliation**; to wit, that God was in Christ, **reconciling** the **world** unto himself, not **imputing their trespasses** unto **them**; and hath **committed** unto us the word of reconciliation. Now then we are **ambassadors** for Christ, as **though** God did **beseech** you by us: we **pray you** in **Christ's stead**, be ye reconciled to God.

R	W	T	H	I	N	G	S	A	R	E	H	R	W	O
R	E	E	S	P	O	U	R	P	T	E	E	E	T	S
F	R	C	D	I	S	T	R	O	P	C	N	C	R	T
A	O	R	O	E	R	A	U	L	O	E	A	O	E	S
B	F	E	J	N	Y	H	O	N	M	U	D	N	S	I
T	E	A	R	Y	C	B	C	O	T	A	L	C	P	R
T	R	T	O	A	E	I	C	N	S	T	R	I	A	H
H	E	U	H	S	L	E	L	S	I	H	O	L	S	C
O	H	R	E	E	B	F	A	I	H	E	W	I	S	E
U	T	E	D	N	I	B	L	C	N	M	B	A	E	D
G	C	U	E	O	M	R	R	E	I	G	N	T	S	A
H	S	V	S	A	T	Y	R	T	S	I	N	I	M	E
H	I	I	S	A	D	E	T	T	I	M	M	O	C	T
G	N	Y	A	W	A	A	L	L	T	H	I	N	G	S
S	I	M	P	U	T	I	N	G	D	L	O	H	E	B

Secret Message

____

____

____

____

____

____

82

Abundant Harvest

Galatians 6:6–10

Let him that is **taught** in the **word communicate** unto him that **teacheth** in all good **things**. **Be not deceived**; **God is not mocked**: for **whatsoever a man soweth**, that **shall he also** reap. For he that soweth to **his flesh** shall of the **flesh reap corruption**; but he that soweth to the **Spirit** shall of the Spirit **reap life everlasting**. And let us not be **weary** in **well doing**: for in due **season** we shall reap, if we **faint not**. As we have therefore **opportunity**, let us **do good** unto **all men**, **especially** unto **them** who are of the **household of faith**.

W	A	H	A	L	L	M	E	N	W	E	A	R	Y	O
S	M	S	G	N	I	H	T	E	E	M	N	S	P	D
P	A	E	R	H	S	E	L	F	I	O	H	R	E	L
H	N	H	T	E	R	L	I	H	I	C	T	E	S	O
T	T	E	E	T	V	S	S	T	C	K	E	A	P	H
S	L	I	V	A	A	E	P	R	I	E	W	P	E	E
G	E	E	A	E	L	U	O	I	S	D	O	L	C	S
H	N	A	D	F	R	S	G	S	R	R	S	I	I	U
T	O	I	S	R	F	L	O	H	T	I	U	F	A	O
E	T	I	O	O	O	O	A	U	T	A	T	E	L	H
H	H	C	A	D	N	W	N	S	B	S	H	A	L	L
C	O	M	M	U	N	I	C	A	T	E	B	W	Y	A
A	B	E	N	O	T	D	E	C	E	I	V	E	D	F
E	H	A	T	Y	H	G	O	D	I	S	N	O	T	E
T	O	N	T	N	I	A	F	R	D	O	O	G	O	D

Secret Message

____

____

____

____

____

____

83

Rich in Mercy

Ephesians 2:6–10

And hath **raised us** up **together**, and **made us** sit together in **heavenly places** in **Christ Jesus**: That in the **ages to come he might** shew the **exceeding riches** of his grace in his **kindness toward** us **through** Christ Jesus. **For by grace are ye saved** through **faith**; and **that not of yourselves**: **it is the gift of God**: not of **works**, lest any man **should boast**. For we are his **workmanship**, **created** in Christ Jesus unto **good** works, **which** God hath **before ordained** that we should **walk** in **them**.

W H C I H W H E D A H T I A F
D E N I A D R O R T H G I M T
N S U L M C G H E A V E N L Y
B U K Y H F O R T R E B E R B
O D D R O T W N E O O C E S R
A E I T S U O J X H W F A C O
S S F E C T R E C M T A E R F
T I G W O R K S E R A E R B G
G A I F M B M U E P D D G D E
E R S F E A A S D L E O E O H
D L U O H S N I I A V T O U T
R I C H E S S T N C A E T G S
T H R O U G H H G E S H S H I
S S E N D N I K R S E O P E T
A N D B A P P C T M Y I S M I

Secret Message

84

Rejoice Evermore

Philippians 4:4–8

Rejoice in the Lord **always**: and again I say, Rejoice. Let your **moderation** be **known** unto all men. The **Lord** is at hand. Be **careful** for **nothing**; but in every thing by **prayer** and **supplication** with **thanksgiving** let your **requests** be made known unto God. And the **peace** of God, which **passeth** all **understanding**, shall keep your **hearts** and **minds through Christ Jesus. Finally, brethren, whatsoever things** are **true**, whatsoever things are **honest**, whatsoever things are **just**, whatsoever things are **pure**, whatsoever things are **lovely**, whatsoever things are of **good report**; if there be any **virtue**, and if there be any **praise**, **think** on these things.

W	T	H	A	C	H	R	I	S	T	J	P	Y	N	T
T	P	R	A	I	S	E	Y	W	U	M	L	U	E	O
H	N	M	O	W	H	A	T	S	O	E	V	E	R	A
R	T	O	N	P	W	P	T	D	V	G	N	R	H	E
O	S	H	I	L	E	F	E	O	H	O	W	E	T	R
U	D	A	A	T	I	R	L	Y	T	O	O	Q	E	E
G	N	I	D	N	A	T	S	R	E	D	N	U	R	V
H	I	D	A	T	K	C	H	C	S	U	K	E	B	I
B	M	L	I	Y	J	S	I	E	S	T	R	S	S	R
H	L	O	E	E	R	O	G	L	A	G	I	T	K	T
Y	N	V	S	P	J	E	R	I	P	R	N	S	N	U
S	L	U	F	E	R	A	C	D	V	P	T	I	I	E
I	S	P	R	A	Y	E	R	D	R	I	U	S	H	E
N	E	A	R	C	G	N	I	H	T	O	N	S	T	T
P	Y	N	A	E	B	H	I	L	I	P	L	G	P	I

Secret Message

85

Clothed with Kindness

Colossians 3:11–15

Where there is **neither Greek** nor Jew, circumcision nor **uncircumcision, Barbarian, Scythian, bond** nor **free**: but **Christ** is all, and in all. Put on therefore, as the **elect** of God, **holy** and **beloved, bowels** of **mercies, kindness, humbleness** of mind, **meekness, longsuffering**; **forbearing** one **another**, and **forgiving** one another, if any man have a **quarrel** against any: even as Christ **forgave** you, so also do ye. And above all these **things** put on **charity**, which is the bond of **perfectness**. And let the **peace** of God **rule** in **your hearts**, to the which also ye are **called** in one **body**; and be ye **thankful**.

S	D	U	S	C	Y	T	H	I	A	N	S	S	P	E
G	A	N	O	T	H	E	R	P	E	A	S	G	C	H
P	N	C	O	G	R	R	E	H	T	I	E	N	S	F
H	E	I	O	B	R	A	U	E	H	R	N	I	L	O
E	D	R	R	B	C	E	E	M	A	A	K	H	E	R
W	L	C	F	E	I	R	E	H	N	B	E	T	H	G
T	C	U	O	E	F	R	H	K	K	R	E	U	N	A
G	H	M	R	Q	C	F	B	R	F	A	M	I	A	V
R	R	C	B	I	U	T	U	E	U	B	V	C	C	E
U	I	I	E	E	S	A	N	S	L	I	E	B	A	A
O	S	S	A	W	H	E	R	E	G	O	H	O	L	Y
Y	T	I	R	A	H	C	N	R	S	N	V	W	L	D
S	O	O	I	N	E	E	O	D	E	S	O	E	E	O
W	I	N	N	T	S	F	T	C	E	L	E	L	D	B
H	W	H	G	S	S	E	N	D	N	I	K	S	A	T

Secret Message

86

Rest Assured

1 Thessalonians 4:15–17

For **this we say unto you by the word** of the Lord, **that** we **which** are **alive and remain** unto the **coming** of the Lord **shall not prevent them** which **are asleep**. For the Lord **himself** shall **descend from heaven** with a **shout**, with the **voice** of the **archangel**, and with the **trump of God**: and the **dead** in **Christ** shall **rise first**: **Then** we which **are alive** and remain shall be **caught up together** with them **in the clouds**, to **meet** the Lord **in the air**: and so shall we ever be **with the Lord**.

N	D	E	A	D	W	H	H	C	I	H	W	O	S	T
E	I	R	H	O	R	I	S	E	F	I	R	S	T	U
U	N	A	O	C	A	U	G	H	T	U	P	T	S	O
E	T	I	M	W	N	W	C	H	T	M	E	H	T	H
R	H	R	T	E	E	M	T	O	N	L	L	A	H	S
I	E	H	U	S	R	H	E	S	M	U	S	T	P	L
A	C	H	A	M	E	D	T	D	O	I	T	H	E	N
E	L	Y	T	L	P	A	N	Y	N	L	N	G	E	F
H	O	P	O	E	H	O	O	A	B	E	N	G	L	R
T	U	R	R	E	G	T	F	O	E	A	C	E	S	O
N	D	N	A	E	N	O	E	G	H	V	S	S	A	M
I	S	V	I	U	V	C	T	C	O	M	I	A	E	W
A	E	V	I	L	A	E	R	A	I	D	H	L	R	D
N	S	A	S	S	A	A	N	H	U	O	T	L	A	T
E	D	B	C	H	R	I	S	T	Y	A	V	M	O	B

Secret Message

____

____

____

____

____

____

87

God Is Just

2 Thessalonians 1:5–9

Which is a **manifest token** of the **righteous judgment** of God, that ye may be **counted worthy** of the **kingdom** of God, for which ye also **suffer**: **Seeing** it is a righteous **thing** with God to **recompense tribulation** to them that trouble you; and to you who are **troubled** rest with us, when the **Lord Jesus shall** be **revealed** from **heaven** with his **mighty angels**, in **flaming** fire **taking vengeance** on them that **know** not God, and that **obey** not the **gospel** of our Lord Jesus **Christ**: who shall be **punished** with **everlasting destruction** from the **presence** of the Lord, and from the **glory** of his **power**.

E	W	G	L	O	R	Y	R	F	R	E	W	O	P	H
A	V	N	B	T	H	D	D	E	L	B	U	O	R	T
S	A	E	E	T	O	R	C	L	F	A	E	S	E	H
U	Y	N	R	V	O	N	R	L	P	F	M	A	S	I
S	U	O	G	L	A	T	I	A	D	D	U	I	E	N
E	W	L	S	E	A	E	G	H	E	A	Y	S	N	G
J	S	A	G	K	L	S	H	S	H	T	B	O	C	G
M	A	N	I	F	E	S	T	U	S	N	T	C	E	T
H	E	N	E	E	O	R	E	I	I	E	T	H	G	K
V	G	S	I	P	U	E	O	W	N	M	O	R	O	I
W	O	N	K	C	M	H	U	O	U	G	K	I	S	N
W	G	O	T	U	L	O	S	D	P	D	E	S	P	G
N	M	I	G	H	T	Y	C	C	O	U	N	T	E	D
O	O	D	E	L	A	E	V	E	R	J	T	W	L	O
N	O	I	T	A	L	U	B	I	R	T	O	R	K	M

Secret Message

____

____

____

____

____

____

88

Remain Resolute

1 Timothy 6:11–14

But thou, O man of God, **flee** these **things**; and **follow** after **righteousness, godliness, faith, love, patience, meekness. Fight** the **good** fight of faith, lay **hold** on **eternal life**, whereunto thou art also **called**, and hast professed a good **profession** before many **witnesses**. I give thee **charge** in the **sight** of God, who **quickeneth** all things, and before **Christ Jesus**, who before **Pontius Pilate witnessed** a good **confession**; that thou **keep** this **commandment without spot, unrebukable**, until the **appearing** of our **Lord** Jesus Christ.

I	N	G	N	I	R	A	E	P	P	A	E	W	J	H
A	T	P	A	T	I	E	N	C	E	W	T	A	E	Y
E	V	O	L	C	G	O	D	L	I	N	E	S	S	D
F	L	E	E	H	H	O	L	D	O	P	R	I	U	E
C	S	B	T	D	T	A	P	I	R	H	N	G	S	A
O	O	I	A	H	E	F	R	O	F	T	A	H	U	S
N	A	M	I	K	O	L	F	G	S	E	L	T	S	L
F	C	N	M	L	U	E	L	E	E	N	C	E	U	A
E	G	H	L	A	S	B	S	A	L	E	N	T	I	L
S	T	O	R	S	N	S	E	T	C	K	D	U	T	T
S	W	A	I	I	E	D	O	R	E	C	I	O	N	T
I	M	O	L	N	S	P	M	E	N	I	O	H	O	H
O	N	O	T	I	S	T	M	E	T	U	H	T	P	G
N	R	I	Y	H	P	E	E	K	N	Q	I	I	S	I
D	W	S	O	D	E	S	S	E	N	T	I	W	N	F

Secret Message

____

____

____

____

____

____

89

A Life of Faith

2 Timothy 4:5–8

But **watch** thou in all **things**, **endure afflictions**, do the **work** of an **evangelist**, make full **proof** of thy **ministry**. For **I am now ready** to be **offered**, and the **time** of my **departure is at hand**. I have **fought** a **good fight**, I have **finished my course**, I have **kept the faith**: **Henceforth** there is **laid up** for me a **crown** of **righteousness**, which the **Lord**, the righteous **judge**, **shall give me at that day**: and **not to me only**, but unto all them also that **love** his **appearing**.

W	W	L	W	H	E	D	N	A	H	T	A	S	I	S
G	O	O	D	A	J	N	A	T	E	D	P	I	D	S
T	P	R	N	U	T	A	D	M	U	K	P	L	Y	E
A	H	D	D	M	Y	C	O	U	R	S	E	D	T	N
T	F	G	E	L	A	T	H	O	R	L	A	L	T	S
T	E	F	U	I	T	I	W	M	A	E	R	D	H	U
H	S	G	L	O	L	O	T	I	R	E	I	E	H	O
A	Y	I	N	I	F	L	D	T	R	O	N	H	Y	E
T	L	V	L	E	C	U	A	U	T	C	G	S	R	T
D	I	E	K	E	P	T	T	H	E	F	A	I	T	H
A	N	M	T	N	G	R	I	F	S	Y	T	N	S	G
Y	W	E	E	O	A	N	O	O	L	M	H	I	I	I
F	O	O	R	P	G	R	A	N	N	A	G	F	N	R
N	R	D	E	S	T	L	O	V	E	S	I	E	I	S
P	C	D	I	H	S	D	E	R	E	F	F	O	M	E

Secret Message

____

____

____

____

____

____

90

Worthy Standard

2 Timothy 3:14–17

But **continue thou** in the **things which** thou hast **learned** and hast **been assured** of, **knowing** of **whom** thou hast learned **them**; and that from a **child** thou hast **known** the **holy scriptures**, which are able to **make** thee **wise** unto **salvation through faith** which is in **Christ Jesus**. All scripture is **given** by **inspiration** of God, and is **profitable** for **doctrine**, for **reproof**, for **correction**, for **instruction** in **righteousness**: that the man of God may be **perfect**, **thoroughly furnished** unto all **good works.**

S	A	L	V	A	T	I	O	N	E	R	T	H	U	E
U	S	F	H	H	L	E	A	R	N	E	D	A	O	T
S	I	E	I	C	T	H	E	P	I	P	O	R	H	H
E	O	N	N	O	I	T	C	E	R	R	O	C	T	O
J	G	F	S	S	T	H	I	R	T	O	G	I	P	R
S	S	W	P	T	U	R	W	F	C	O	A	R	M	O
K	O	E	I	T	R	O	H	E	O	F	O	Y	D	U
R	W	U	R	S	A	U	E	C	D	F	H	E	S	G
O	B	N	A	U	E	G	C	T	I	C	H	O	N	H
W	E	I	T	O	T	H	F	T	H	S	H	I	L	L
K	E	T	I	M	W	P	A	R	I	G	W	I	H	Y
A	N	N	O	A	T	B	I	N	N	O	I	H	L	A
T	I	O	N	K	L	S	R	R	N	O	N	R	O	D
N	A	C	W	E	T	U	L	K	C	I	T	H	E	M
G	I	V	E	N	F	D	E	R	U	S	S	A	T	Y

Secret Message

91

Relentlessly Seeking Righteousness

Titus 2:11–15

For the **grace** of God that **bringeth salvation** hath appeared to all men, **teaching** us that, **denying ungodliness** and **worldly lusts**, we should live **soberly**, **righteously**, and **godly**, in this **present** world; looking for that **blessed** hope, and the **glorious appearing** of the **great** God and our **Saviour Jesus Christ**; who gave **himself** for us, that he **might redeem** us from all **iniquity**, and **purify** unto himself a **peculiar people**, **zealous** of good **works**. These things **speak**, and **exhort**, and **rebuke** with all **authority**. Let no man **despise** thee.

E	X	H	O	R	T	R	U	O	I	V	A	S	D	P
K	S	P	A	U	Y	L	R	E	B	O	S	E	L	U
U	Z	I	W	A	S	W	Y	R	G	E	N	Y	I	R
B	Y	E	P	T	S	L	I	N	N	Y	A	T	G	I
E	C	L	A	S	D	A	T	I	I	L	P	I	O	F
R	T	H	S	L	E	I	L	N	H	D	P	U	T	Y
U	S	W	R	U	O	D	G	V	C	O	E	Q	T	H
G	L	O	R	I	O	U	S	O	A	G	A	I	W	B
R	W	T	A	G	S	E	S	S	E	T	R	N	R	L
A	O	N	N	U	M	T	T	P	T	O	I	I	W	E
C	H	U	S	E	S	S	E	H	H	H	N	O	A	S
E	T	E	E	U	S	O	P	T	G	G	G	I	N	S
S	J	D	L	L	P	E	U	E	E	I	A	I	N	E
P	E	C	U	L	I	A	R	T	A	E	R	G	M	D
R	F	L	E	S	M	I	H	P	S	K	R	O	W	D

Secret Message

____

____

____

____

____

____

92

Paul's Plea

Philemon 15–19

For **perhaps** he **therefore departed** for a **season**, that **thou shouldest receive** him for ever; not now as a **servant**, but **above** a servant, a **brother beloved**, **specially** to me, but how **much more** unto thee, **both in the flesh**, and in **the Lord**? If thou count me therefore a **partner**, receive **him as myself**. If he hath **wronged** thee, or **oweth** thee **ought**, put that on mine **account**; I **Paul** have **written** it with **mine own hand**, I **will repay** it: **albeit** I do not say to thee how thou **owest** unto me **even thine own self besides**.

Y	S	E	D	I	S	E	B	B	E	L	O	V	E	D
W	L	N	R	E	H	T	O	R	B	O	W	E	S	T
H	A	L	A	P	G	T	N	A	V	R	E	S	A	T
H	W	S	A	L	H	N	A	S	C	T	T	H	E	N
A	O	U	M	I	B	S	O	T	E	C	H	O	D	W
N	L	F	N	E	C	E	H	R	H	W	O	R	T	R
W	H	T	E	V	E	E	I	O	W	I	O	U	D	I
O	H	H	S	I	R	H	P	T	U	L	N	E	N	T
E	L	G	A	E	O	I	A	S	E	L	T	E	F	T
N	V	U	F	C	M	M	R	H	V	R	D	E	L	E
I	B	O	E	E	H	A	T	I	A	E	N	E	E	N
M	R	G	B	R	C	S	N	P	R	P	E	T	S	U
E	V	E	N	A	U	P	E	R	H	A	P	S	N	T
F	L	E	S	Y	M	D	R	L	R	Y	N	E	W	D
T	O	P	H	I	L	E	M	O	F	N	T	H	O	U

Secret Message

93

Persistence Triumphs

Hebrews 12:1–3

Wherefore seeing we also are **compassed** about with so **great** a **cloud** of **witnesses**, let us lay **aside every weight**, and the sin which doth so **easily** **beset us**, and **let us run** with **patience** the **race** that is set before us, **looking** unto **Jesus** the **author** and **finisher** of **our faith**; who for the joy that was set before him **endured** the **cross**, **despising** the **shame**, and is set down at the **right hand** of the **throne** of God. For **consider** him that endured such **contradiction** of **sinners against himself**, lest ye be **wearied** and **faint** in **your minds**.

I	R	M	N	C	T	T	H	R	O	N	E	D	F	I
D	W	O	I	O	S	U	T	E	S	E	B	E	A	M
E	E	H	H	N	Y	L	I	S	A	E	E	S	I	G
W	A	S	E	T	D	P	A	A	A	S	C	P	N	T
D	E	S	S	R	U	S	F	H	G	O	N	I	T	J
W	U	A	I	A	E	A	R	S	D	A	E	S	W	E
E	H	O	R	D	P	F	U	S	I	E	I	I	D	S
N	I	D	L	I	E	M	O	O	S	G	T	N	O	U
D	M	R	A	C	E	G	O	R	T	N	A	G	S	S
U	S	D	S	T	N	D	P	C	E	H	P	E	I	T
R	E	H	S	I	N	I	F	S	T	Y	G	N	A	S
E	L	K	K	O	T	O	S	H	A	R	N	I	H	T
D	F	O	H	N	E	E	G	F	E	E	U	A	E	A
T	O	C	O	N	S	I	D	E	R	V	M	O	H	W
L	E	T	U	S	R	U	N	S	G	E	E	R	Y	S

Secret Message

94

Genuine Religion

James 2:12–17

So **speak** ye, and so do, as they that **shall** be **judged** by the law of **liberty**. For he shall have **judgment without mercy**, that hath **shewed** no mercy; and mercy **rejoiceth against** judgment. What doth it **profit**, my **brethren**, **though** a man say he hath **faith**, and have not **works**? can faith save him? If a **brother** or **sister** be **naked**, and **destitute** of **daily food**, and one of you say unto them, **Depart** in **peace**, be ye **warmed** and **filled**; **notwithstanding** ye give them not **those things** which are **needful** to the **body**; what doth it profit? **Even** so faith, if it hath not works, is **dead, being alone**.

W	W	H	A	T	P	A	R	T	O	J	F	T	T	G
A	T	H	E	W	I	T	H	O	U	T	I	B	N	Y
R	K	R	S	H	E	W	E	D	O	F	Y	I	L	D
M	Y	A	A	Y	I	E	G	B	O	T	D	I	S	A
E	C	A	E	P	D	M	V	R	R	N	A	K	E	D
D	T	L	I	P	E	O	P	E	A	D	T	T	S	E
R	L	U	F	N	S	D	B	T	N	E	T	M	O	A
E	E	E	T	I	M	I	S	H	L	Y	H	F	H	D
H	B	J	S	I	L	H	E	R	U	C	O	O	T	R
T	B	T	O	S	T	L	U	E	F	R	U	O	T	B
O	E	O	H	I	A	S	E	N	D	E	G	D	U	J
R	S	A	W	I	C	T	E	D	E	M	H	S	G	R
B	L	T	E	A	N	E	T	D	E	N	O	L	A	T
L	O	B	E	I	N	G	T	S	N	I	A	G	A	H
N	I	N	W	O	R	K	S	H	T	I	A	F	G	S

Secret Message

95

Stand Firm

1 Peter 5:8–11

Be **sober**, be **vigilant**; **because** your **adversary** the **devil**, as a **roaring lion, walketh** about, **seeking whom** he may **devour**: whom **resist stedfast** in the **faith, knowing** that the same **afflictions** are **accomplished** in your **brethren** that are in the **world**. But the God of all **grace**, who hath **called** us **unto** his **eternal glory** by **Christ Jesus**, after that ye have **suffered** a **while**, make you **perfect, stablish, strengthen, settle** you. To him be glory and **dominion** for ever and ever. **Amen.**

T K T A N O I N I M O D P E T
S N S U F F E R E D E L I H W
I O A E R F E S G H T I A F A
R W F L Y S L S S R T H E Y A
H I D A I H S I L B A T S M R
C N E S E G L A C A S C E H O
H G T L L P I D Y T N N E J A
T T S O M D E V R N I G K E I
E O R O E L N E E U N O I S A
K Y C V L N N R T I O T N U D
L C I A T G H S R E W V G S H
A L C W T T A A P E R F E C T
W I H H E W O R L D B N T D K
I O E R S R N Y D O F O A P E
M N B E C A U S E O P L S L E

Secret Message

____

____

____

____

____

____

96

The Lord Is Patient

2 Peter 3:8–10

But, **beloved**, be not **ignorant** of this **one thing**, that one day is with the Lord as a **thousand years**, and a thousand years as **one day**. The Lord is **not slack** **concerning** his **promise**, as some men **count slackness**; but is **longsuffering** to **us-ward**, not **willing** that **any should** **perish**, but that **all should** come to **repentance**. But the **day of the Lord** will come as a **thief** in the **night**; in the which the **heavens shall** **pass away** with a **great noise**, and the **elements** shall melt with **fervent heat**, the **earth** also and the **works** that are therein shall be **burned** up.

T N U O C W H S A T T D G O E
D N A S U O H T T S H N P E T
O N E T H I N G E N I D R S A
Y S C T P S D C G R E A T S O
F D E N R U B R E V F M S F P
E R S A O O D F O R A E E E F
T H E R M N F L E L N E R L L
A Y S O I U E P U K Y I G T E
S S I N S B E D C O S S N H H
H K O G E N H A A H H U I G T
A R N I T V L E T Y O S L I F
L O P A S S A W A Y U W L N O
L W N F E R V E N T L A I L Y
K C A L S T O N H D D R W A A
E A R T H Y W I L L A D S K D

Secret Message

97

Walk in the Light

1 John 1:5–9

This then is the **message** which we have **heard** of **him**, and **declare** unto **you**, that **God is light**, and in him is **no darkness** at all. If we **say** that we have **fellowship** with him, and walk in darkness, we **lie**, and do not the **truth**: But if we **walk in the light**, as he is in the light, we **have** fellowship one with **another**, and the **blood** of **Jesus Christ** his **Son cleanseth** us from all **sin**. If we say that we have no sin, we **deceive ourselves**, and the truth is not in us. If we **confess** our sins, he is **faithful** and **just** to **forgive** us our **sins**, and to cleanse us **from** all **unrighteousness**.

S	A	Y	H	F	A	I	T	H	F	U	L	O	T	W
M	A	C	O	N	F	E	S	S	N	N	Y	H	C	H
A	T	S	U	S	E	J	P	T	E	R	G	R	S	A
T	S	T	R	U	T	H	P	E	V	I	G	R	O	F
H	I	P	S	E	A	Y	O	U	L	G	R	I	S	D
G	R	D	E	C	E	I	V	E	N	H	N	I	T	E
I	H	H	L	E	N	E	H	O	W	T	N	T	E	C
L	C	S	V	T	A	T	D	M	E	E	N	R	M	L
S	H	T	E	S	N	A	E	L	C	O	T	E	I	A
I	B	O	S	I	R	O	K	O	F	U	S	H	H	R
D	F	I	K	K	D	H	S	I	N	S	H	T	M	E
O	R	L	N	O	E	T	S	T	A	N	A	O	O	J
G	A	E	O	A	S	O	H	G	N	E	V	N	R	S
W	S	L	R	U	X	X	E	I	L	S	E	A	F	O
S	B	D	J	F	E	L	L	O	W	S	H	I	P	N

Secret Message

98

Love One Another

1 John 4:7–12

Beloved, let us **love one another**: for love is of God; and every one that **loveth** is **born** of God, and **knoweth** God. He that loveth not knoweth not God; for **God is love**. In this was **manifested** the love of God **toward** us, **because** that God sent his **only begotten** Son into the **world**, that we **might live through** him. **Herein** is love, not that we loved God, but that he loved us, and **sent his Son** to be the **propitiation** for our sins. Beloved, if God so loved us, we **ought also** to love one **another**. No **man hath** seen God at any **time**. If we love one another, God **dwelleth** in us, and his love is **perfected** in us.

D	E	T	C	E	F	R	E	P	W	H	I	N	L	C
H	S	F	O	U	W	O	R	L	D	R	B	O	O	O
T	U	H	A	T	H	K	S	O	F	T	V	S	H	E
H	A	M	A	N	I	F	E	S	T	E	D	S	V	E
G	C	A	N	I	B	I	B	E	O	T	L	I	T	E
U	E	N	O	E	C	O	M	N	O	T	L	H	H	N
O	B	T	T	R	A	I	E	W	H	I	A	T	R	N
T	B	H	H	E	T	A	A	G	E	W	L	N	O	N
O	E	R	E	H	N	R	I	D	B	E	S	E	U	E
G	L	I	R	O	D	M	O	N	L	Y	O	S	G	T
N	O	I	T	A	I	T	I	P	O	R	P	N	H	T
N	V	H	I	N	G	I	N	T	V	H	E	I	R	O
F	E	I	R	S	K	N	O	W	E	T	H	T	V	G
R	D	E	D	W	E	L	L	E	T	H	R	S	E	E
E	V	O	L	S	I	D	O	G	H	X	N	R	O	B

Secret Message

99

Build on Faith

Jude 20–25

But ye, **beloved**, building up **yourselves** on your most **holy faith**, praying in the **Holy Ghost**, keep **yourselves** in the **love** of God, looking for the **mercy** of our **Lord** Jesus **Christ** unto **eternal life**. And of some have **compassion**, making a **difference**: and others save with **fear**, pulling them **out** of the **fire**; hating even the **garment** spotted by the **flesh**. Now unto him that is able to keep you from **falling**, and to **present** you **faultless** before the **presence** of his glory with **exceeding joy**, to the only wise God our **Saviour**, be **glory** and **majesty**, **dominion** and **power**, both **now and ever**. **Amen.**

D	I	F	F	E	R	E	N	C	E	B	W	H	A	R
O	U	T	T	M	E	R	C	Y	T	E	W	O	O	E
L	D	N	T	A	R	E	W	O	P	L	E	S	E	V
R	A	E	F	J	T	A	M	D	R	O	L	X	E	E
E	N	M	S	E	R	I	F	T	T	V	C	C	I	D
F	P	R	E	S	E	N	C	E	N	E	O	H	S	N
I	H	A	V	T	T	A	H	I	E	D	M	O	S	A
L	O	G	L	Y	E	M	R	D	S	S	P	L	E	W
L	L	A	E	R	E	E	I	O	E	F	A	Y	L	O
A	Y	G	S	N	A	N	S	M	R	L	S	G	T	N
N	F	L	R	M	G	E	T	I	P	E	S	H	L	D
R	A	O	U	J	I	N	J	N	U	S	I	O	U	D
E	I	R	O	E	S	L	E	I	T	H	O	S	A	T
T	T	Y	Y	S	A	V	I	O	U	R	N	T	F	E
E	H	R	F	A	L	L	I	N	G	X	E	V	O	L

Secret Message

____

____

____

____

____

____

100

Alpha and Omega

Revelation 1:9–11

I **John**, **who** also am your **brother**, and **companion** in **tribulation**, and in the **kingdom** and **patience** of **Jesus Christ**, was in the **isle** that is called **Patmos**, for the **word of God**, and for the **testimony** of Jesus Christ. I was in the **Spirit** on the **Lord**'s **day**, and heard behind me a **great voice**, as of a **trumpet**, saying, I am **Alpha** and **Omega**, the **first** and the **last**: and, What thou **seest**, write in a **book**, and **send** it unto the **seven churches** which are in **Asia**; unto **Ephesus**, and unto **Smyrna**, and unto Pergamos, and unto Thyatira, and unto Sardis, and unto Philadelphia, and unto Laodicea.

J O H N W A D O G F O D R O W

E H A T M H Y M T S M Y R N A

S H I C E P H E S U S A T L S

U C E R E L A G T A K R E U P

S R C E A A P A S P I E S A I

R S N O S I Y I N B N R T E R

V O E E M A A T U L G A I T I

T M I R D P S L E I D C M E T

O T T E N A A S L T O H O P W

E A A H L T L N S F M R N M S

S P P T I T H C I H A I Y U E

E B O O K L O R D O P S T R N

E W N R E F I R S T N T R T D

S H X B X E C I O V T A E R G

T O S E V E N C H U R C H E S

Secret Message

____

____

____

____

____

____

101

The End of the Book

Revelation 22:18–21

For I **testify** unto **every man** that **heareth the words** of the **prophecy** of **this book**, If **any man** shall **add unto** these things, **God** shall add unto him the **plagues** that are **written** in this book: And if any man shall **take away from** the words of the book of this prophecy, God shall take away **his part** out of **the book of life**, and out of the **holy city**, and from the things which are written in this book. He which **testifieth** these things **saith, Surely I come quickly. Amen. Even so, come, Lord Jesus.** The **grace** of our Lord Jesus **Christ** be with **you all**. Amen.

W	S	U	S	E	J	T	R	A	P	S	I	H	H	P
E	T	O	D	R	E	C	C	M	E	G	T	I	L	R
F	E	H	R	G	W	H	V	E	E	E	R	A	D	O
I	S	T	O	H	E	R	R	N	I	E	G	A	I	P
L	T	D	W	L	V	I	I	F	E	U	L	T	C	H
F	I	A	E	E	Y	S	I	T	E	T	H	I	O	E
O	F	O	H	N	V	T	O	S	T	I	F	J	M	C
K	Y	E	T	S	S	E	U	S	S	E	C	Y	E	Y
O	H	R	H	E	I	S	R	B	T	A	N	O	S	L
O	N	Y	T	I	C	D	O	Y	R	A	E	U	U	K
B	E	V	E	N	S	O	C	O	M	E	C	A	R	C
E	O	R	R	D	K	E	D	Y	I	A	L	L	E	I
H	T	S	A	I	T	H	N	F	O	O	N	L	L	U
T	A	K	E	A	W	A	Y	F	R	O	M	R	Y	Q
U	S	T	H	O	D	A	D	D	U	N	T	O	A	Y

Secret Message

____

____

____

____

____

____

ANSWER KEYS

1-The Better Things

1. WOMAN
2. MOURNING
3. FOLLY
4. WISDOM
5. MADNESS
6. DEFENCE
7. STRAIGHT
8. MONEY
9. CROOKED

A Good Name

2-Praise!

1. SALVATION
2. JUDGE
3. TOGETHER
4. VICTORY
5. FLOODS
6. LOUD
7. PSALM
8. HANDS
9. REJOICE
10. VOICE
11. SOUND
12. MERCY

A Joyful Noise

3-The Joy of Parenting

1. SEASON
2. WRATH
3. DISPERSE
4. TREASURE
5. DEPART
6. SCORN
7. FORSAKE
8. REVENUE

A Wise Son

4-Ultimate Authority

1. MAGICIAN
2. MIRACLE
3. SERPENT
4. COMMAND
5. DOWN
6. STREAMS
7. SERVE
8. POOLS
9. HARDEN

Aaron's Rod

5-Poof! They're Gone!

1. EXALT
2. CHILDREN
3. MIGHTY
4. SLAUGHTER
5. HIGH
6. FLAME
7. PLAIN
8. CALAMITY
9. HOLINESS
10. SPOKEN

All the Heathen

6-Cut Apart

1. LEBANON
2. POTTER
3. SLAUGHTER
4. VISIT
5. YOUNG
6. ASUNDER
7. ABHOR
8. DARKEN
9. CEDAR
10. FLESH

Beauty and Bands

7-Right Hand Clan

1. TRIBE
2. BORDER
3. TAKEN
4. REJECTED
5. FAMILY
6. SAMUEL
7. GARRISON
8. PRESENT

Benjamin

8-Prayer and Praise

1. BONES
2. RESTORE
3. HOLY
4. DRINK
5. REPROVE
6. OFFER
7. PERISH
8. ALTAR
9. RANSOM
10. SHOUT

Book of Psalms

9-Good Reading

1. BREACH
2. HOUSE
3. MASONS
4. HILKIAH
5. WORDS
6. FORSAKEN
7. MIGHT
8. JUDAH
9. EVIL
10. KINDLE
11. REPAIR
12. WARDROBE

Book of the Law

10-Stone by Stone

1. CHAMBER
2. AUDIENCE
3. LODGE
4. BREAD
5. PORTERS
6. SHEAVES
7. WARDS
8. CLEANSE
9. ISRAEL
10. SELLERS

Build the Wall

11-Aiming to Please

1. LAMBS
2. FLOUR
3. ANOINT
4. WHEAT
5. COATS
6. OFFICE
7. WAFERS
8. SIN
9. YOUNG

Burnt Offering

12-Praise before the Ark

1. COVENANT
2. DEPART
3. HATH
4. SERVANT
5. REJOICE
6. NATION
7. BLESSED
8. DAVID
9. INSTRUMENT

10. SOUND

Certain Levites

13-Terrors

1. CLOUD
2. SOLITARY
3. PURSUE
4. YOUTH
5. FORCE
6. AFTER
7. BRIDLE
8. CALAMITY
9. CAST
10. DERISION
11. SINEWS

Days of Affliction

14-Faithfulness

1. DELIGHT
2. SLAY
3. SMOKE
4. MERCIFUL
5. FORSAKE
6. CONDEMN
7. INHERIT
8. ABUNDANCE

Days of Famine

15-"Ungolden" Years

1. BREAD
2. VANITY
3. SOUTH
4. FLESH
5. WITHHOLD
6. EMPTY
7. TRULY
8. CLOUDS
9. SPIRIT
10. HEART

Days of Thy Youth

16-Deceptive Love

1. MOCKED
2. AVENGED
3. LEAN
4. AFFLICT
5. LOCKS
6. RAZOR
7. PHILISTINES

Delilah

17-Massacre at Nob

1. DEPART
2. CONSPIRE
3. LEAGUE
4. AGAINST
5. THINE
6. PRIEST
7. DWELT
8. FOOTMEN
9. FIELD
10. CAPTAIN
11. HOUSE

Doeg the Edomite

18-Watch What You Say!

1. WOOD
2. VOICE
3. SOUL
4. TRUST
5. REPROVE
6. FORTH
7. CALAMITIES
8. PRAYER
9. LIFTING
10. PLACES

Door of My Lips

19-Hungry for Prophecy

1. OPENED
2. LANGUAGE
3. STRANGE
4. STRONG
5. RUSHING
6. WICKED
7. REQUIRE
8. NOISE
9. CHILDREN
10. SHALT

Eat the Roll

20-Second Visit

1. TREAD
2. LEVI
3. JEWEL
4. CALVES
5. HEART
6. HEALING
7. OPPRESS
8. SOLES
9. POUR
10. SHALL
11. PLEASANT

Elijah the Prophet

21-Two of a Kind

1. BEGAT
2. SISTER
3. GARMENT
4. STRUGGLED
5. NATION
6. BRETHREN
7. DEATH
8. SOJOURN
9. DEPART
10. PLACE
11. FOUND
12. BROTHER

Esau and Jacob

22-Amazing Wonders

1. FIRMAMENT
2. BUZI
3. LIKENESS
4. KING
5. WHEELS
6. EAGLE
7. CRYSTAL
8. LIVING
9. NOISE
10. WINGS
11. TOWARD
12. LION

Ezekiel's Vision

23-Woe to Them!

1. SAFELY
2. PASTORS
3. FLOCK
4. SHAME
5. REPROACH
6. ANGER
7. SODOM
8. PROPHESY
9. HEARD
10. DREAMS
11. FORGET
12. FOLDS

False Prophets

24-The Leftovers

1. AFFLICTED
2. SUFFICED
3. GLEANED
4. DAMSEL
5. KINDRED

6. GROUND
7. FIND
8. HUSBAND
9. WOMAN
10. PHAREZ

Field of Boaz

25-A Barrier

1. FIRST
2. LIKENESS
3. MORNING
4. DOMINION
5. SEASONS
6. IMAGE
7. EVENING
8. HEAVEN
9. MULTIPLY

Firmament

26-It Was a Long Week!

1. FRUIT
2. WISE
3. APRONS
4. SERPENT
5. SECOND
6. GARDEN
7. BRUISE
8. BREATH
9. THISTLES
10. MOTHER

First Sabbath

27-A Dark Night...

1. FAMILIES
2. OBSERVE
3. BASON
4. POSTS
5. BEAST
6. ROAST
7. REMAIN
8. SELFSAME
9. HYSSOP
10. LINTEL
11. EATEN

Firstborn Smote

28-Hot Ones!

1. FOUNDED
2. ANGELS
3. VALLEY
4. AMONG
5. FIELD
6. QUENCH
7. SING
8. FOWLS
9. CURTAIN
10. CHAMBER
11. CATTLE

Flaming Fire

29-Smart Man!

1. AFFINITY
2. THRONE
3. UPRIGHT
4. BETWEEN
5. INCENSE
6. DISCERN
7. DWELL
8. HONOUR
9. DREAM

For Wisdom

30-Spirits of Heaven

1. LIFTED
2. COUNTRY
3. CROWNS
4. BLACK
5. HEAD
6. MEMORIAL
7. HORSE
8. TEMPLE
9. COUNSEL

Four Chariots

31-Mighty Warrior

1. REALM
2. PRINCE
3. GREAT
4. REBEL
5. JUDGES
6. LAWS
7. OBEYED
8. SANCTUARY
9. VISION
10. DREADFUL
11. ISRAEL

Angel Gabriel

32-An Eyeful

1. GRAPES
2. BRING
3. SAYING
4. CITIES
5. TENTS
6. STRONGER
7. HONEY
8. SOUTH
9. FATHER
10. JORDAN
11. COURAGE
12. MILK

Giants, Sons of Anak

33-Moral Virtues

1. GRACE
2. PRECIOUS
3. DILIGENCE
4. GLORY
5. FAITH
6. ABOUND
7. PURGED
8. STIR
9. PLEASED

Godliness

34-Something to Count On

1. GOODNESS
2. OLIVE
3. DESTROY
4. SHARP
5. HIMSELF
6. RICHES
7. ENDURE
8. MISCHIEF
9. THYSELF

God's Mercy

35-A Light to See

1. GREAT
2. BEHOLD
3. LOOKED
4. EYES
5. ANGEL
6. CRYING
7. PLAIN
8. HANDS
9. TALKED
10. HEADSTONE
11. FINISH
12. CAME
13. WAKENED

Golden Candlestick

36-Water-Proofing

1. DAUGHTERS
2. CORRUPT
3. PITCH

4. CATTLE
5. CHILDREN
6. WINDOW
7. RENOWN
8. FASHION
9. DESTROY

Gopher Wood

37-Watch Out!

1. GOLAN
2. CREEP
3. TABLES
4. VOICE
5. HEATHEN
6. FIGURE
7. MERCY
8. DARKNESS
9. EGYPT
10. WINGED
11. BEAST

Graven Images

38-Belly Tremble

1. SPEECH
2. SCATTER
3. BONES
4. HABITATION
5. NAKED
6. WORK
7. DEVOUR
8. KNOWN

Habakkuk

39-A Perfect Yet Troubled Man!

1. MOUTH
2. PRINCES
3. SLEPT
4. CURSED
5. BIRTH
6. CONCEIVE
7. DAWNING
8. TWILIGHT
9. JOYFUL
10. WOMB

His Servant Job

40-A Glorious Outfit

1. HASTE
2. MOUNTAIN
3. FOWLS
4. THUNDER
5. HEAVENS
6. PLANTED
7. MANIFOLD
8. REJOICE
9. SPIRITS
10. GLORY

Honour and Majesty

41-The Lord Gives a Sign

1. CHILD
2. DAMASCUS
3. TEMPT
4. ASSYRIA
5. FORSAKEN
6. CONDUIT
7. PREVAIL
8. FULLER

Immanuel

42-Back to School

1. DILIGENT
2. SNARED
3. TROUBLE
4. RENDER
5. CRUEL
6. WICKED
7. TRUTH
8. RIGHTEOUS
9. CONDEMN

Instruction

43-Looking for Love in All the Wrong Places

1. WILDERNESS
2. HARLOT
3. ANGER
4. POLLUTE
5. SHAME
6. WICKED
7. TREACHEROUS
8. BACKSLIDE
9. NATIONS
10. ADULTERY
11. SURELY

Israel's Idolatry

44-An Old Phrase. . .

1. JERUSALEM
2. ENTRANCE
3. HUNDRED
4. SODOMITES
5. AHAB
6. PROVOKE
7. HORNS
8. GATHER

Jehoshaphat

45-A New Name

1. SOJOURNER
2. WITHHELD
3. SHORE
4. SILVER
5. CAVE
6. SHEKELS
7. JIDLAPH
8. ABIDE
9. STRETCHED
10. HAND

Jehovah-Jireh

46-Because He Was Sad

1. JUDAH
2. PRESENCE
3. FATHER
4. SEPULCHRE
5. FOREST
6. WASTE
7. REBELLION
8. NOBLES
9. MOREOVER

Jerusalem

47-Warrior Gives Thanks

1. JUDGES
2. STONES
3. HALF
4. BURNT
5. AGAINST
6. SEIZE
7. ACCORD
8. BLESSINGS
9. FORTH
10. AMBUSH
11. STRANGER

Joshua's Altar

48-Glory to Shame

1. LANGUISH
2. REJECTED
3. KILLING

4. SHADOW
5. FORGET
6. BREAK
7. CONTROVERSY
8. SWEAR
9. LEFT
10. DECLARE
11. DOINGS
12. HEIFER

Lack of Knowledge

49-Heavy Heart

1. ISRAEL
2. ASSEMBLY
3. ASHES
4. TURNED
5. BASKET
6. WATCHMEN
7. GRIEF
8. SACKCLOTH
9. ANGUISH

Lamentation

50-Jaws

1. CONCEAL
2. SHINE
3. VAIN
4. BRIDLE
5. CALDRON
6. TERRIBLE
7. LIGHT
8. BARBED
9. NOSTRILS

Leviathan

51-He Knew God Well

1. BLOT
2. SALVATION
3. SINNER
4. TONGUE
5. MAKING
6. BURNT
7. HIDDEN
8. TENDER
9. SINNED
10. GLADNESS

Lovingkindness

52-Refiner's Fire

1. FORMER
2. SPARE
3. JACOB
4. SERVE
5. SWIFT
6. PURIFY
7. PROFIT
8. CAST
9. FATHERS
10. WITNESS
11. PLEASANT

Majesty of Christ

53-We're Covered

1. CHERUBIM
2. LENGTH
3. BORNE
4. COVER
5. OVERLAY
6. STAVES
7. GOLDEN
8. PLACES
9. CUBIT

Mercy Seat

54-Little Known

1. NIMROD
2. ZION
3. INCURABLE
4. PROPHET
5. BRETHREN
6. FAMILY
7. FOREST
8. RAISE
9. SHEAVES
10. STRONG
11. HORN
12. WITHIN
13. DIVINE

Micah the Morasthite

55-A Threshing Floor

1. BEAMS
2. AMOUNT
3. HUNDRED
4. TALENTS
5. IMAGE
6. SCORE
7. CRIMSON
8. PILLARS
9. CHERUB

Mount Moriah

56-Kingdom Come

1. MULE
2. CONSUME
3. WINTER
4. FORTH
5. CORNER
6. FLESH
7. FOUGHT
8. PLAGUE
9. CAPTIVITY
10. VALLEY
11. HORSE
12. SAINTS

Mount of Olives

57-A Furnace!

1. COMMAND
2. CLOUD
3. TOUCH
4. RETURNED
5. TRUMPET
6. SANCTIFY
7. WINGS
8. WAXED
9. LIGHTNING

Mount Sinai

58-Hot Rocks!

1. MOSES
2. BEHOLD
3. SIMILITUDE
4. LEARN
5. EASTWARD
6. MIDST
7. NEITHER
8. POSSESS
9. FISH
10. FIGURE
11. CREEP
12. CLEAVE

Mountain of Fire

59-Vile Verbage

1. ABOMINATION
2. REFUSE
3. MOTHER
4. REPROOF
5. WRATH
6. APPEASE
7. WISE
8. CORRECT
9. FORSAKE
10. MERRY
11. DINNER

Mouth of the Wicked

60-They Wouldn't Stop

1. MOSES
2. ROUND
3. WORMS
4. RULERS
5. MORNING
6. STANK
7. NOTHING
8. SPEAK

Murmurings

61-Only for the Lord

1. BARREN
2. UNCLEAN
3. RAZOR
4. HUSBAND
5. DRINK
6. DETAIN
7. COUNTENANCE
8. OBSERVE

Nazarites

62-Short but Powerful

1. SWALLOW
2. STUBBLE
3. CAPTIVITY
4. LAID
5. REMAIN
6. REWARD
7. HOLINESS
8. DECEIVE
9. DESPISED
10. POSSESS
11. KINDLE
12. WOUND

Obadiah's Vision

63-A Heart Transplant

1. VISION
2. BORDER
3. KINDRED
4. PRINCE
5. DETESTABLE
6. FALLEN
7. SCATTER
8. SPEAK
9. STATUTES

Ordinances

64-Vision Impaired

1. PROSPER
2. MOCK
3. WRATH
4. WICKED
5. PRISONERS
6. HEBREWS
7. MANNER
8. GREATER

Potiphar

65-Gave Up One of Seven

1. PHARAOH
2. CRIED
3. SECOND
4. SHEPHERDS
5. STOOD
6. FLOCK
7. SMITE
8. DAUGHTER
9. RIVER
10. STRANGER
11. BONDAGE

Priest of Midian

66-Road Work

1. PURGE
2. RETURN
3. PROVE
4. FEARED
5. COVENANT
6. HIRELING
7. REFINER
8. SWIFT
9. ABIDE
10. HAPPY

Prepare the Way

67-A Great Light

1. OPPRESSOR
2. REJOICE
3. INCREASE
4. STRETCH
5. STOUTNESS
6. STAFF
7. SPOIL
8. EVERLASTING
9. COUNSEL
10. JUSTICE

Prince of Peace

68-Lighten Up

1. SCORPION
2. FOURSCORE
3. HEAVY
4. GRIEVOUS
5. BURNT
6. CHARIOT
7. CHASTISE
8. PERFORM

Rehoboam

69-Judgment

1. APPAREL
2. MERCHANT
3. CRASHING
4. SETTLE
5. HOUSETOPS
6. FISHES
7. BLOCKS
8. RIDDANCE
9. CANDLES

Remnant of Baal

70-Refreshing Grace

1. PASTURES
2. ENEMIES
3. ANOINT
4. COMFORT
5. MAKE
6. DEATH
7. NAME
8. SURELY
9. SHEPHERD
10. GOODNESS
11. HOUSE
12. STILL

Restoreth My Soul

71-True Value

1. COMPARE
2. RECEIVE
3. CLOUDS
4. RIGHTEOUS
5. DURABLE
6. FOUNTAINS
7. PRUDENCE
8. PREPARE
9. PLACE

Rich Treasure

72-Built Strong

1. ARISE

2. NOSTRILS
3. CONSUME
4. BUCKLER
5. CLEAN
6. FALLEN
7. GIRDED
8. FROWARD
9. DEPART
10. CHERUB
11. BRIGHTNESS
12. WINGS

Rock and Fortress

73-Strike One

1. ELDERS
2. FOUGHT
3. CHOOSE
4. BOOK
5. CHIDE
6. EGYPTIANS
7. THIRST
8. JOSHUA
9. PREVAIL
10. BUILT

Rock in Horeb

74-King Me!

1. FIRSTBORN
2. BAKER
3. MAIDS
4. JUDGE
5. BEHOLD
6. APPOINT
7. CHOSEN
8. CAPTAIN
9. GROUND
10. PEOPLE
11. REHEARSE
12. HARVEST

Samuel the Prophet

75-David's Desire

1. SERVANT
2. THRONE
3. WALKEST
4. ESTABLISH
5. YEARS
6. SEVEN
7. LIFE
8. PEACEABLY
9. WISDOM
10. ACCORDING

Shew Thyself a Man

76-Job's Trial

1. SOLE
2. WALKING
3. FOOLISH
4. PRESENCE
5. FORTH
6. DESTROY
7. POTSHERD
8. SPRINKLE
9. BOILS
10. MANTLE

Skin for Skin

77-Pass It On

1. HEWERS
2. THOUSAND
3. CONVEY
4. OFFICER
5. CEDAR
6. SERVANT
7. BUILD
8. DESIRE

Son of David

78-Calling Out

1. FLOWERS
2. SHORN
3. CROWNED
4. GRAPE
5. COMELY
6. FOXES
7. TOWER
8. BELOVED
9. PERFUME
10. LEBANON
11. FOUNTAIN

Song of Solomon

79-A Promise

1. STRANGER
2. MOUTH
3. UNDERSTAND
4. WOMAN
5. EQUITY
6. SEARCH
7. DISCRETION
8. JUDGMENT

Sound Wisdom

80-Thanksgiving

1. GATHER
2. FEAST
3. BRANCHES
4. SERVILE
5. MONTH
6. SHEAF
7. PROCLAIM
8. BLEMISH
9. SOLEMN

Tabernacles

81-Bedtime Story

1. NIGHT
2. ESTHER
3. RECORDS
4. COVERED
5. HORSE
6. GALLOWS
7. BANQUET
8. MOURNING
9. CHAMBERLAIN
10. BEFALLEN
11. MINISTER

The Chronicles

82-Lies and Deceit

1. TEACHER
2. HERESY
3. FEIGN
4. ANGEL
5. PUNISH
6. BRUTE
7. PERNICIOUS
8. PROVERB
9. UPON
10. HOLY
11. TEMPEST
12. COVETOUS

The False Prophets

83-Night Sight

1. CHARIOT
2. FIFTH
3. DISCREET
4. FAVOUR
5. PHARAOH
6. TIME
7. LINEN
8. DUNGEON
9. DEVOUR

The Famine

84-Sate Your Appetite

1. CONTENT

2. NAUGHTY
3. REPROOF
4. WICKED
5. LAMP
6. BEAUTY
7. CLOTHES
8. FALSE
9. EYELIDS
10. INNOCENT
11. FRIEND

The Way of Life

85-Changing Times

1. NOTHING
2. PURPOSE
3. EMBRACE
4. REFRAIN
5. SILENCE
6. LABOUR
7. DUST
8. PERCEIVE
9. MANIFEST
10. PORTION
11. INIQUITY

There Is a Season

86-Never Forget

1. SECRET
2. PREACHER
3. EVERY
4. CONCLUSION
5. MOURN
6. PLEASURE
7. ALMOND
8. TREMBLE
9. WINDOWS
10. PROVERBS

Thy Creator

87-A Dog's Life

1. CONCEIT
2. ARROW
3. HINGES
4. FIREBRAND
5. SLOTHFUL
6. FORMED
7. VOMIT
8. MEDDLE
9. TALEBEARER
10. BELLY

To His Folly

88-Not Just for Tasting

1. SERVANT
2. COUNSEL
3. RIGHTEOUS
4. RENDER
5. SWORD
6. MISCHIEF
7. MOUTH
8. OVERTHROWN
9. TENDER
10. WITNESS
11. HEAVINESS
12. SATISFIED

Tongue of the Wise

89-Then There Were Many

1. EARTH
2. FLOOD
3. WHOLE
4. ABROAD
5. CONFOUND
6. BUILD
7. SCATTERED
8. BRICK
9. SPEECH
10. LANGUAGE

Tower of Babel

90-Ram Tough

1. GARMENTS
2. TABERNACLE
3. INCENSE
4. STRANGERS
5. CENSER
6. SEAT
7. SOULS
8. FINGER
9. BLOOD
10. SKIN
11. SPRINKLE

Transgressions

91-Special Diet

1. VULTURE
2. SANCTIFY
3. CLOVEN
4. SCALES
5. PELICAN
6. AMONG
7. CHAMELEON
8. TORTOISE
9. OSPRAY
10. LOCUST

Unclean Meat

92-A Little Flat!

1. HOUSE
2. MIDNIGHT
3. SPOILED
4. SAYING
5. PASSOVER
6. URGENT
7. SACRIFICE
8. DESTROYER
9. BROUGHT
10. ARMIES
11. FEAST
12. HERDS

Unleavened Bread

93-Lamentable Demise

1. DIVISIONS
2. FAMILIES
3. PEOPLE
4. DISGUISED
5. WILLINGLY
6. OFFERINGS
7. MOURNED
8. SINGERS
9. KINGS
10. DEEDS
11. AMBASSADOR

Valley of Megiddo

94-Graven Images

1. DIVINERS
2. HEAVEN
3. WORSHIP
4. TOKENS
5. CYRUS
6. ROAST
7. OFFSPRING
8. DECAY
9. COMPASS
10. DECLARE
11. RAISED

Vanity of Idols

95-Good Grief

1. FOREVER
2. EXERCISED
3. ESTATE
4. VANITY
5. CONCERN

6. PROFIT
7. ARISE
8. PERCEIVE
9. INCREASE
10. CIRCUIT

Vexation of Spirit

96-Don't Be Lame

1. WANTING
2. FALSE
3. KINDNESS
4. WEALTH
5. SHAME
6. DELIVER
7. INIQUITY
8. ANGER
9. INTREAT
10. DROPPING
11. REPROVE
12. ROARING
13. CALAMITY

Walketh in Integrity

97-Definition of Bitter

1. SWALLOW
2. STATUTES
3. ENCAMPED
4. THREESCORE
5. ORDINANCE
6. SATISFIED
7. TIMBREL
8. DANCES
9. PRAISES
10. TRIUMPH

Waters of Marah

98-Marvelous Work

1. AWAKE
2. TONGUE
3. DARKNESS
4. SECRET
5. HEART
6. AFAR
7. PRECIOUS
8. CURIOUSLY
9. SURELY

Wonderfully

99-Seven Times Seven

1. CITY
2. OPPRESS
3. SAFETY
4. GROWTH
5. FALLEN
6. JUDGE
7. SUBURBS
8. BOUGHT
9. VILLAGES
10. YEARLY
11. ISRAEL

Year of Jubile

100-Easy Load

1. AWAY
2. PEOPLE
3. THICKETS
4. MOUNT
5. LIFTING
6. BEHIND
7. TURNED
8. LEADERS
9. ANCIENT

Yoke of Burden

101-Freedom

1. NATURE
2. BONDAGE
3. FORTH
4. APPOINT
5. INJURE
6. TUTORS
7. GOVERNORS
8. AFRAID
9. OBSERVE
10. BORN
11. ELEMENTS

Adoption of Sons

102-A Bad Read

1. SERVANT
2. ANGEL
3. BLOOD
4. APOSTLE
5. CHURCH
6. MARVEL
7. PREACH
8. RELIGION
9. PERSUADE
10. PERVERT
11. CERTIFY
12. DELIVER

Another Gospel

103-Looking Good!

1. MASTER
2. WRATH
3. ADMONITION
4. UTTERANCE
5. PROMISE
6. AFFAIRS
7. MAKING
8. OBEDIENCE
9. BOLDLY

Armour of God

104-Labor On!

1. BURDEN
2. RESTORE
3. SEASON
4. CONSTRAIN
5. CORRUPT
6. WRITTEN
7. GRACE
8. FAULT
9. OVERTAKEN
10. ESPECIALLY

Be Not Weary

105-Fearless

1. BISHOP
2. ABOUND
3. DESIRE
4. REJOICE
5. SINCERE
6. FURTHER
7. STRIFE
8. BETWIXT
9. MANIFEST

Bonds in Christ

106-One Big Family

1. SOBERLY
2. TOWARD
3. SLOTHFUL
4. PREFER
5. FERVENT
6. POSSIBLE
7. SIMPLICITY
8. DEARLY
9. EXHORT
10. AVENGE

Brotherly Love

107-Phrase of Praise

1. ABSENCE
2. HUMBLE
3. SERVANTS
4. VAINGLORY
5. BOWELS
6. REPUTATION

7. BECAUSE
8. HARMLESS
9. SORROW
10. ROBBERY
11. SOLDIER

Christ Is Lord

108-The Removal

1. CHRIST
2. EDIFY
3. REPROACH
4. GRACE
5. MOUTH
6. MINDED
7. CARNAL
8. HINDERED
9. PARTAKERS
10. STRIVED
11. DEBTORS
12. REIGN

Circumcision

109-Stay Awake!

1. BESEECH
2. AMONG
3. HELMET
4. OBTAIN
5. BRETHREN
6. BLAMELESS
7. CEASING
8. FAITHFUL
9. PATIENT
10. FEEBLE
11. COMFORT

Cometh as a Thief

110-Contentment

1. STAND
2. FELLOW
3. ABOUND
4. LOVELY
5. FLOURISH
6. SALUTE
7. THANKS
8. GLORIOUS
9. WOMEN
10. HUNGRY
11. CAESAR

Do All Things

111-Beware

1. GRIEVOUS
2. CONCISION
3. FLESH
4. TOWARD
5. COUNT
6. CONFORM
7. STOCK
8. ENSAMPLE
9. SUFFER
10. DOUBTLESS

Evil Workers

112-In the Light

1. THEREFORE
2. WORKING
3. LEAVE
4. WRINKLE
5. REPROVE
6. WRATH
7. CHERISH
8. REVERENCE
9. SPIRIT

Followers

113-Confused Christians

1. FORESEE
2. SCHOOL
3. BEWITCH
4. MASTER
5. TRUTH
6. HEARING
7. DISANNUL
8. FLESH
9. MEDIATOR
10. JUSTIFIED
11. ORDAIN
12. BLESSING

Foolish Galatians

114-Holy Matrimony

1. GREAT
2. HIMSELF
3. SAVIOUR
4. IDOLATER
5. UNWISE
6. PRESENT
7. CHERISH
8. NOURISH
9. COVET
10. WASHING

Glorious Church

115-An Earthly Picture

1. LENGTH
2. MINISTER
3. REVEAL
4. ACCESS
5. EFFECTUAL
6. MANIFOLD
7. FAMILY
8. RICHES
9. ETERNAL
10. HEIGHT
11. DARKNESS
12. WHEREBY

Great Mystery

116-Above All

1. GATHER
2. MENTION
3. ADOPT
4. BELIEVE
5. EARNEST
6. ENLIGHTEN
7. PRAYERS
8. POWER
9. GOSPEL
10. SEALED
11. CHOSEN
12. WISDOM

Heavenly Places

117-A Promise

1. CONTINUE
2. MANNER
3. FOOLISH
4. LEARN
5. MIRACLE
6. WRITTEN
7. ADDED
8. NATIONS
9. CRUCIFY
10. EVIDENT

Inheritance

118-The Only Way

1. JESUS
2. HEATHEN
3. MIGHTY
4. FALSE
5. PRIVATELY
6. FORWARD
7. LIBERTY
8. FRUSTRATE
9. COMMIT

10. SOMEWHAT

Justified by Faith

119-Working Hard

1. SHAMEFUL
2. APOSTLES
3. BEHAVE
4. SOULS
5. ENTREAT
6. PLEASING
7. DESIRE
8. TRUTH
9. ENDEAVOR
10. FLATTERING
11. GUILE

Labour and Travail

120-Hanging On

1. GLORY
2. DEVOUR
3. UNCLEAN
4. ENVYING
5. FLESH
6. JUSTIFY
7. OFFENCE
8. SERVE
9. PROFIT
10. ENTANGLE
11. AGAINST

Longsuffering

121-The Highest

1. FELLOW
2. FORGIVE
3. AGES
4. GIVEN
5. WORTHY
6. HOPE
7. WISDOM
8. REDEMPTION
9. RICHLY
10. VISIBLE
11. LIGHT

Love in the Spirit

122-Not a Pretty Sight

1. FULFILL
2. MURDERS
3. STRIFE
4. CONTRARY
5. FRUIT
6. OTHERWISE
7. TESTIFY
8. GENTLE
9. MEEKNESS
10. HATRED

Lust of the Flesh

123-Deception

1. GLORY
2. DESTROY
3. PERDITION
4. TAUGHT
5. ALWAYS
6. OPPOSE
7. SHAKEN
8. ALREADY
9. HEARTS
10. GOSPEL

Lying Wonders

124-Another Lie

1. PERFECT
2. RENDER
3. PATIENT
4. ESCAPE
5. ABSTAIN
6. DESPISE
7. EPISTLE
8. SANCTIFY
9. ESTEEM
10. UNRULY

Peace and Safety

125-A Good Work Here

1. RESPECT
2. BESEECH
3. SACRIFICE
4. SALUTE
5. AGAIN
6. PRAYER
7. REPORT
8. THINGS
9. LEARNED
10. HUNGRY
11. REQUESTS

Philippians

126-Stand Strong

1. PROVOKE
2. TREMBLE
3. SINGLE
4. SINCERITY
5. PROMISE
6. AFFAIRS
7. PLATE
8. MIGHT
9. WILES
10. PERSONS

Principalities

127-A Gift

1. REMISSION
2. TONGUE
3. ESTABLISH
4. SWIFT
5. MISERY
6. ORACLES
7. UNBELIEF
8. SINNER
9. UNDERSTAND
10. POISON
11. SLANDER

Righteousness

128-To the Finish

1. COMFORT
2. LABOUR
3. LIKENESS
4. FASHION
5. OBEDIENT
6. HEAVINESS
7. ABSENCE
8. SPIRIT
9. NATURAL

Run in Vain

129-Held High

1. SERVANTS
2. WRATH
3. DOING
4. BELOVED
5. WRESTLE
6. DEVIL
7. ARMOUR
8. FINALLY
9. FEAR
10. PLEASERS
11. SAINTS
12. HEAVEN

Shield of Faith

130-Be Gentle

1. STEAL
2. FATHER
3. FULNESS
4. DECEIVE

5. DARKENED
6. RATHER
7. JOINED
8. APOSTLES
9. IGNORANCE
10. CREATED
11. SEALED

Tenderhearted

131-A Good Pace

1. WITCHCRAFT
2. TROUBLE
3. DRUNK
4. LIBERTY
5. VARIANCE
6. ANOTHER
7. GENTLENESS
8. TEMPERANCE
9. FRUIT
10. HATRED
11. DESIRE
12. FAITH

Walk in the Spirit

132-Singing with Grace

1. WISDOM
2. FORGAVE
3. APPEAR
4. HUSBANDS
5. BOWELS
6. FLESH
7. RESPECT
8. HUMBLE
9. RISEN
10. SUBMIT
11. MERCIES
12. MOUTH

Word of Christ

133-Radiant Appearance

1. PIERCED
2. BEGOTTEN
3. FURNACE
4. WHITE
5. STRENGTH
6. HEARD
7. GARMENT
8. CANDLE

Countenance

134-God's Right-Hand Man

1. JUDGMENT
2. PERISHED
3. EXECUTE
4. SPEECHES
5. ETERNAL
6. FEAST
7. APOSTLES

Michael

135-An Assiduous Plan

1. CONTEND
2. SAINTS
3. UNGODLY
4. DEFILE
5. ARCHANGEL
6. CREPT
7. STRANGE
8. GRACE
9. DIGNITIES

Diligence

136-No Favoritism

1. OPPRESS
2. FOOTSTOOL
3. WORTHY
4. TRANSGRESS
5. APPAREL
6. PARTIAL
7. RAIMENT
8. WARMED

Royal Law

137-Highly Regarded

1. FRIENDS
2. RECORD
3. HIMSELF
4. PROSPER
5. TRUE
6. FORTH
7. BRING
8. CHURCH
9. SORT

Demetrius

138-A Trusted Helper

1. ACCOMPLISH
2. WITNESS
3. EXAMPLE
4. OVERSIGHT
5. CHARITY
6. ROARING
7. SUFFERED
8. SUPPOSE

Silvanus

139-A Chosen Woman

1. ENTERED
2. WALKING
3. REWARD
4. COMMANDMENT
5. WRITE
6. ELDER
7. SAKE
8. DOCTRINE
9. GREATLY

Elect Lady

140-All Christians

1. BODY
2. PRAISE
3. CONSCIENCE
4. MOUTH
5. SHEEP
6. SUPREME
7. FEAR
8. FOOLISH
9. HONEST
10. ORDINANCE

Brotherhood

141-Treat Others Kindly

1. FACE
2. GOLD
3. AMAZEMENT
4. PITIFUL
5. MANNER
6. CHASTE
7. COURTEOUS
8. HIDDEN
9. HOLY
10. TONGUE

Compassion

142-No Fire Damage

1. QUAKE
2. WROUGHT
3. FIRE
4. BONDS

5. VIOLENCE
6. FLIGHT
7. CAVES
8. SWORD

Quenched

143-More Than Just a King

1. TESTAMENT
2. PRIEST
3. SALEM
4. RECEIVE
5. TENTH
6. KING
7. SURETY
8. ORDER
9. TITHES
10. DESCENT

Melchisedec

144-Take Heed!

1. ELDER
2. DEFILED
3. PEACE
4. TALKERS
5. CHILDREN
6. LOVER
7. CONVINCE
8. TEMPERATE
9. FABLES

Deceivers

145-Our High Priest

1. CONFIRMATION
2. OATH
3. ANCHOR
4. HEIRS
5. STRONG
6. SOUL
7. DILIGENCE
8. NAME
9. COUNSEL
10. INHERIT

Forerunner

146-Heaven's Gift

1. FAITH
2. DOCTRINE
3. ETERNAL
4. CRUCIFY
5. ENLIGHTENED
6. WORLD
7. TASTED
8. THORNS

Holy Ghost

147-God Sees Everything

1. MARROW
2. WRATH
3. CERTAIN
4. JOINTS
5. PROFESSION
6. HARDEN
7. SIGHT
8. HEART

Manifest

148-Bless His House

1. POWER
2. HANDS
3. GOSPEL
4. SAVED
5. GIFT
6. KEEP
7. HOUSE
8. MERCY
9. PURPOSE
10. SOUND

Onesiphorus

149-Among Paul's Travels

1. MINISTER
2. JANGLING
3. CHARGE
4. PURE
5. ABIDE
6. IMMORTAL
7. PROFANE
8. LIARS

Macedonia

150-A Fortunate Church

1. ALPHA
2. PRINCE
3. TRIBULATION
4. KINGDOM
5. ISLE
6. CLOUDS
7. COMPANION
8. BROTHER
9. VOICE
10. OMEGA

Philadelphia

151-Very Happy

1. GREATLY
2. COME
3. JOURNEY
4. GODLY
5. WITNESS
6. MALICIOUS
7. CONTENT
8. ELDER

Rejoiced

152-A High Office

1. PATRIARCH
2. VERILY
3. TRIBE
4. TENTH
5. DESCENT
6. CONSECRATED
7. HOPE
8. OATH
9. ORDER

Priesthood

153-From Root to Fruit

1. FULFILLED
2. DAVID
3. PROPHET
4. JOSEPH
5. MOTHER
6. HUSBAND
7. CONCEIVED
8. VIRGIN
9. EMMANUEL

Firstborn

154-John the Baptist

1. STRAIGHTWAY
2. BAPTIZED
3. UNLOOSE
4. JORDAN
5. DESCENDING
6. REPENTANCE
7. MESSENGER
8. HEAVENS
9. LOCUSTS
10. REMISSION

Wilderness

155-Blessed among Women

1. FORASMUCH
2. ZACHARIAS
3. GENERATION
4. BLESSED
5. KINGDOM
6. GABRIEL
7. MAGNIFY
8. ESPOUSED
9. ELISABETH
10. SALUTATION

A Handmaiden

156-CNN in the Wilderness

1. WITNESS
2. HEAVEN
3. ESAIAS
4. LATCHET
5. BAPTIZING
6. MOSES
7. BEGINNING
8. BEGOTTEN
9. PREFERRED
10. REMAINING
11. COMPREHEND

The Lamb of God

157-Forty Days

1. JERUSALEM
2. UPPER ROOM
3. ORDAINED
4. MINISTRY
5. MATTHIAS
6. SUPPLICATION
7. DISCIPLES
8. ASSEMBLED

Apostles

158-When in Rome…

1. CREATOR
2. FAITH
3. GREEKS
4. GLORIFIED
5. UNDERSTOOD
6. SERVANT
7. APOSTLESHIP
8. GRACE
9. HOLINESS

The Gospel

159-Idiot's Domain

1. WRITTEN
2. RIGHTEOUSNESS
3. BRETHREN
4. FOOLISHNESS
5. CONFOUND
6. GLORY
7. MIGHTY

Worldly

160-Yea Yea and Nay Nay

1. SIMPLICITY
2. SUFFERINGS
3. ACKNOWLEDGE
4. TESTIMONY
5. SALVATION
6. LIGHTNESS
7. DESPAIRED
8. PARTAKERS

Promises

161-As Thou Has Believed

1. SELFSAME
2. TORMENT
3. GNASHING
4. SERVANT
5. BELIEVED
6. CAPERNAUM
7. WORTHY
8. FOLLOWED
9. HEALED
10. WEEPING
11. CENTURION
12. ABRAHAM

So Great Faith

162-A Swine Time Was Had by All

1. STEEP
2. COMPASSION
3. ASUNDER
4. SUFFERED
5. CHOKED
6. THOUSAND
7. BESOUGHT
8. ADJURE
9. CLOTHED

Possessed

163-An Offer You Can Refuse

1. TEMPLE
2. ANGELS
3. COMMAND
4. SPIRIT
5. STONE
6. JERUSALEM
7. MOUNTAIN
8. DELIVERED
9. WORSHIP
10. WILDERNESS

Temptation

164-Wheat or Rye?

1. TIBERIAS
2. HIMSELF
3. RABBI
4. MIRACLES
5. MANNA
6. DISEASED
7. LOAVES
8. FISHES
9. DISCIPLES
10. THIRST
11. SUFFICIENT

The Bread of Life

165-The Good, the Bad, and the Martyred

1. MATTHIAS
2. JAMES
3. JUDAS
4. DAVID
5. PETER
6. NICANOR
7. CAIAPHAS
8. PROCHORUS
9. STEPHEN
10. PILATE
11. ANDREW

Heavens Open

166-Walk This Way

1. CHILDREN
2. JOINT-HEIRS
3. INTERCESSION
4. ADOPTION
5. FULFILLED
6. MORTAL
7. PREDESTINATE

8. LIBERTY
9. BONDAGE

Condemned

167-Till Death Us Do Part

1. SUPPOSE
2. DEFRAUD
3. FASTING
4. VIRGIN
5. BENEVOLENCE
6. MARRIED
7. SANCTIFIED
8. ABIDE
9. RECONCILED
10. STEDFAST
11. COMMANDMENTS

Put God First

168-Happy Birthday, Herod

1. BEHEADED
2. PROPHET
3. CHARGER
4. BROUGHT
5. DANCED
6. PRISON
7. BAPTIST
8. PLEASED

Herodias

169-Happy Birthday, Dear Jesus

1. HIGHEST
2. WONDERED
3. HEAVENLY HOST
4. SWADDLING
5. BETHLEHEM
6. GLORIFYING
7. DELIVERED
8. FIRSTBORN
9. MANGER
10. AUGUSTUS

Good Tidings

170-A Leopard Changes His Spots

1. BARNABAS
2. SYNAGOGUES
3. SLAUGHTER
4. CONFOUNDED
5. BROTHER
6. BASKET
7. STRAIGHT
8. SCALES
9. DAMASCUS
10. VESSEL

Saul of Tarsus

171-Present Gifts

1. REASONABLE
2. SOBERLY
3. MEASURE
4. CONFORMED
5. MEMBERS
6. REJOICE
7. FERVENT
8. SERVICE
9. OVERCOME
10. PATIENT

A Sacrifice

172-Love-eth

1. VAUNTETH
2. HOPETH
3. PROFITETH
4. SUFFERETH
5. BELIEVETH
6. ENDURETH
7. THINKETH
8. BEARETH
9. REJOICETH
10. SEEKETH

These Three

173-Paul: Man of Action

1. ESCAPED
2. SUPPLIED
3. FASTING
4. TRANSFORMED
5. PREACHED
6. ROBBED
7. THINK
8. PRESENT
9. BOASTING
10. STONED

Sufferings

174-This Is My Body

1. JUDAS
2. EVEN
3. BLESSED
4. TESTAMENT
5. BETRAY
6. VINE
7. FEAST
8. THANKS
9. TWELVE
10. DRINK

Unleavened

175-Mission Possible

1. DISEASES
2. DUST
3. TOWNS
4. SHAKE
5. GOSPEL
6. PREACHING
7. HEALING
8. TWELVE
9. JOURNEY

Authority

176-Here Comes the Bride

1. KINGDOM
2. AROSE
3. VIRGINS
4. TRIMMED
5. FOOLISH
6. LAMPS
7. BRIDEGROOM
8. VESSELS

Marriage

177-Share and Share Alike

1. GHOST
2. HEART
3. TEMPT
4. POSSESSORS
5. HOUSES
6. ANANIAS
7. BURIED
8. LACKED

Sapphira

178-Follow the Leader (Part 1)

1. SAVED
2. CEPHAS
3. MEMORY
4. THIRD
5. GOSPEL
6. STAND
7. BURIED
8. BRETHREN

9. PREACHED
10. PRESENT

Scriptures

179-Follow the Leader (Part 2)

1. FAITH
2. RISEN
3. LABOURED
4. ASLEEP
5. DEATH
6. FALLEN
7. GRACE
8. CHURCH
9. ALIVE
10. COMETH
11. PERISHED

Firstfruits

180-Follow the Leader (Part 3)

1. STARS
2. CORRUPTION
3. CELESTIAL
4. EARTH
5. IMAGE
6. SOWEST
7. NATURAL
8. HEAVEN
9. FLESH

Spiritual

181-Follow the Leader (Part 4)

1. STING
2. WRITTEN
3. STEDFAST
4. LAST TRUMP
5. MORTAL
6. SOUND
7. TWINKLING
8. MYSTERY
9. ABOUNDING

Swallowed

182-Judgment Day

1. GLORY
2. DISSOLVED
3. TERROR
4. COMMEND
5. SOBER
6. SPIRIT
7. BEHOLD
8. ETERNAL
9. AMBASSADORS

Good or Bad

183-Know Jesus, Know Peace; No Jesus, No Peace

1. REJOICE
2. UNGODLY
3. SINNERS
4. HEARTS
5. EXPERIENCE
6. FIGURE
7. PATIENCE
8. PEACE
9. BLOOD

Justified

184-The End of the World (Part 1)

1. OFFENDED
2. AFFLICTED
3. SORROWS
4. DESOLATION
5. PESTILENCES
6. BETRAY
7. RUMOURS
8. PLACES
9. HATED
10. DECEIVE
11. INIQUITY
12. FAMINES

False Prophets

185-The End of the World (Part 2)

1. TRUMPET
2. NATIONS
3. WITNESS
4. GATHER
5. DARKENED
6. EAGLES
7. ELECT
8. WONDERS
9. ENDURE
10. DAYS

Power and Glory

186-Trial by (Guilty) Jury

1. ACCUSE
2. GROUND
3. FINGER
4. ADULTERY
5. WROTE
6. TEMPTING
7. STONED
8. MASTER
9. HEARD

Condemned

187-Amazing Talent

1. SLOTHFUL
2. RULER
3. JOURNEY
4. GIVEN
5. GAINED
6. TAKEN
7. TALENTS
8. GOODS

Servants

188-It Is Done

1. CROSS
2. VINEGAR
3. SCOURGED
4. SCARLET
5. SIMON
6. FORSAKEN
7. THIEVES
8. YIELDED
9. MOCKED

Crucified

189-Scrambled Word Pictures

1. PEARLS
2. TALENTS
3. VINEYARD
4. GENERATION
5. BUSHEL
6. LEAVEN
7. WEDDING
8. SOWER

Parables

190-It's a Miracle! (Part 1)

1. FINGERS
2. SPIT
3. ASTONISHED
4. SPEECH
5. CHARGED
6. PLAIN
7. TONGUE
8. HEAR

9. SPAKE

Ephphatha

191-It's a Miracle! (Part 2)

1. COMETH
2. HEALED
3. FOUND
4. GOETH
5. AUTHORITY
6. WORTHY
7. FAITH
8. SOLDIERS
9. SERVANT

Centurion

192-It's a Miracle! (Part 3)

1. WORSE
2. FEAST
3. MOTHER
4. MARRIAGE
5. GOVERNOR
6. DISCIPLES
7. BRIDEGROOM
8. TASTED
9. STONE

Waterpots

193-It's a Miracle! (Part 4)

1. FISHES
2. REMAIN
3. FIVE THOUSAND
4. GATHER
5. MOUNTAIN
6. LOAVES
7. PENNYWORTH
8. THANKS
9. PASSOVER

Fragments

194-It's a Miracle! (Part 5)

1. SIGHT
2. SILOAM
3. SEEING
4. OPENED
5. SABBATH
6. WORKS
7. BEGGED
8. SINNED
9. SPITTLE
10. WASHED

His Parents

195-Our Eyes Can Deceive Us

1. ANGELS
2. MARY MAGDALENE
3. SEPULCHRE
4. TAKEN
5. AWAY
6. WEEPEST
7. STONE
8. WOMAN
9. BORNE

Empty Tomb

196-A Job Well Done

1. GIVEN
2. POWER
3. WORLD
4. WORDS
5. LIFE ETERNAL
6. SANCTIFY
7. MANIFESTED
8. PERFECT

God's Name

197-All That and a Bag of Chips

1. LIGHT
2. THE WAY
3. MESSIAS
4. MIRACLE WORKER
5. GOOD SHEPHERD
6. BREAD
7. THE LIFE
8. SAVIOUR
9. THE LAMB

The Christ

198-A Great Day's Catch

1. DRAUGHT
2. FISHES
3. JOHN
4. PARTNERS
5. JAMES
6. SIMON
7. LAUNCH
8. FISHERMEN
9. ZEBEDEE
10. MULTITUDE

Gennesaret

199-Yet Shall He Live

1. JEWS
2. GRAVE
3. SISTERS
4. LAZARUS
5. SICKNESS
6. AWAKE
7. BETHANY
8. SLEEPETH
9. COME FORTH

Jesus Wept

200-How Does Your Garden Grow?

1. ANOTHER
2. BURNED
3. FRUIT
4. REMAIN
5. LOVED
6. WITHERED
7. BRANCHES
8. CHOSEN

True Vine

201-Waste Not, Want Not

1. PORTION
2. FATHER
3. BROTHER
4. WASTED
5. SWINE
6. YOUNGER
7. FATTED CALF
8. LIVING

Prodigal

202-The Reading of Father's Will

1. JESUS
2. PURPOSE
3. SPIRIT
4. BONDAGE
5. LIBERTY
6. CHILDREN
7. FREELY
8. ADOPTION
9. CONQUERORS
10. SUFFERING

Joint-Heirs

Puzzle 1

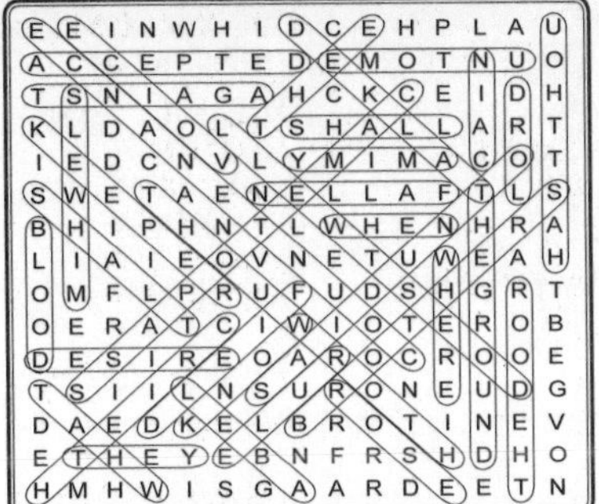

In which place did Cain live after being driven from his garden?

The land of Nod (Genesis 4:16)

Puzzle 2

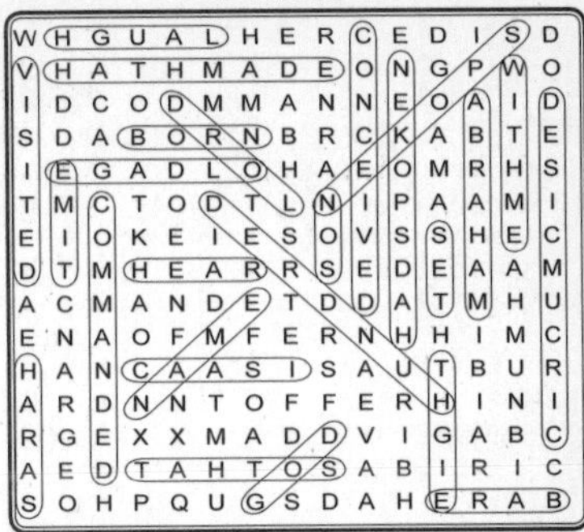

Where did God command Abraham to take Isaac and then offer him as a burnt offering?

The land of Moriah (Genesis 22:2)

Puzzle 3

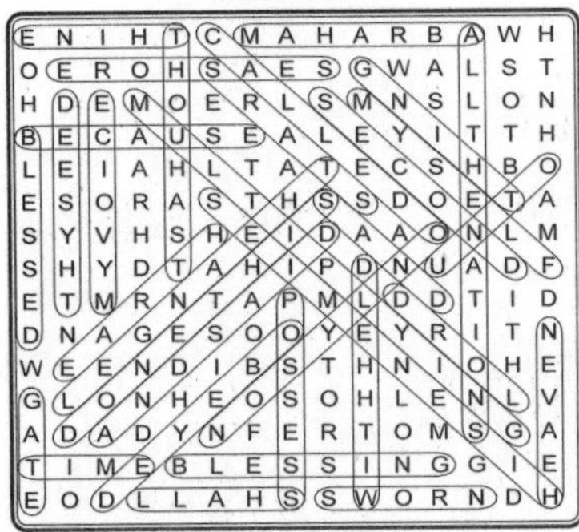

Who was the son that Abraham did not withhold from God?

Isaac (Genesis 22:2)

Puzzle 4

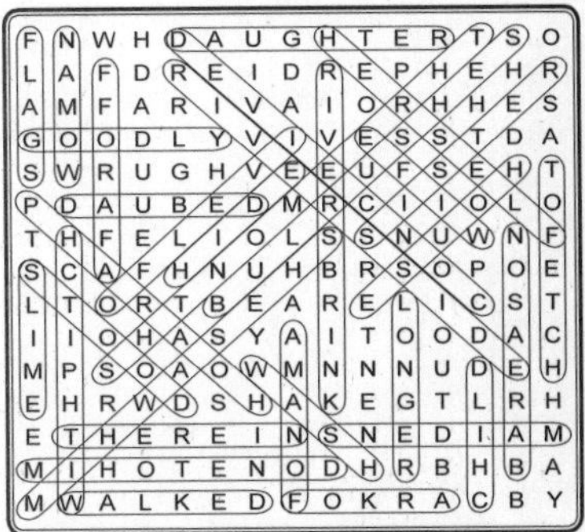

Who did Pharaoh's daughter pay to nurse the baby?

The child's mother (Exodus 2:7–9)

Puzzle 5

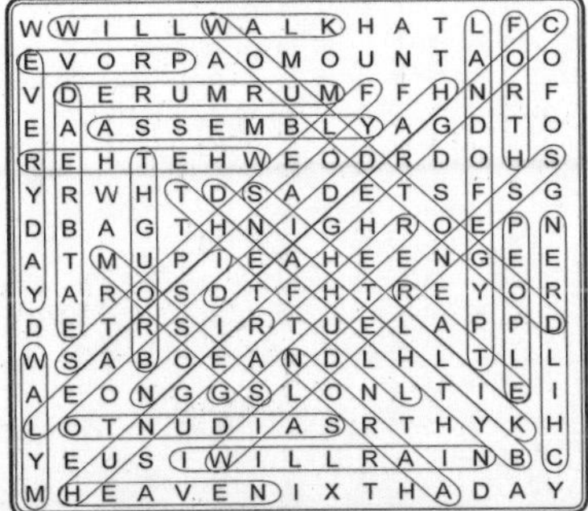

What amount of food was gathered on the sixth day?

Twice as much (Exodus 16:5)

Puzzle 6

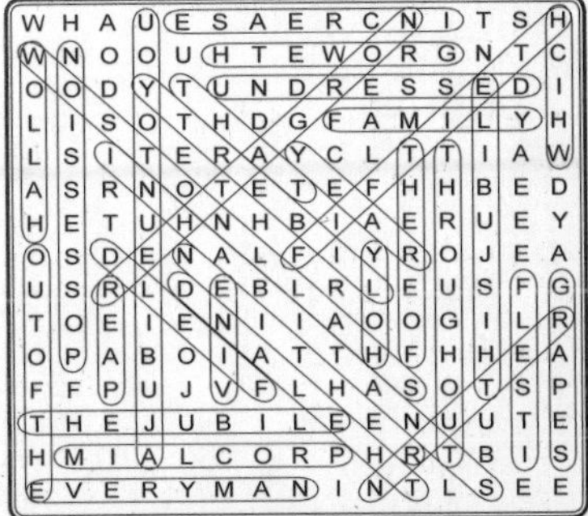

What sound declared the Year of Jubilee?

A trumpet sound (Leviticus 25:9)

Puzzle 7

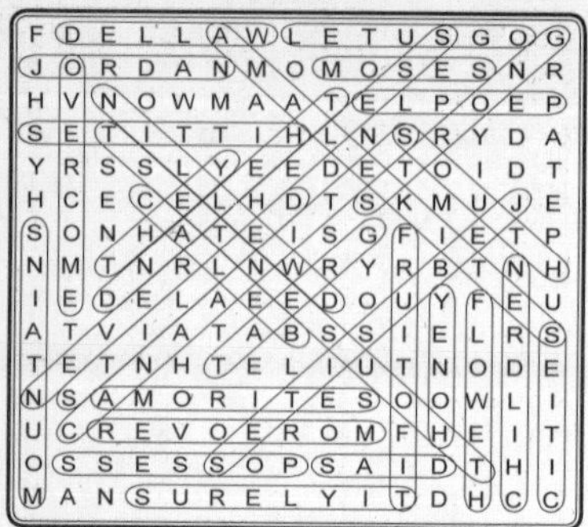

For how many days did the men spy out the land?

Forty (Numbers 13:25)

Puzzle 8

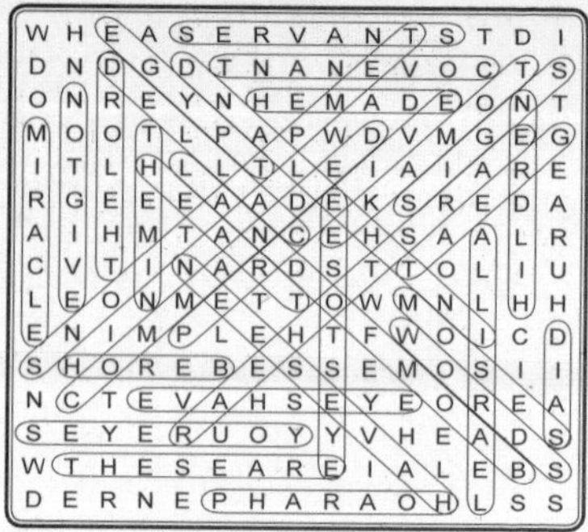

What did not wear out while in the wilderness?

Clothes and shoes (Deuteronomy 29:5)

Puzzle 9

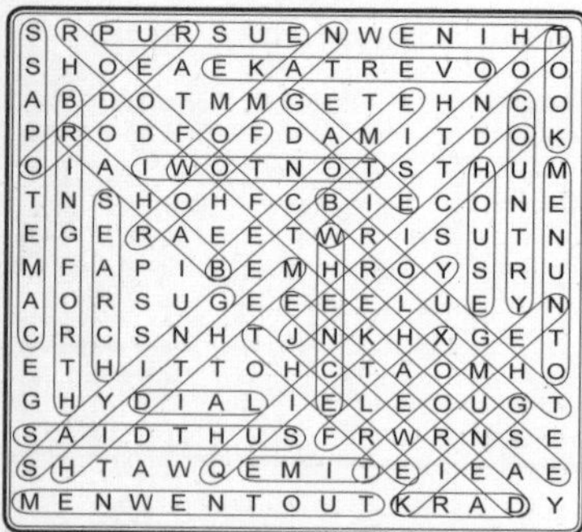

What method did the spies use to get away?

A cord through a window (Joshua 2:15)

Puzzle 10

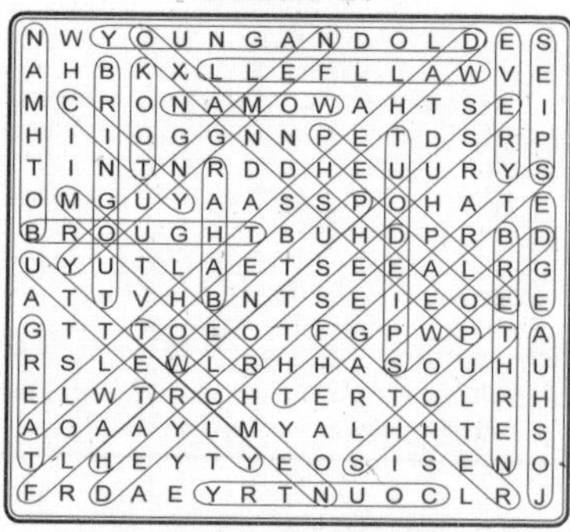

What sign did Rahab leave to show her loyalty to Israel?

A scarlet thread (Joshua 2:21)

Puzzle 11

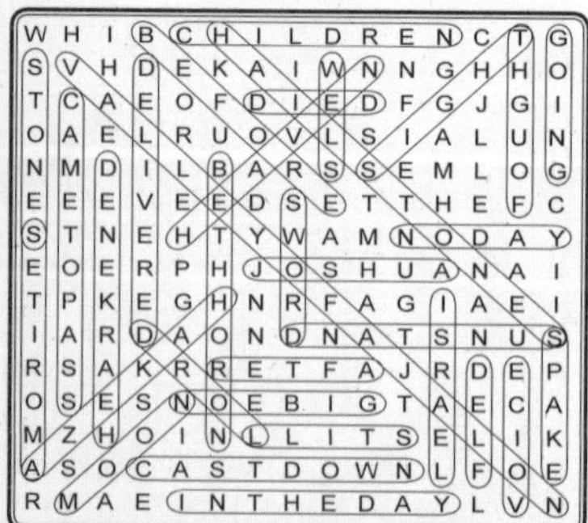

Which king of Jerusalem led the campaign against Israel?

Adonizedec (Joshua 10:3–4)

Puzzle 12

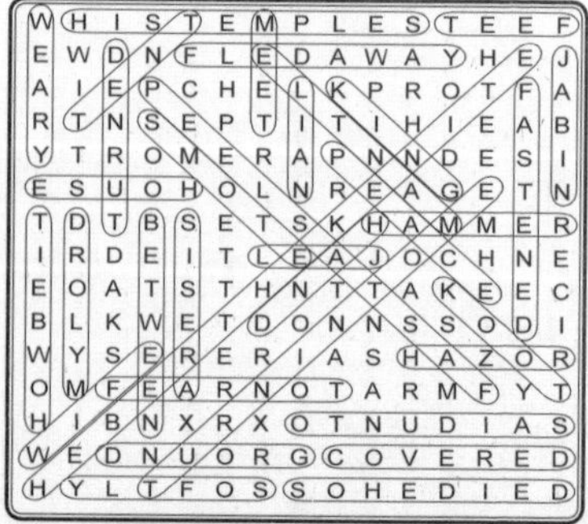

Which prophet ordered the attack on Sisera's army?

Deborah (Judges 4:14)

Puzzle 13

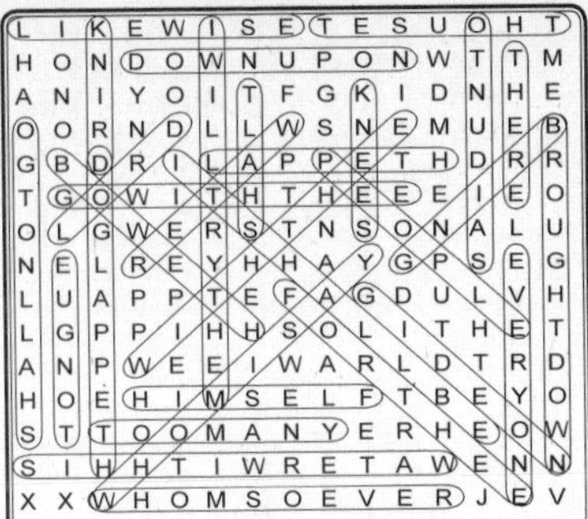

How many of Gideon's men lapped up the water?

Three hundred (Judges 7:7)

Puzzle 14

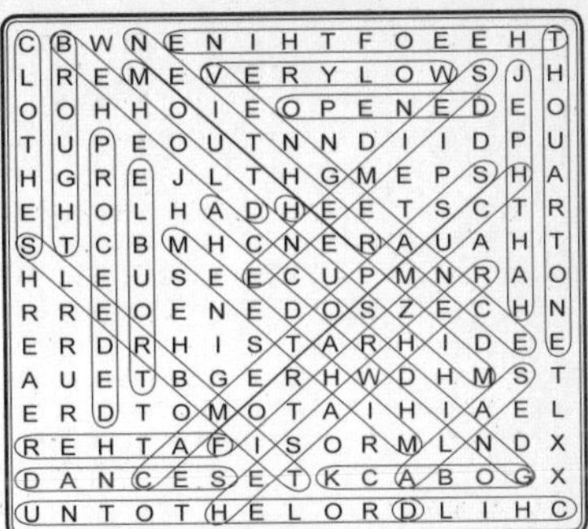

When did Jephthah surrender his daughter to the Lord?

After two months (Judges 11:39)

Puzzle 15

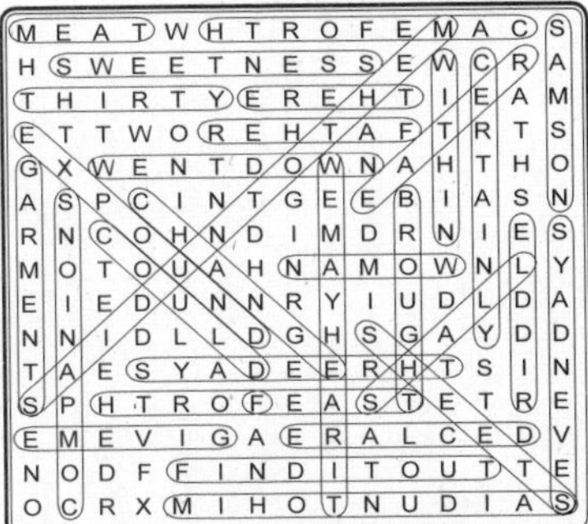

What two things did the riddle stand for?

Honey and a lion (Judges 14:18)

Puzzle 16

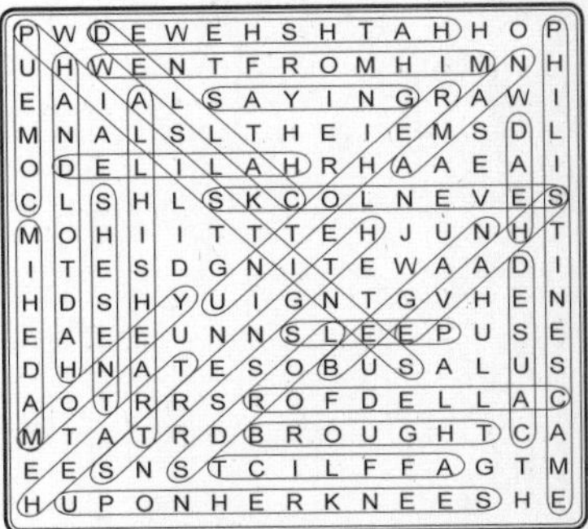

Who was the Israelite judge with unusual strength?

Samson (Judges 16:6)

Puzzle 17

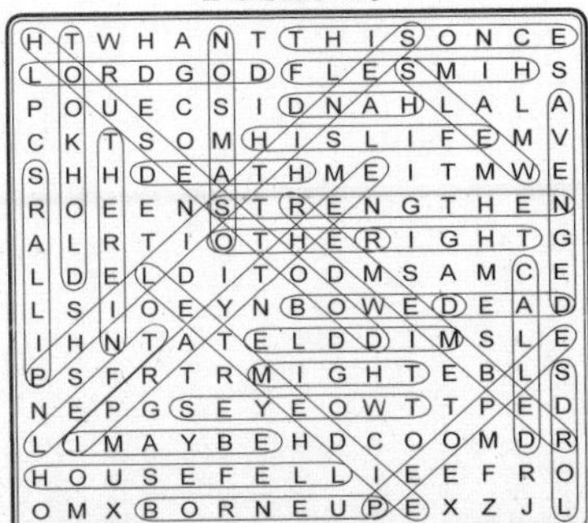

What special commitment did Samson's strength come from?

The Nazarite vow (Judges 13:7)

Puzzle 18

T F E L W H B E R E L E A V E
D I D N A O U M I A Y N D R U
L T H L I T R A P E L P O E P
V O E B E F I O R E T T H E S
Y T R R T S E I D A S T V E P
M L E D D T D O G H A H E T E
E T S E O G H E T R F E T O A
H A T H E O L U A S D E N T K
E E D D O D R F D J E U D H I
L R A E H E E X E X T G Y G N
H T K A H E T W D L S E D U G
T N S T I J U E N V R O L O G
E I I H E U R R I O B E T N L
B H U W E I N E M A C Y E H T
W M T W O N G N I W O L L O F

Where did Naomi and Ruth live before they traveled together to the land of Judah?

Moab (Ruth 1:1–4)

Puzzle 19

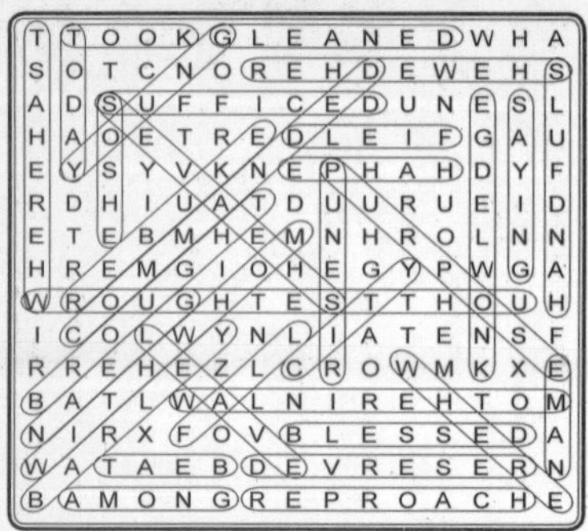

What country did Ruth originate from?

Moab (Ruth 1:4)

Puzzle 20

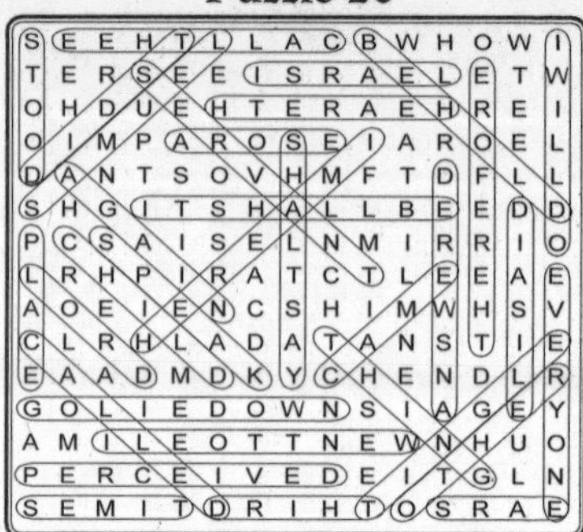

Who were the parents of this miracle child named Samuel?

Elkanah and Hannah (1 Samuel 1:19)

Puzzle 21

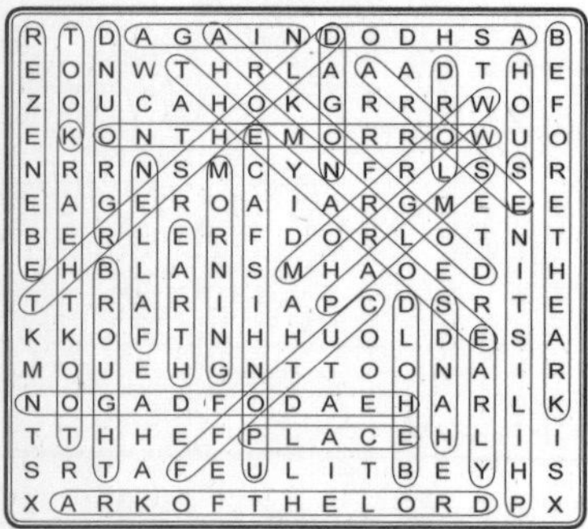

What carried the ark home to the Israelites?

An oxen cart (1 Samuel 6:11–12)

Puzzle 22

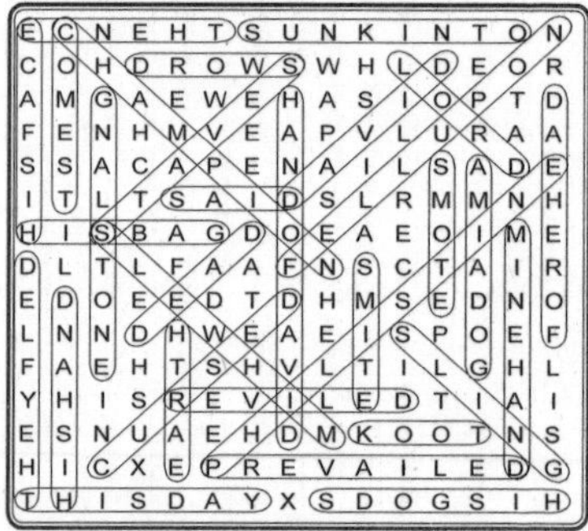

Where was the place Israel faced the Philistines?

Shochoh (1 Samuel 17:1)

Puzzle 23

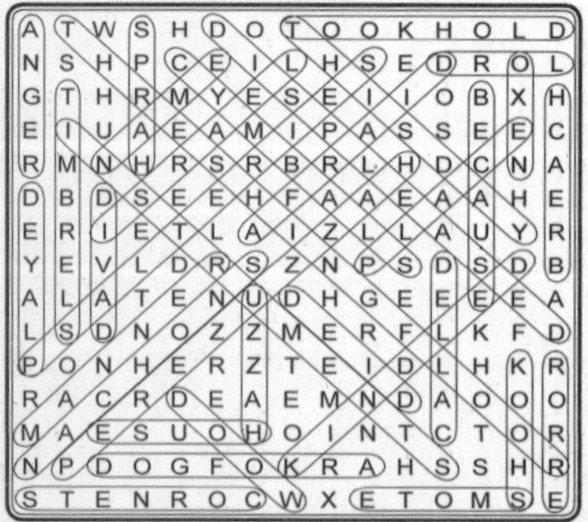

Whose house held the ark for three months?

Obed-edom's (2 Samuel 6:11)

Puzzle 24

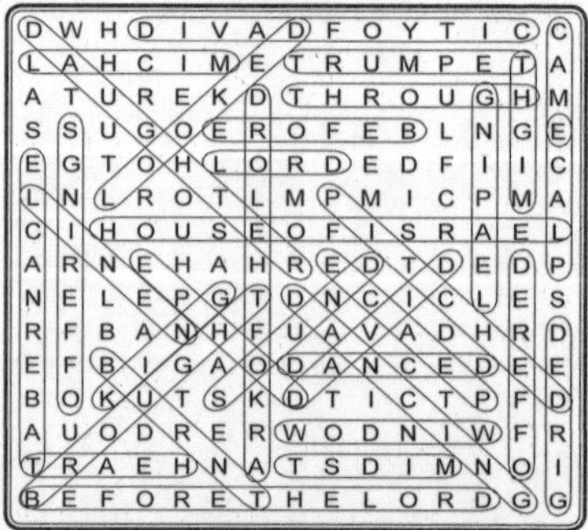

What resulted from Michal's bad attitude?

She was barren (2 Samuel 6:23)

Puzzle 25

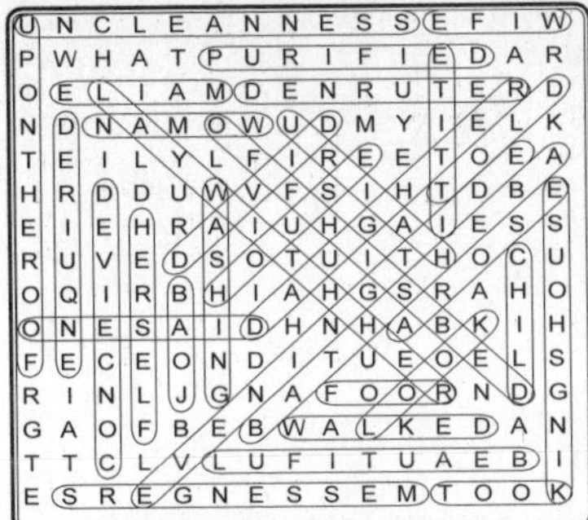

What army killed Uriah during a battle?

The Ammonites (2 Samuel 11)

Puzzle 26

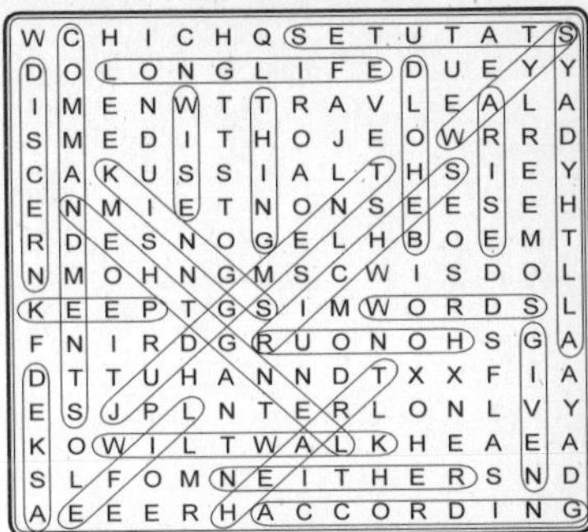

Which queen traveled to Jerusalem to see Solomon's wisdom firsthand?

The queen of Sheba (1 Kings 10:1)

Puzzle 27

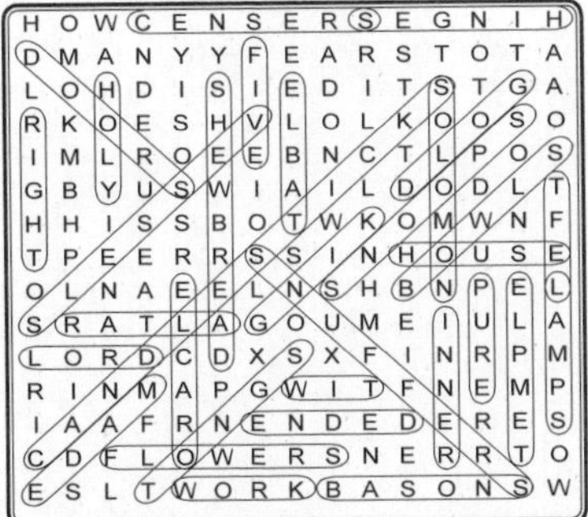

How many years total did it take Solomon to build his own personal home?

Thirteen (1 Kings 7:1)

Puzzle 28

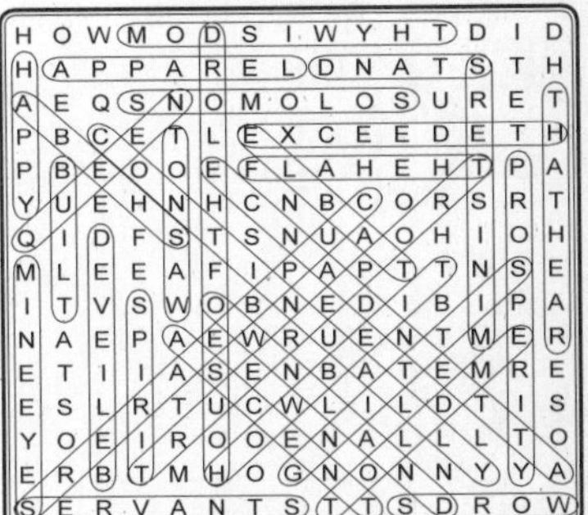

How did the queen of Sheba test Solomon?

With hard questions (1 Kings 10:1)

Puzzle 29

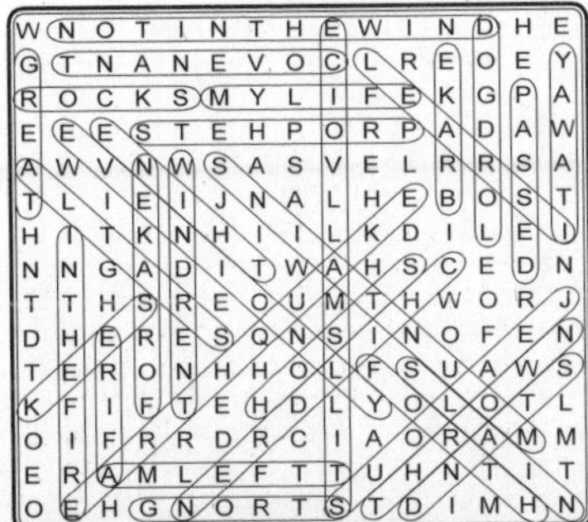

Where was Elijah hiding when the word of the Lord came to him?

In a cave (1 Kings 19:9)

Puzzle 30

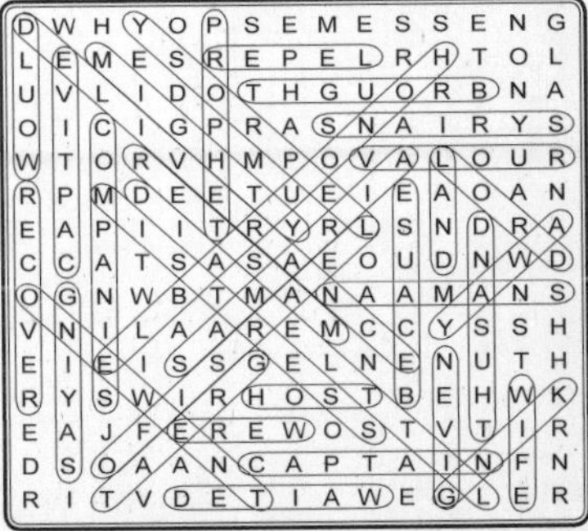

Whose messenger told Naaman to wash in the Jordan River?

Elisha's (2 Kings 5:10)

Puzzle 31

N	L	I	T	T	L	E	R	E	H	T	A	R	B	R
S	E	V	E	N	T	I	M	E	S	W	H	A	E	T
Y	N	A	P	M	O	C	W	A	S	T	H	T	F	E
T	A	E	R	G	B	E	H	O	L	D	U	D	O	L
E	G	N	I	Y	A	S	N	A	D	R	O	J	R	P
E	A	R	N	S	T	O	O	D	N	G	A	A	E	M
A	I	E	K	A	P	S	N	E	F	H	T	R	A	E
D	N	P	S	I	P	T	D	O	C	A	M	E	O	S
E	I	R	T	T	I	N	N	O	N	U	K	N	O	W
P	N	A	D	H	E	A	R	T	H	T	E	W	K	I
P	N	Y	G	O	M	V	F	T	E	H	P	O	R	P
I	S	Y	L	E	A	R	S	I	R	I	I	D	A	H
D	L	I	H	C	L	E	A	N	X	N	X	O	A	S
I	D	E	B	L	E	S	S	I	N	G	L	J	F	A
B	E	L	F	H	S	E	L	F	A	T	H	E	R	W

What was the leper Naaman's position under the king of Syria?

Captain of the host (2 Kings 5:1)

Puzzle 32

W	H	K	I	N	G	S	O	R	O	F	D	E	L	F
K	T	F	I	L	O	R	D	R	S	C	T	E	E	P
D	I	R	T	S	N	I	A	G	A	R	F	V	U	I
S	S	N	A	I	R	Y	S	M	A	T	E	E	T	C
O	D	S	G	P	H	V	P	E	T	N	S	S	H	E
R	L	E	E	O	D	O	H	H	A	O	O	N	E	T
W	O	T	R	T	F	H	E	N	R	M	R	A	I	A
T	H	S	S	S	I	I	O	T	R	A	A	I	R	H
E	E	E	Y	O	R	T	S	E	S	N	Y	T	L	A
S	B	R	N	T	H	D	T	R	Y	T	E	P	I	N
E	I	R	E	E	E	T	M	I	A	H	H	Y	F	D
A	M	N	R	R	U	I	A	A	H	E	T	G	E	F
S	T	O	I	R	A	H	C	E	D	R	L	E	A	L
S	N	H	C	S	H	W	H	E	R	E	F	O	R	E
A	D	F	L	E	T	W	I	L	I	G	H	T	D	D

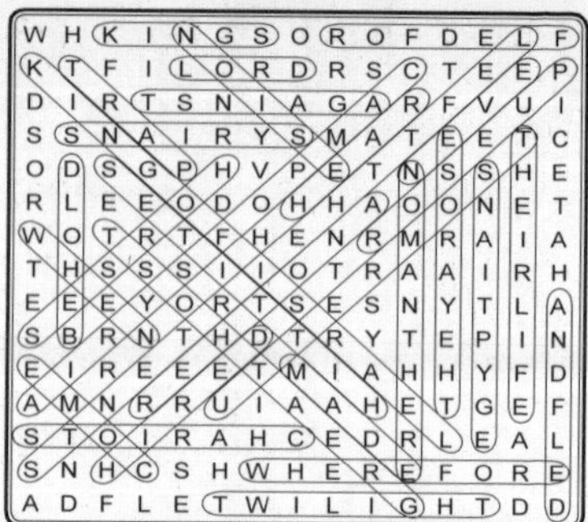

Who first discovered that the Syrians had fled?

Four leprous men (2 Kings 7:3)

Puzzle 33

E	B	D	N	A	W	H	P	Y	F	G	N	I	O	D
S	S	A	R	B	W	M	O	R	E	O	V	E	R	R
U	E	R	A	E	R	E	H	T	E	N	R	O	A	O
O	T	R	O	U	B	L	E	S	O	P	L	T	D	F
H	S	A	B	V	I	M	D	R	N	D	A	O	H	N
T	A	R	L	E	L	R	I	O	W	E	B	R	C	E
E	D	E	E	T	W	D	E	T	O	R	U	U	E	M
E	B	V	U	K	N	I	H	B	D	D	N	I	V	D
O	S	L	T	A	R	E	T	N	M	N	D	W	A	L
F	L	I	I	A	R	O	A	H	I	U	A	O	H	O
S	D	S	R	E	L	S	W	N	T	H	N	R	I	G
T	N	F	F	A	U	E	G	A	H	H	C	K	O	F
O	U	O	F	O	R	E	N	N	A	M	E	M	S	O
N	R	T	H	G	I	E	W	T	E	E	V	E	R	Y
E	F	T	O	H	E	W	E	R	S	R	G	N	O	D

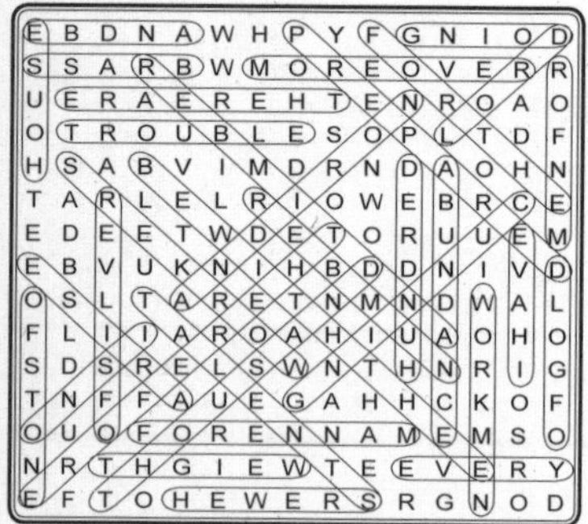

Why was David not allowed to build a house for God?

He had shed much blood (1 Chronicles 22:8)

Puzzle 34

P	R	A	Y	E	R	W	H	O	B	D	N	E	H	T
U	E	I	F	O	R	G	I	V	E	H	L	L	O	T
Y	A	R	P	D	N	A	T	I	U	H	L	P	E	T
H	P	O	P	O	U	S	F	M	C	L	E	O	H	E
T	H	L	T	E	A	I	B	T	A	N	S	E	Y	E
G	M	N	A	H	T	L	O	H	L	E	M	P	W	N
E	U	Y	I	C	E	U	S	W	L	S	A	Y	I	E
A	D	K	N	S	E	I	A	I	E	O	D	M	C	V
R	T	A	E	A	R	H	R	L	D	H	E	A	K	A
S	S	T	R	E	M	I	V	L	L	C	F	A	E	E
E	D	C	E	W	S	E	E	I	A	Y	S	H	D	H
S	O	S	H	N	S	D	E	H	M	N	E	Y	N	T
U	O	I	T	S	T	A	N	E	T	N	D	N	A	C
O	C	H	E	A	R	T	L	A	E	H	L	L	I	W
H	T	I	B	F	Y	T	U	R	N	F	R	O	M	M

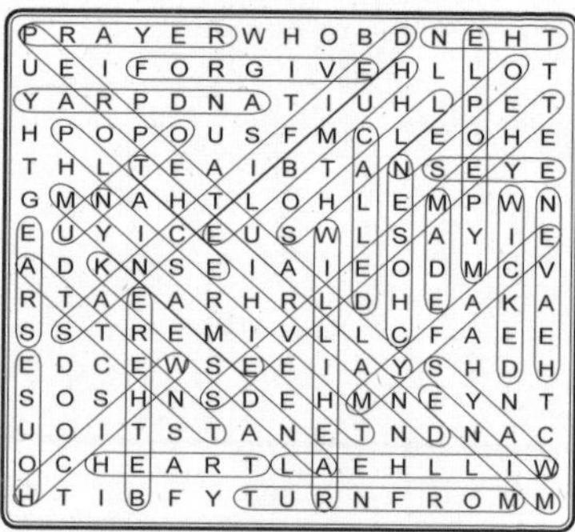

Who built the house that God had chosen to sanctify?

Solomon (2 Chronicles 7:11)

Puzzle 35

L	K	W	D	O	G	R	U	O	F	O	H	E	A	D
M	I	H	K	E	E	S	T	A	H	T	R	E	F	E
W	N	T	N	E	M	E	S	R	O	H	H	S	F	T
A	G	N	T	E	S	I	E	D	Z	R	P	G	L	A
A	A	O	G	L	N	R	A	O	N	O	I	O	I	E
B	B	P	N	G	E	E	F	L	K	A	U	W	C	R
E	A	U	H	Q	S	O	M	E	C	R	H	N	T	T
F	N	S	U	U	R	E	N	Y	S	O	A	E	T	N
O	D	I	A	S	H	A	M	E	D	T	R	E	H	I
R	R	C	A	T	V	W	L	N	S	H	E	P	G	T
E	E	K	L	A	R	V	A	B	S	K	E	D	U	F
B	E	L	H	A	E	O	U	F	O	R	G	O	O	D
R	A	A	T	S	V	S	O	L	D	I	E	R	S	A
S	A	H	G	N	I	Y	A	S	F	A	S	T	E	D
F	E	J	O	U	R	E	W	O	P	R	N	E	B	Y

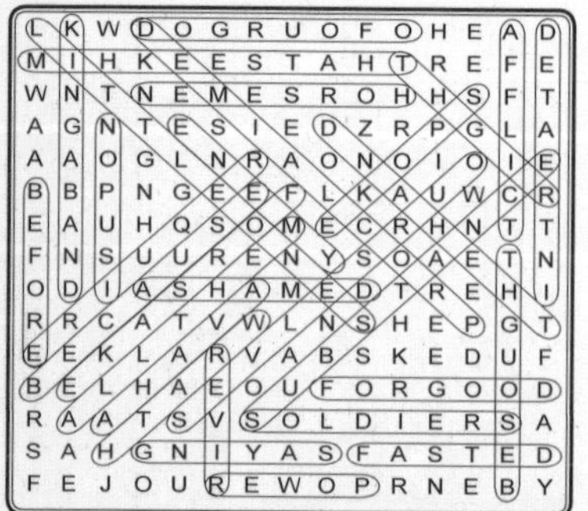

Where was Ezra going when he asked for a safe journey?

To Jerusalem (Ezra 8:31)

Puzzle 36

E	T	S	A	W	W	W	I	T	H	F	I	R	E	A
N	S	H	H	F	A	S	O	R	R	O	W	O	F	F
T	E	P	T	E	A	O	S	T	S	E	U	Q	E	R
T	D	V	C	H	A	T	D	I	A	R	D	N	E	A
H	L	E	A	O	G	R	H	R	M	E	I	A	H	I
D	U	M	H	E	U	I	T	E	N	H	A	Y	S	D
I	O	A	F	V	H	N	S	O	R	T	S	M	E	E
A	W	Y	W	A	O	F	T	Y	B	S	E	F	P	I
S	T	B	D	T	V	H	O	E	H	E	R	O	U	H
G	K	U	S	F	I	O	S	D	N	T	V	Y	L	I
N	J	I	N	N	O	A	U	G	O	A	A	T	C	A
I	C	L	G	R	D	U	T	R	A	G	N	I	H	X
K	E	D	E	M	U	S	N	O	C	R	T	C	R	X
E	V	I	L	G	N	I	K	D	P	R	A	Y	E	D
E	S	T	H	E	C	I	T	Y	P	L	E	A	S	E

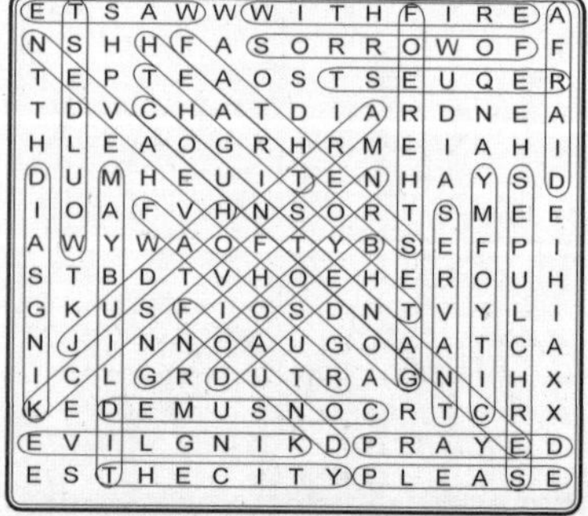

What post did Nehemiah have with King Artaxerxes?

Cupbearer (Nehemiah 1:11)

Puzzle 37

```
A D K N O W E T H H O W W W A
D N E N R E S U O H S E H S H
E T S L I U E H F A T H E R S
S P I W I R T R U H E A T E I
T R W R E V D E H S L E H H R
R E E R E R E R R T H C E T E
O S K G N I D R O C C A R O P
Y E I L A T E G A N D E N N I
E N L A R G E M E N T P G A T
D T H I S T I M E T C A C S H
A O R E H T I E N M T E E H G
R O F E Y T S A F H D D C A I
I O R E H T S E E R L A A L N
S N E D I A M R O O R Y L L D
E K I N G D O M H E C S P A I
```

How was Esther related to Mordecai?

She was Mordecai's adopted daughter; the daughter of Mordecai's uncle (Esther 2:7)

Puzzle 38

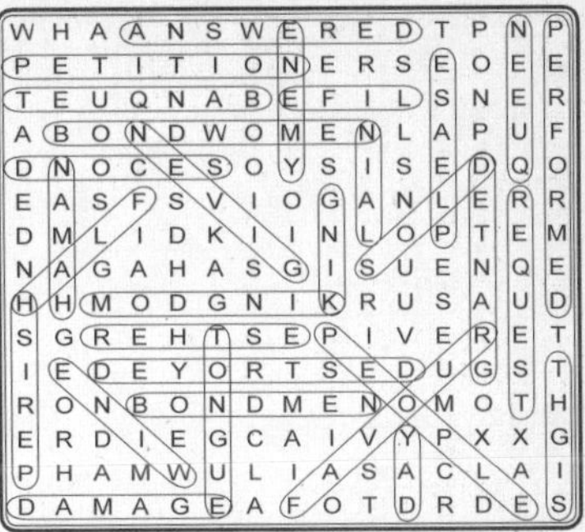

What personal possession did King Ahasuerus give to Mordecai?

His ring (Esther 8:2)

Puzzle 39

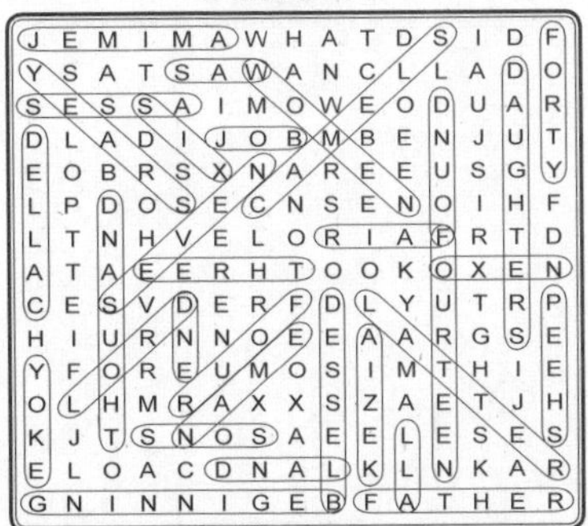

What did Satan claim would be Job's response if the Lord took everything from him?

Satan claimed Job would curse God to His face (Job 1:9–11)

Puzzle 40

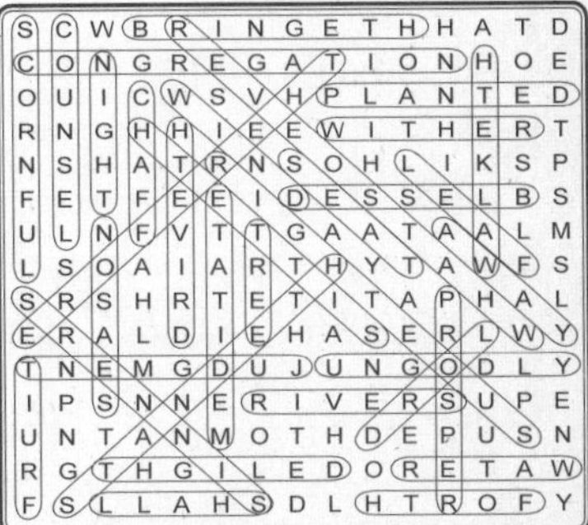

What does this psalm say shall happen to the ungodly?

They shall perish (Psalm 1:6)

Puzzle 41

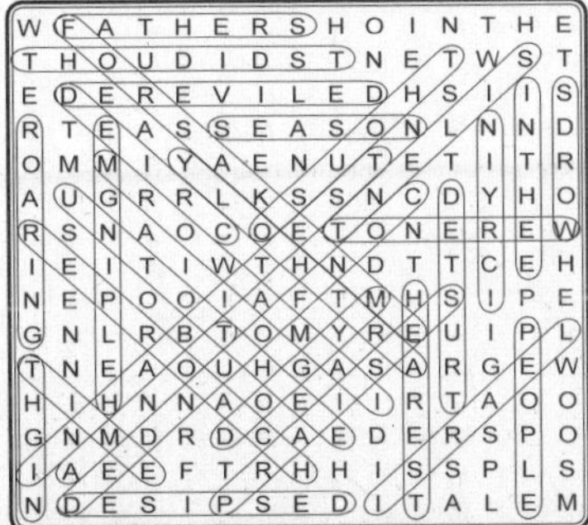

Who in the New Testament said the opening words of this psalm?

Jesus (Matthew 27:46)

Puzzle 42

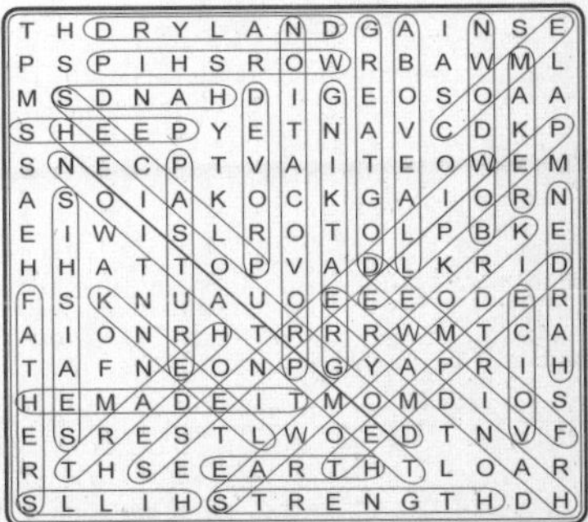

This psalm says to make what kind of noise to the Lord?

A joyful noise (Psalm 95:1)

Puzzle 43

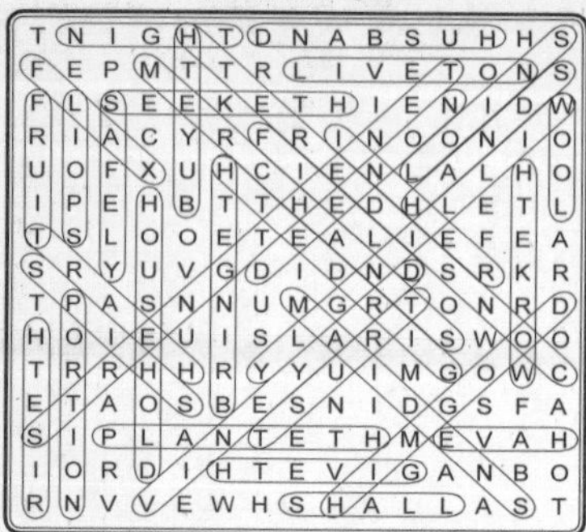

The price of a virtuous woman is far above what?

Rubies (Proverbs 31:10)

Puzzle 44

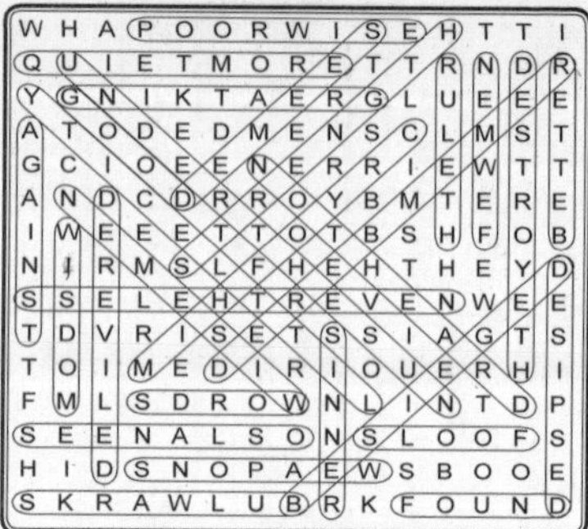

What title describes the writer of this book?

The Preacher (Ecclesiastes 1:1)

Puzzle 45

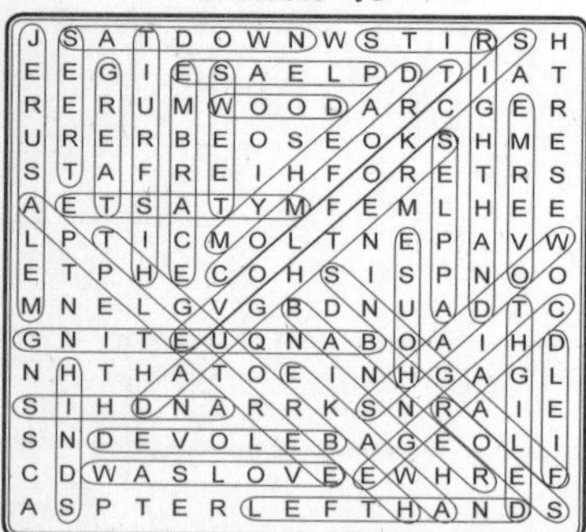

What rose is mentioned in this chapter?

Rose of Sharon (Song of Songs 2:1)

Puzzle 46

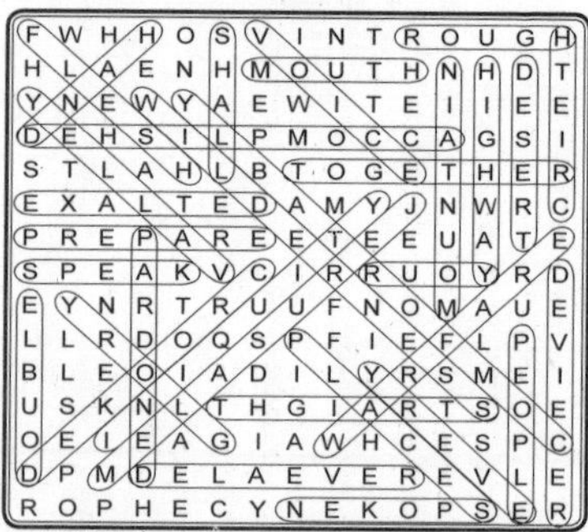

Who in the New Testament fulfilled Isaiah's prophecy?

John the Baptist (Matthew 3:1–3)

Puzzle 47

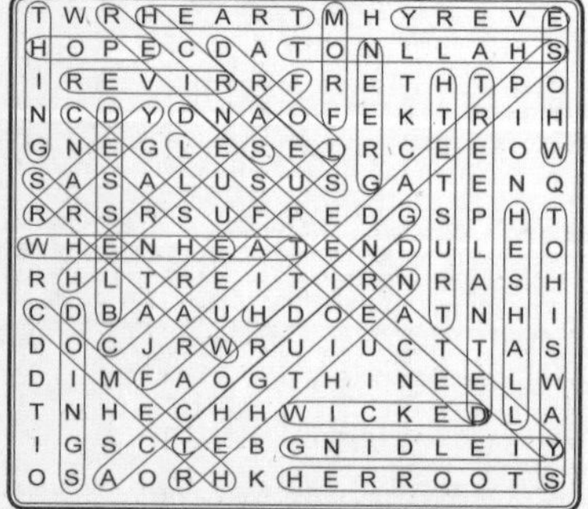

What king conquered Judah in this book?

Nebuchadnezzar (Jeremiah 24:1)

Puzzle 48

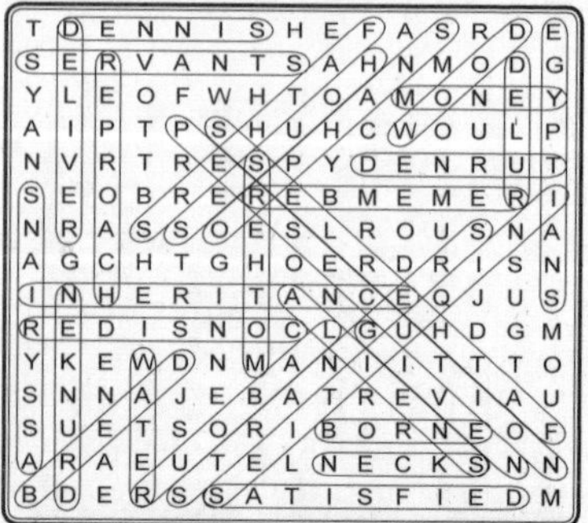

The army of what country brought God's judgment on Jerusalem?

Babylon (Jeremiah 52:12–13)

Puzzle 49

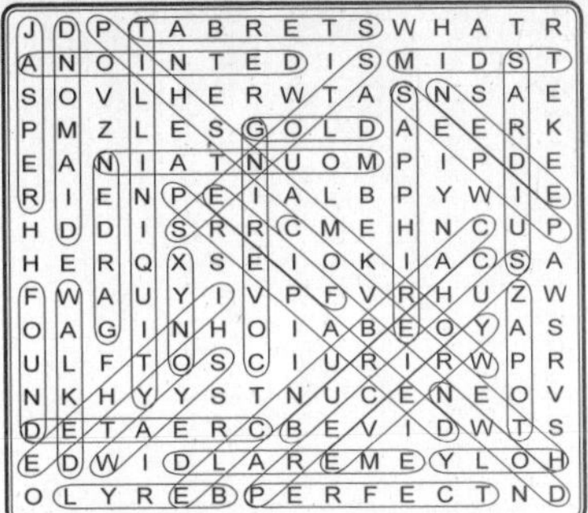

What river was Ezekiel by when he saw his first vision?

The river Chebar (Ezekiel 1:3)

Puzzle 50

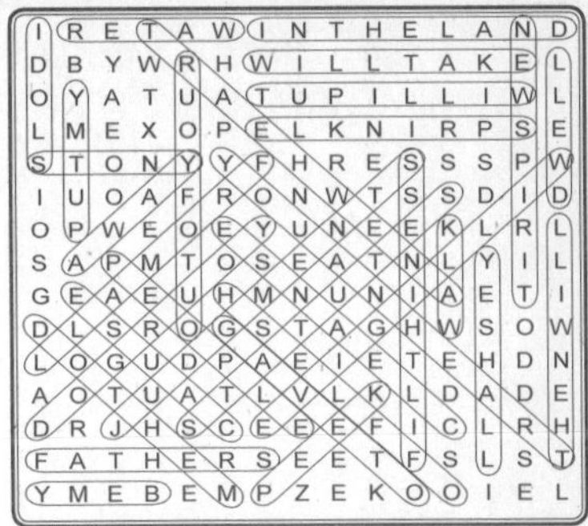

By what expression does God address Ezekiel?

Son of man (Ezekiel 36:1)

Puzzle 51

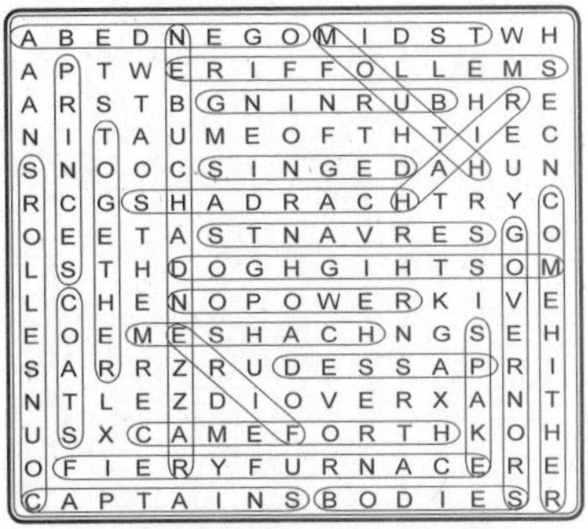

What was the name of the country the king ruled over?

Babylon (Daniel 1:1)

Puzzle 52

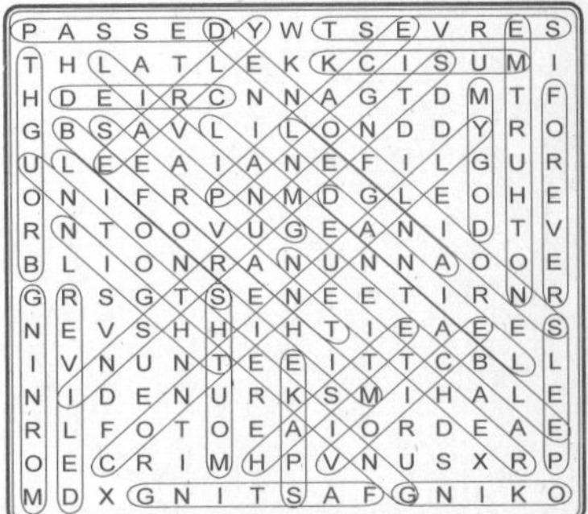

What king did Daniel serve under after Darius?

Cyrus the Persian (Daniel 6:28)

Puzzle 53

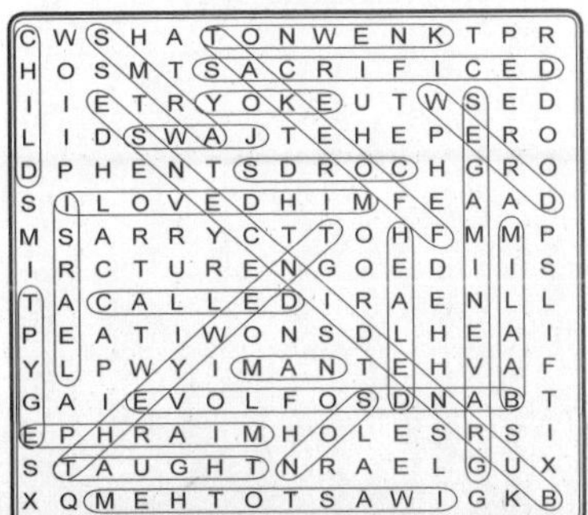

What prostitute did the prophet Hosea marry to picture God's relationship with faithless Israel?

Gomer (Hosea 1:3)

Puzzle 54

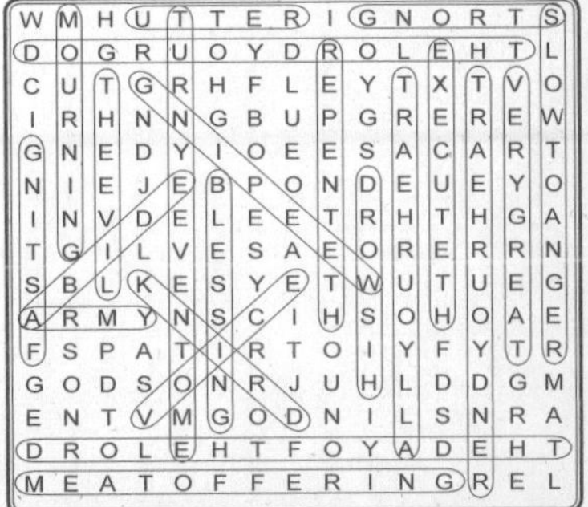

Which flying bug does Joel say is part of God's judgment on Israel?

Locust (Joel 1:4)

Puzzle 55

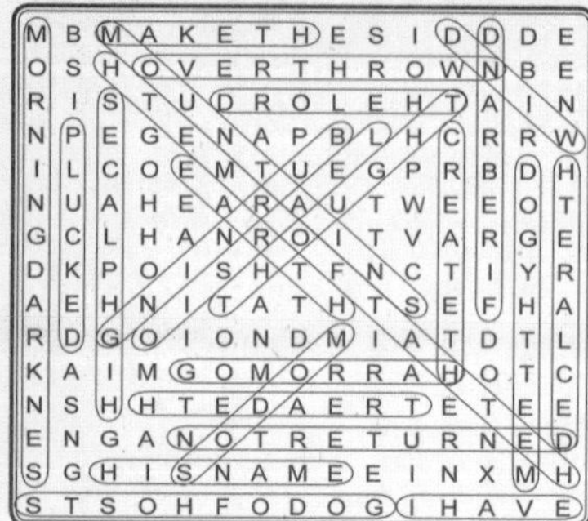

Besides being a prophet, what vocation did Amos engage in?

Herdman (Amos 1:1)

Puzzle 56

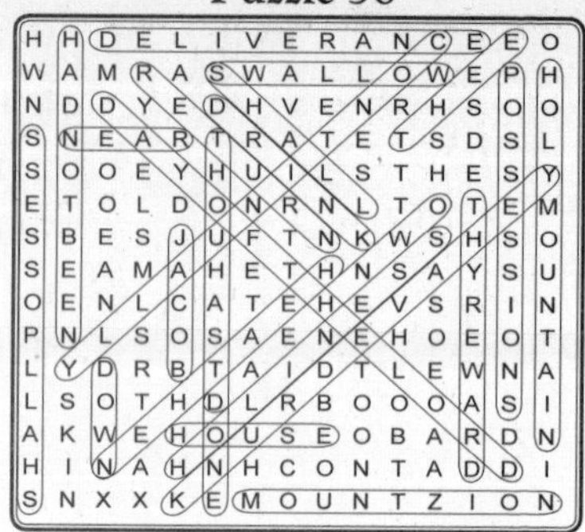

How many verses does the Old Testament's shortest book, Obadiah, contain?

Twenty-one

Puzzle 57

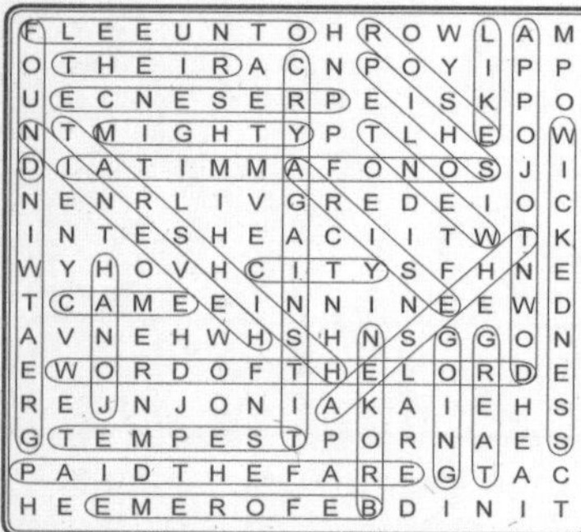

How many people lived in the city of Nineveh when Jonah preached in it?

Six-score thousand, that is, 120,000 (Jonah 4:11)

Puzzle 58

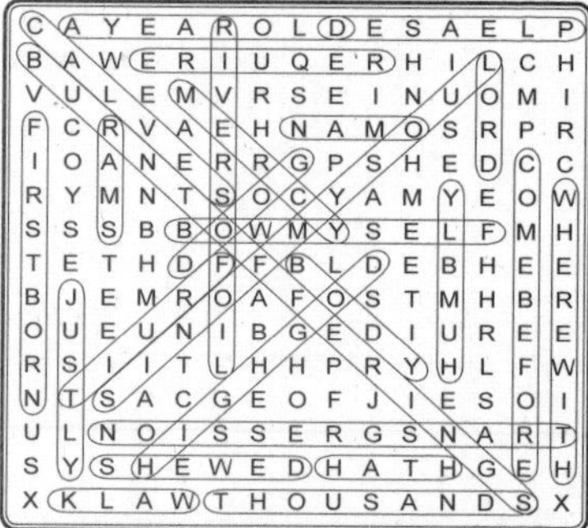

Which verse in Micah's prophecy names Bethlehem as the birthplace of Jesus?

Micah 5:2

Puzzle 59

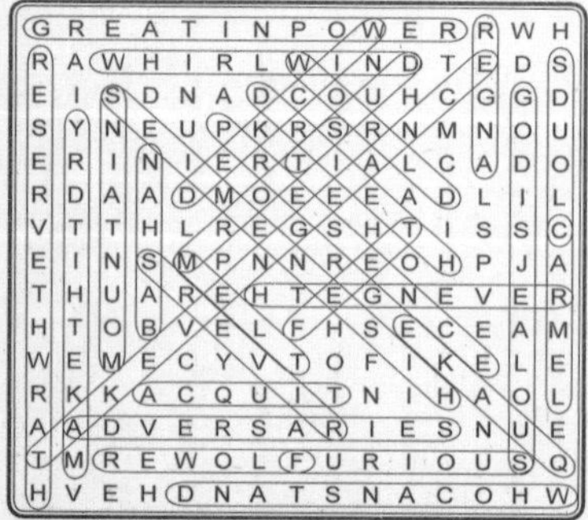

What did Nahum call his prophecy of Nineveh?

"The burden" (Nahum 1:1)

Puzzle 60

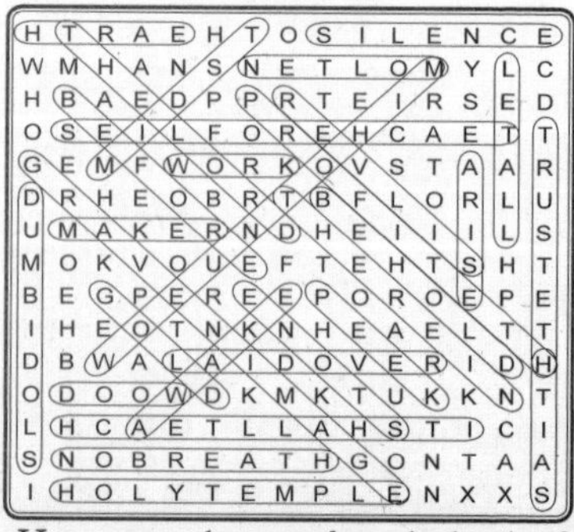

How many chapters does the book of the prophet Habakkuk contain?

Three

Puzzle 61

H E A R T O N U O H T R A E F
I K I N G O F I S R A E L J G
N N J E R U S A L E M S W U L
T D O G Y H T H A T A T S D A
H W I T H J O Y T H G I M G D
A G N I S S L O R D Y N R M I
T S D I M E H T N I A H N E R
D A U G H T E R O F Z I O N E
A C K C A L S E S C A S P T J
Y A Y E E I L D V T D L A S O
L S W M N V N E E I L O L K I
N T O W E A A N A T L V O J C
O O N A H N W S H R I E S D E
O U O M E D E A B Y S H O U T
Z T E P H B A N Y I A I H X X

What Assyrian capital, well known to Jonah, is doomed by Zephaniah?

Nineveh (Zephaniah 2:13)

Puzzle 62

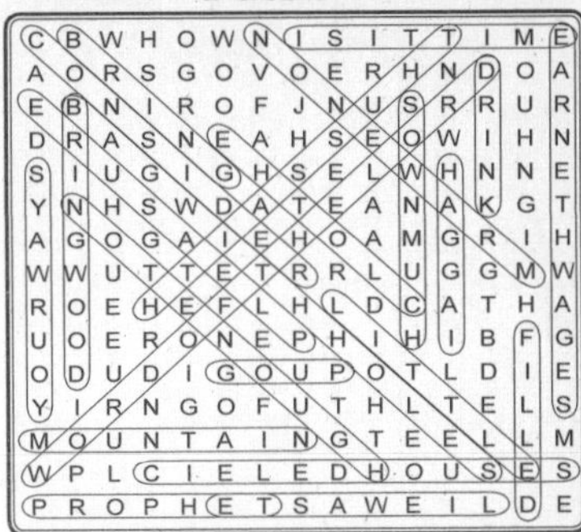

Who was governor of Judah when Haggai urged the rebuilding of the temple?

Zerubbabel (Haggai 1:1)

Puzzle 63

E S O O H C J E A L O U S W H
S L A T K D E S A E L P S I D
A I I N S D R O C O M F O R T
E H F N T T U R E E Y S D E I
T E D D E T S H E T P R D T O
A L C E P H A O I E T Z E U E
F P I N C H L R H A Z R H R I
F E T U A H E S A F I U C N N
L D I M B P M H E G O E T E A
I L E M S I E S C H N D E D N
C M S O E A U S T S A E R N G
T G R C T O E Y R E S T T O E
I P A H H N R D R E R O S A L
O M E Y O C N P M E R C I E S
N N M T H U S S A I T H G X X

What kind of trees did the prophet Zechariah's angelic messenger stand among?

Myrtle (Zechariah 1:8)

Puzzle 64

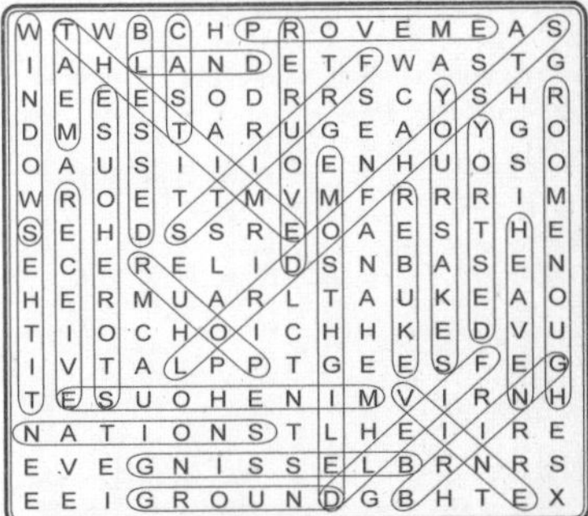

What was God's charge against Israel in Malachi chapter three, verse eight?

"Ye have robbed me" (Malachi 3:8)

Puzzle 65

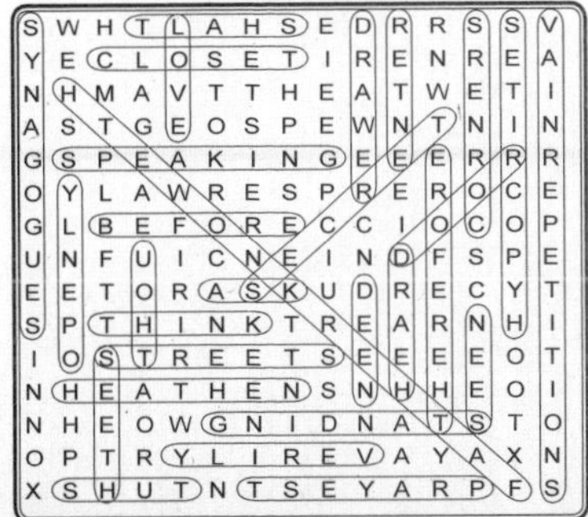

Where in Matthew's Gospel are specific instructions on how to pray?

Matthew 6:9–13

Puzzle 66

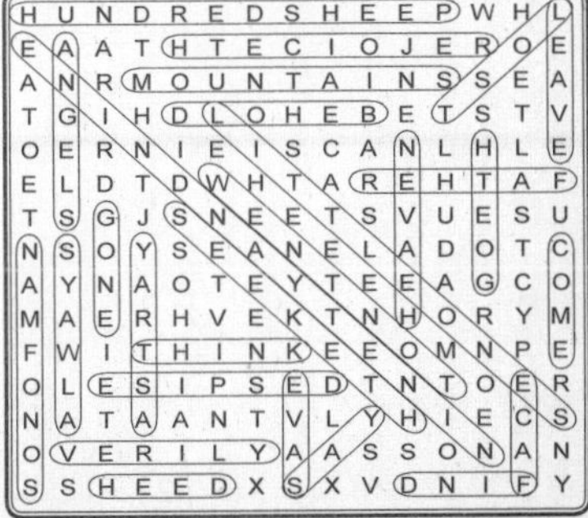

What are the stories called that Jesus used to teach very important lessons?

Parables (Matthew 13:3)

Puzzle 67

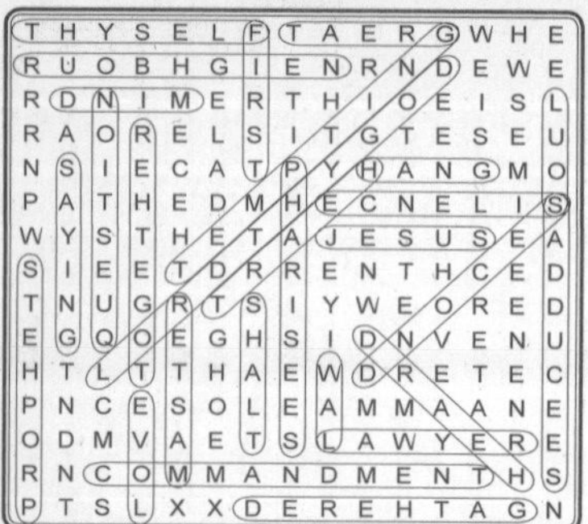

Where were the Israelites encamped when they were given the Ten Commandments?

Near Mount Sinai (Exodus 19)

Puzzle 68

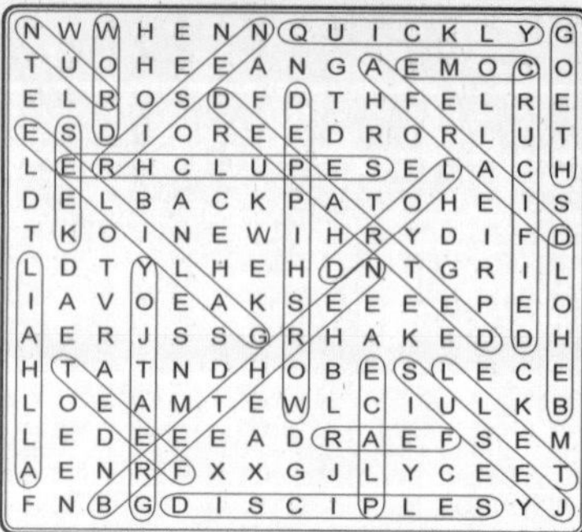

When the angel of the Lord rolled back the stone, why did the grave keepers shake and become like dead men?

"For fear of him" (Matthew 28:4)

Puzzle 69

W H Y J E R U S A L E M P Y C
S O L O E U L D C J E S L P E
M F T R U S S N R D O L A R D
A O I D O P U N I G E R G E U
L L A A E I N S E A T N U S T
L L R N E R C R D A O A E S I
S O T T O I W N O R P E S E T
H W S E P T N L H E A L E D L
I E E L Y S A T Y R E C F O U
P D E R T T E R H E A N K G M
H S E I D U M A E A D U N F T
A L A E D H A M A N U W O O A
I W H C U O T T H L J E W N E
P R O S G A L I L E E Y N O R
I N S O M U C H W N O D I S G

Why could Jesus no longer enter a town openly after He healed a man with leprosy?

Because the man shared freely that Jesus had healed him (Mark 1:40–45)

Puzzle 70

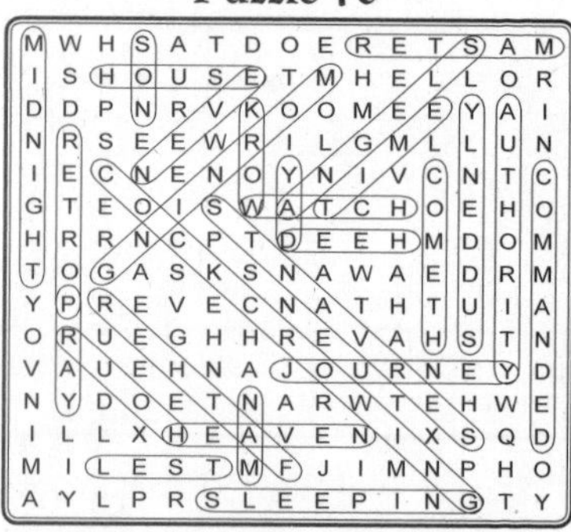

What does the Lord promise will never pass away—even though heaven and earth will?

His Word (Mark 13:31)

Puzzle 71

B W H Y D S E U G N O T W E N
A I D J E E R E V O C E R S S
P N U W O R L D S R E B A E U
T E G O S P E L K E H V T R H
I K E D B E L I E V E T H E I
Z O D A M N E D R D A S E H C
E P I P L T E S I B V E R W F
D S I G N S O R G E E H U Y E
T O W O L L O F H L N D T R S
P D T H G N I H T Y L D A E D
E R R M T O P R H U R T E V N
E A E I L C H T A H E G R E A
O S D A N O P E N L X X C E H
L O S I C K R X D E V I L S X
G F O R T H O D E V I E C E R

Why did Jesus rebuke the disciples before He told them to preach the gospel?

For their lack of faith and unbelief that He was risen (Mark 16:14)

Puzzle 72

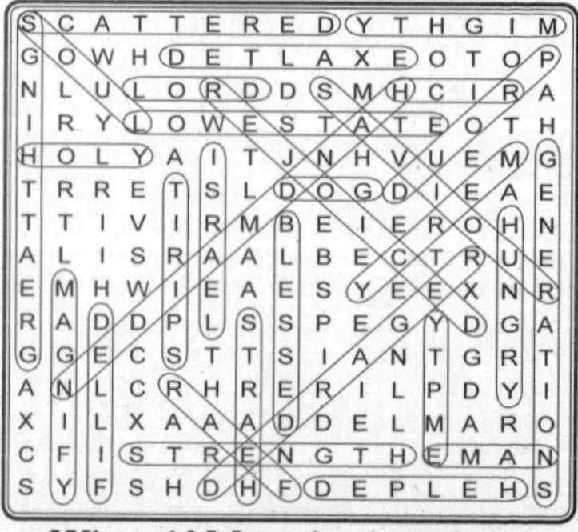

Who told Mary that her relative Elisabeth was expecting a child?

The angel Gabriel (Luke 1:26–36)

Puzzle 73

A W H S A T R E G N A M W A S
C M A W R H Y G D E P P A R W
C S R A E P A A C T I S O N D
O F W D M E H E L H T E B H E
M I E D N S T N H E E H A N R
P R D L G O E I W L L T F I E
L S L I R J S L I T R O O M V
I T I N N L N L F A A L P P I
S B H G E A A R E E E C D T L
H O C O G G Z I I D A Y S V E
E R H E Y R A M D H D E R N D
D N T E W S R A H O U S E E B
O U I T J E E S U S J B X I R
T H W X C I T Y O F D A V I D
S O N X C C H A R D T O N X B

What was Mary's reaction when the angel first appeared to give her news about Jesus' birth?

She was troubled (Luke 1:29)

Puzzle 74

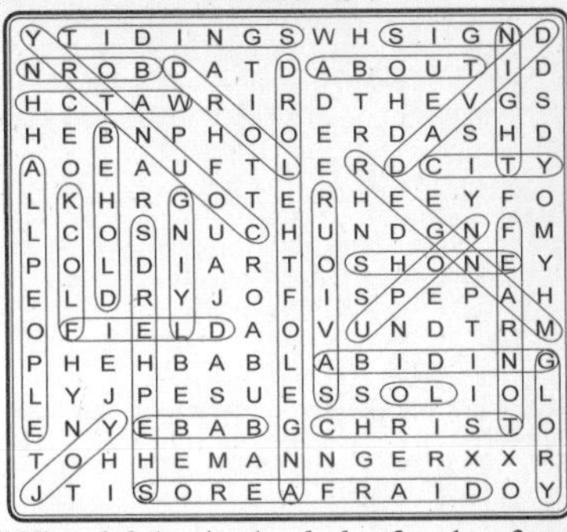

What did the shepherds do after they found Mary, Joseph, and the baby Jesus in the manger?

They spread the word to others about the birth of Jesus (Luke 2:17)

Puzzle 75

C O M M A N D E T H W H A T A
C S O U N T R Y G W E D N I W
R E I J E P R S U N S A N D O
T L H D E D E P I S I C I B K
M A S T E R T E P D L G E Y E
E U R S T R A R L E A Y A D V
E N E O L I W I N S G T O R W
A C B H S E N S J A A E K A L
F H U E S E U H S E C L A P L
R E K M I D N G O C F T L O H
A D E E E S D I S C I P L E S
I T D L O R M T H A O O K J F
D P I L A C E X I L X E O K C
E A S H T I A F P M A N N E R
S T O R M O F W I N D X M O C

What country were Jesus and the disciples traveling to when Jesus' calming of the storm took place?

The country of the Gadarenes (Luke 8:26)

Puzzle 76

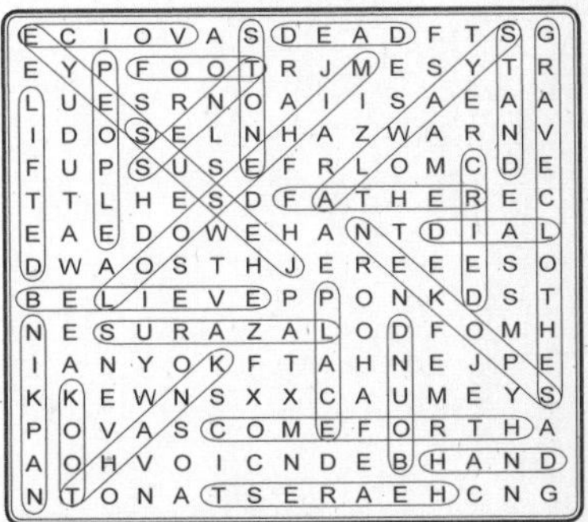

After Jesus raised Lazarus from the dead, what was the response of many of the Jews?

They believed in Jesus (John 11:45)

Puzzle 77

J K G N I E E S T H G I L W N
G O I N T O T H E C I T Y H E
Y S U C I S D F A A D I D S V
A U A R K R E R S R O U N D A
H H S U N L A T O L D T H E E
I C U S L E O E U L T F S S H
M I S U L N Y J H C R S O I S
S H E C I O V E O U E R N R K
T W J S H A L L D L M S A A C
O N H A D E N I H S B E R M I
O E E M E M A C E H L Y T E R
D M A A T H E E T O I T T T P
O D R D A E S A Y I N G H O M
A T D S P T S N I A G A O D C
H U S S U D D E N L Y X U O X

Why did Saul journey to Damascus?

To persecute Christians and bring them bound to Jerusalem (Acts 9:2)

Puzzle 78

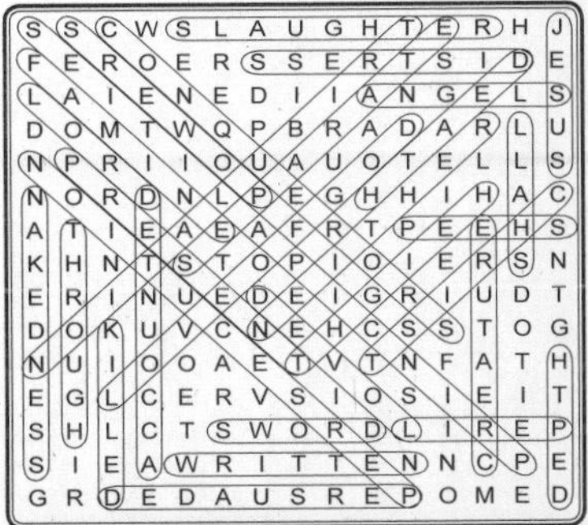

Where did Paul intend to go after visiting Rome?

Spain (Romans 15:24)

Puzzle 79

S	W	H	A	A	D	M	O	N	I	S	H	H	R	M
T	S	I	R	H	C	T	F	W	E	O	A	E	I	S
G	N	E	G	R	A	C	E	L	R	V	H	N	H	S
O	S	E	L	I	T	N	E	G	E	T	I	O	K	E
S	A	D	T	E	R	O	M	P	O	S	U	G	D	N
P	B	R	E	T	H	R	E	N	T	L	Y	I	B	D
E	O	D	G	I	I	T	A	E	D	A	P	M	E	O
L	U	W	D	O	F	R	R	T	D	E	B	D	L	O
E	N	R	E	G	F	I	W	E	A	E	A	L	I	G
T	D	P	L	R	N	F	T	C	V	U	L	Y	E	L
G	O	S	W	G	T	I	E	C	S	E	I	L	V	L
H	G	U	O	R	H	T	T	R	N	U	N	D	I	U
O	S	S	N	F	G	O	E	T	I	A	U	L	N	F
S	L	E	K	F	I	P	L	I	U	N	S	O	G	L
T	L	J	F	O	M	R	P	Y	A	P	G	B	U	L

What work did Tertius fulfill for Paul?

He transcribed the epistle to the Romans (Romans 16:22)

Puzzle 80

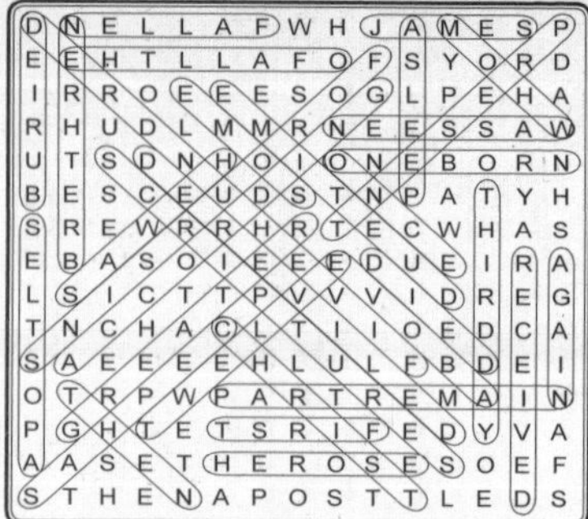

Why does Paul say he was the least of the apostles?

He persecuted the church of God (1 Corinthians 15:9)

Puzzle 81

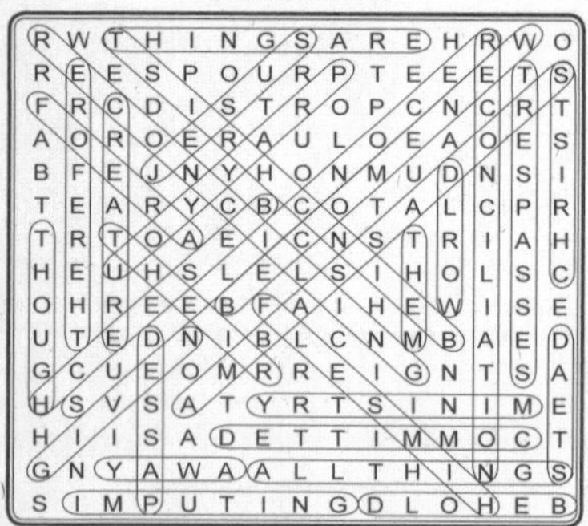

Who reported to Paul about the Corinthians?

Titus (2 Corinthians 7:6–7)

Puzzle 82

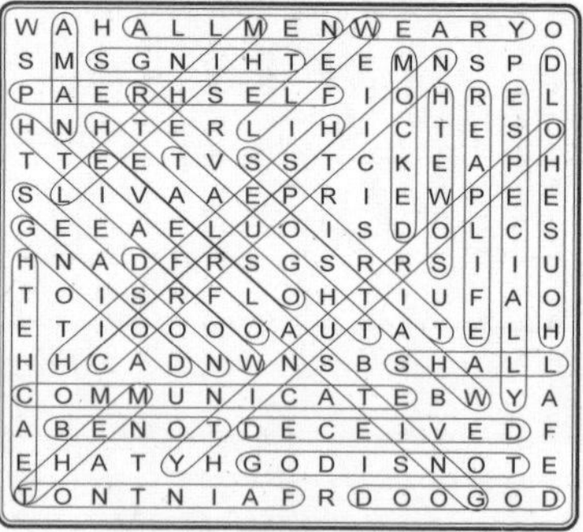

Whose Spirit cries out, "Abba, Father"?

The Spirit of His Son (Galatians 4:6)

Puzzle 83

W	H	C	I	H	W	H	E	D	A	H	T	I	A	F
D	E	N	I	A	D	R	O	R	T	H	G	I	M	T
N	S	U	L	M	C	G	H	E	A	V	E	N	L	Y
B	U	K	Y	H	F	O	R	T	R	E	B	E	R	B
O	D	D	R	O	T	W	N	E	O	O	C	E	S	R
A	E	I	T	S	U	O	J	X	H	W	F	A	C	O
S	S	F	E	C	T	R	E	C	M	T	A	E	R	F
T	I	G	W	O	R	K	S	E	R	A	E	R	B	G
G	A	I	F	M	B	M	U	E	P	D	D	G	D	E
E	R	S	F	E	A	A	S	D	L	E	O	E	O	H
D	L	U	O	H	S	N	I	I	A	V	T	O	U	T
R	I	C	H	E	S	S	T	N	C	A	E	T	G	S
T	H	R	O	U	G	H	H	G	E	S	H	S	H	I
S	S	E	N	D	N	I	K	R	S	E	O	P	E	T
A	N	D	B	A	P	P	C	T	M	Y	I	S	M	I

What number describes faith, hope, and baptism?

One (Ephesians 4:5)

Puzzle 84

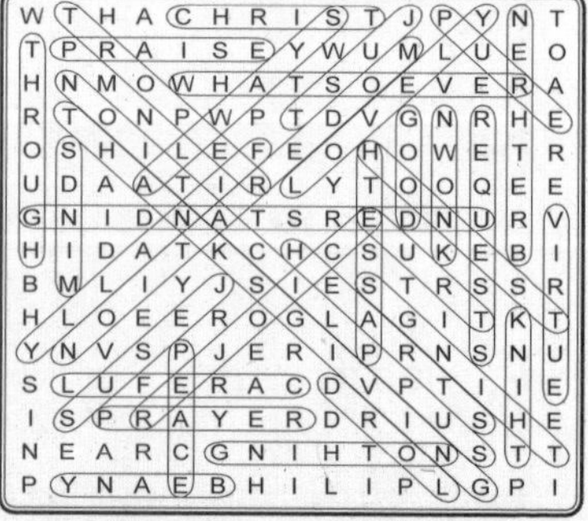

What woman prayed by the riverside near Philippi?

Lydia (Acts 16:12–14)

Puzzle 85

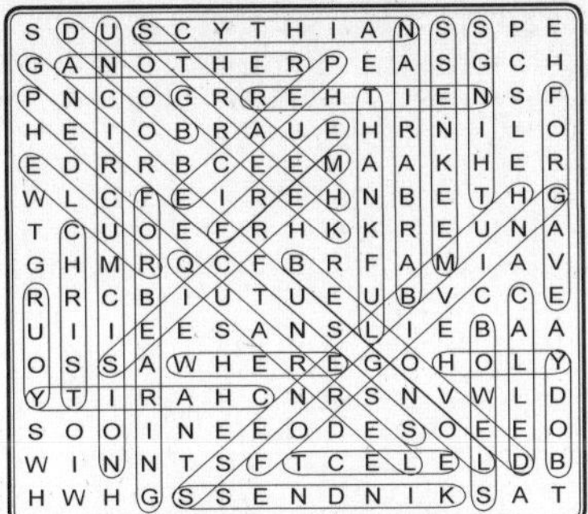

Speech should be with grace seasoned with what?

Salt (Colossians 4:6)

Puzzle 86

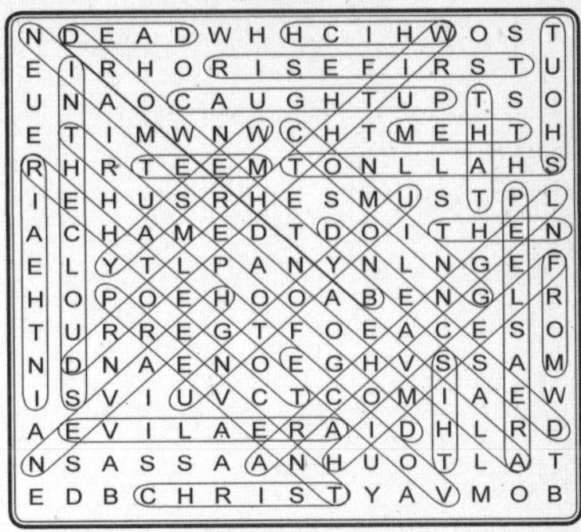

Whose house in Thessalonica was assaulted by a mob?

Jason's (Acts 17:1, 5)

Puzzle 87

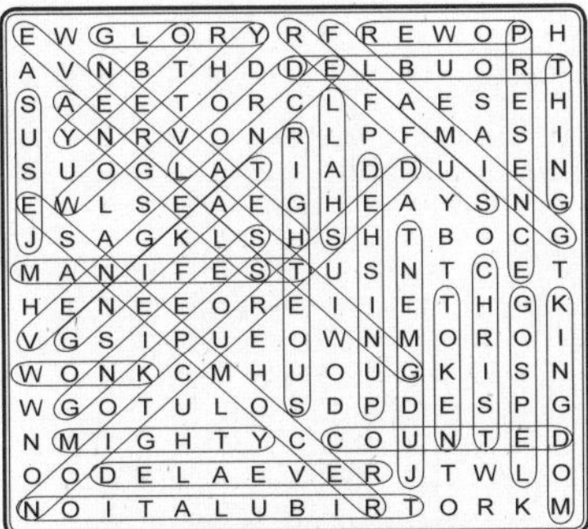

What does Paul say about those who would not work?

Neither should they eat (2 Thessalonians 3:10)

Puzzle 88

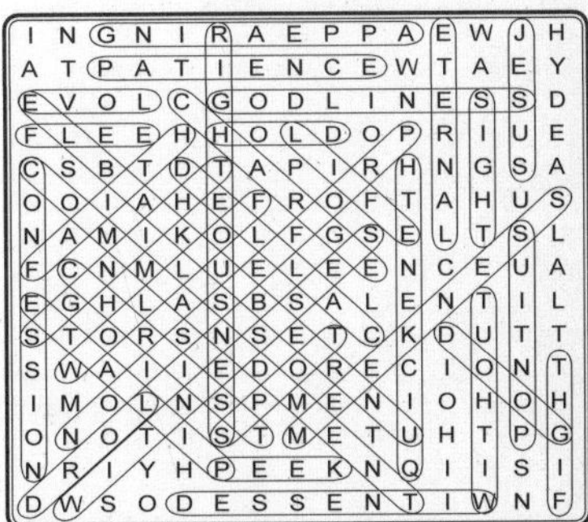

In what way does Paul call Timothy his son?

Son in the faith (1 Timothy 1:2)

Puzzle 89

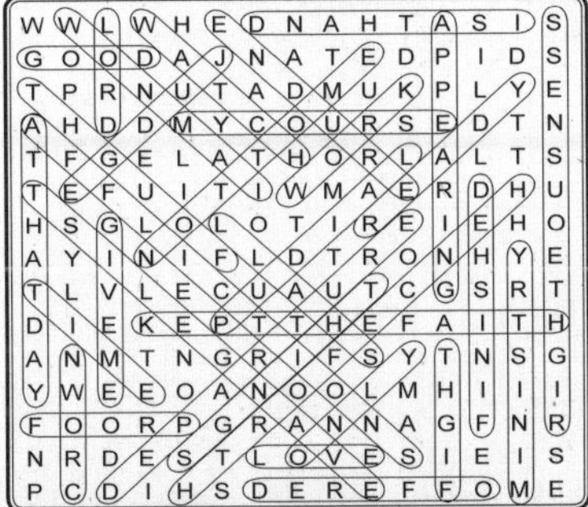

What did Paul tell Timothy to let no man despise?

His (Timothy's) youth (1 Timothy 4:12)

Puzzle 90

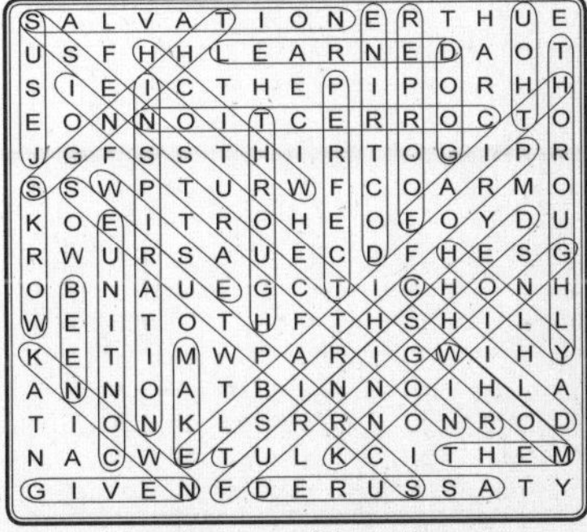

The father of Timothy was of what nationality?

Greek (Acts 16:1)

Puzzle 91

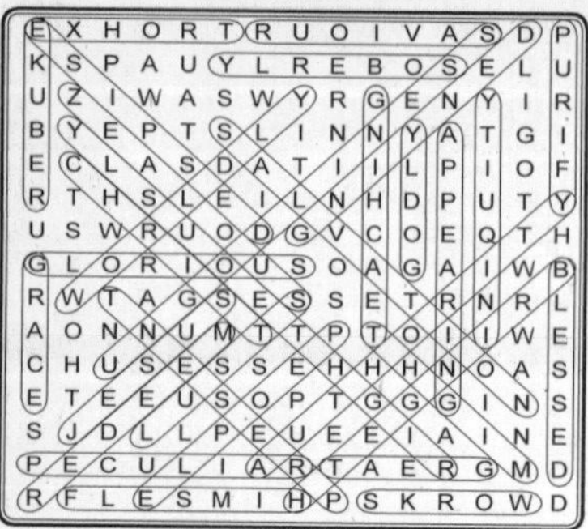

Paul was writing to Titus who was on what island?

Crete (Titus 1:5)

Puzzle 92

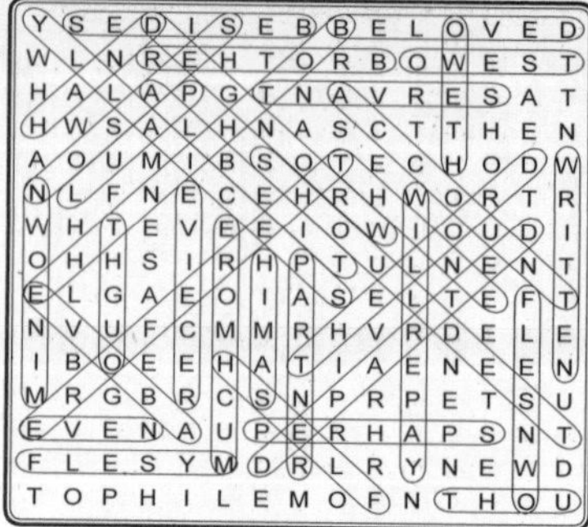

What was the name of the slave being returned to Philemon?

Onesimus (Philemon 10)

Puzzle 93

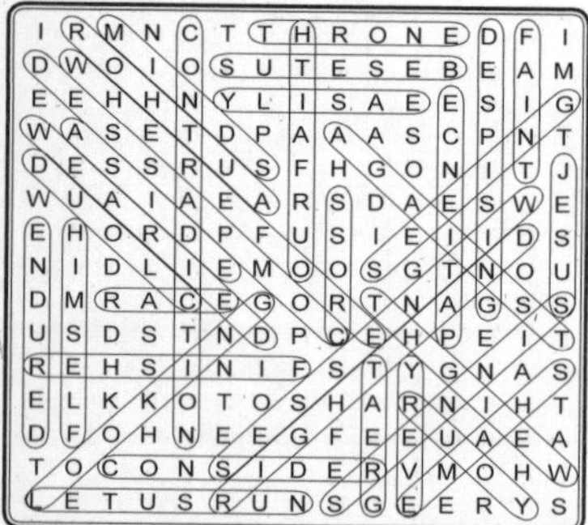

In time past, how did God speak to the fathers?

By the prophets (Hebrews 1:1)

Puzzle 94

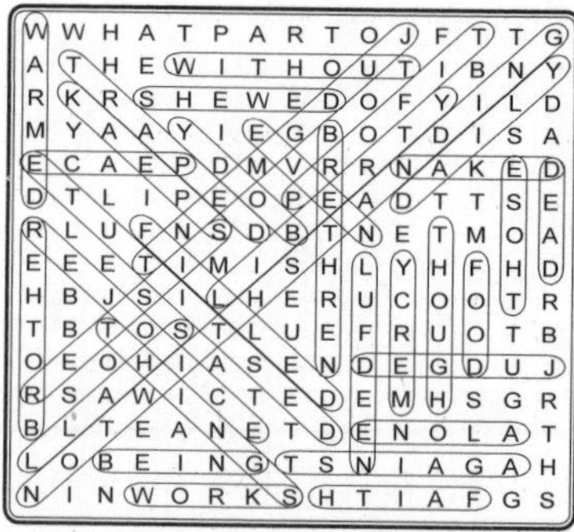

What part of the body is a little member but boasts great things?

The tongue (James 3:5)

Puzzle 95

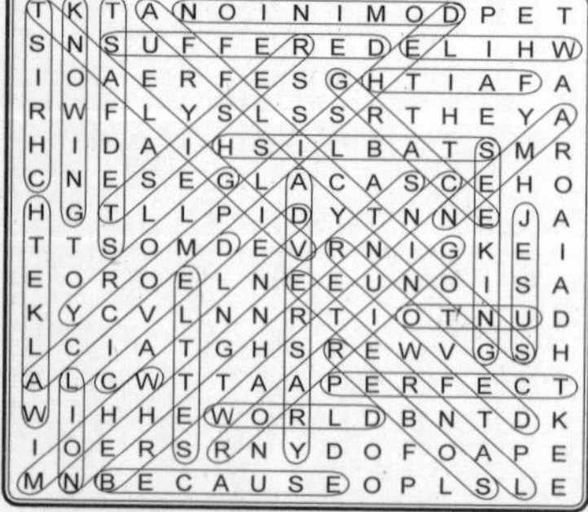

Peter says they are a holy nation and what kind of people?

Peculiar (1 Peter 2:9)

Puzzle 96

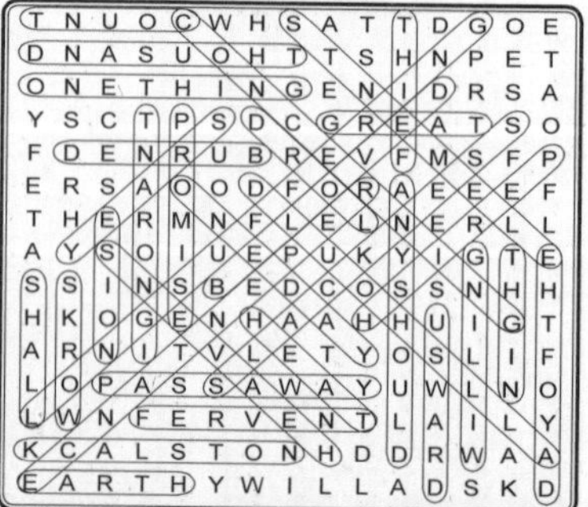

What does Peter say scoffers of the last day will ask?

Where is the promise of His coming? (2 Peter 3:3–4)

Puzzle 97

S A Y H F A I T H F U L O T W
M A C O N F E S S N N Y H C H
A T S U S E J P T E R G R S A
T S T R U T H P E V I G R O F
H I P S E A Y O U L G R I S D
G R D E C E I V E N H N I T E
I H H L E N E H O W T N T E C
L C S V T A T D M E E N R M L
S H T E S N A E L C O T E I A
I B O S I R O K O F U S H H R
D F I K K D H S I N S H T M E
O R L N O E T S T A N A O O J
G A E O A S O H G N E V N R S
W S L R U X X E I L S E A F O
S B D J F E L L O W S H I P N

How many chapters appear in the New Testament book of First John?

Five

Puzzle 98

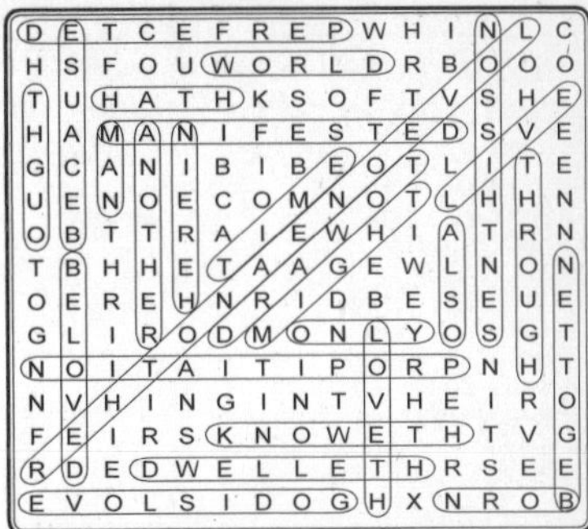

Which four books of the Bible contain the word "beginning" in their first verse?

Genesis, Mark, John, and 1 John

Puzzle 99

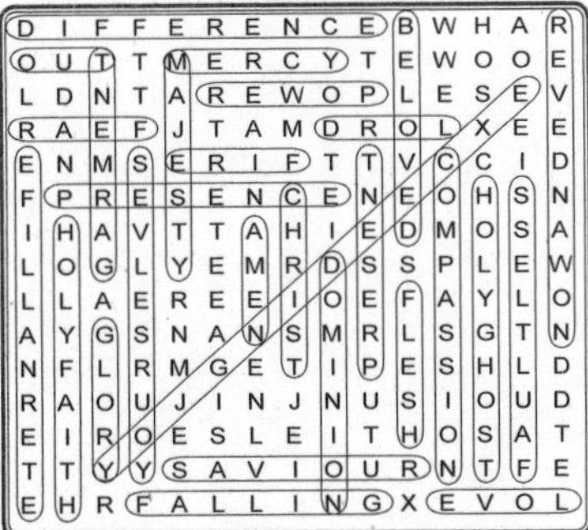

What two Old Testament cities are named in Jude's letter?

Sodom and Gomorrah (Jude 7)

Puzzle 100

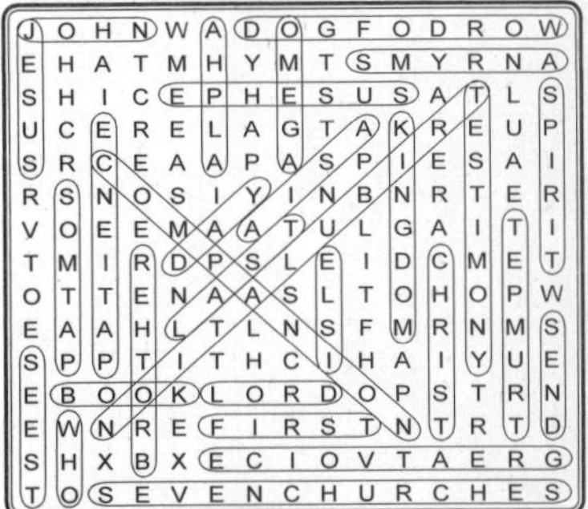

What mythical creature appears in Revelation's twelfth chapter?

A dragon (Revelation 12:3)

Puzzle 101

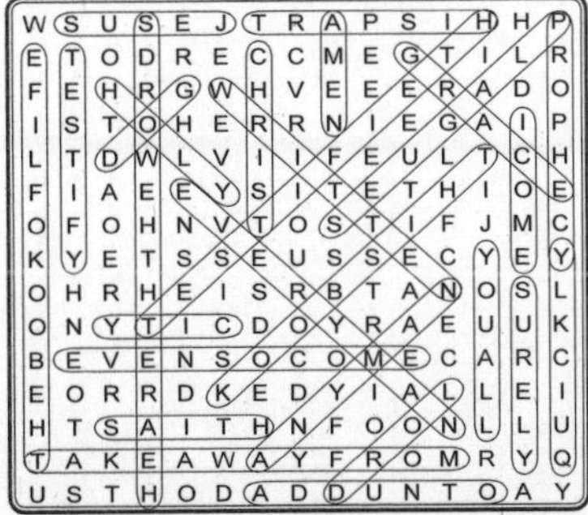

Who received the Revelation of Jesus Christ and recorded it for us today?

John (Revelation 1:1)